MW00639727

THE
OVERVIEW EFFECT

Space Exploration and Human Evolution

THE
OVERVIEW
EFFECT

Space Exploration
and Human Evolution

Frank White

Houghton Mifflin Company
Boston 1987

Library of Congress Cataloging-in-Publication Data

White, Frank, date.
The overview effect.

Bibliography: p.
Includes index.
1. Outer space — Exploration.   2. Astronautics and civilization.   I. Title.
TL790.W48   1987   303.4'83   87-15920
ISBN 0-395-43084-4

Printed in the United States of America

P 10 9 8 7 6 5 4 3 2 1

The author is grateful for permission to quote from the following works:

We Seven, by the Astronauts Themselves. Copyright © 1962, by Simon & Schuster, Inc.

"An Astronaut's Diary," audiotape (Washington, D.C.: National Public Radio, 1985). From René Daumal, *Mount Analogue*, trans. Roger Shattuck. Translation copyright © 1959 by Vincent Stuart Ltd. Reprinted by permission of Pantheon Books, a division of Random House, Inc.

"Conversations with the *Christian Science Monitor*," conducted by Bob MacDonald, September 10, 1985. Reprinted by permission from *Conversations with the Christian Science Monitor*. © 1985 by the Christian Science Publishing Society. All rights reserved.

Earth's Answer: Explorations of Planetary Culture at the Lindisfarne Conferences (West Stockbridge, Mass: Lindisfarne/Harper & Row, 1977). Used by permission of Russell L. Schweickart.

To
the Astronauts and Cosmonauts
of Planet Earth

Acknowledgments

One of the lessons I have learned in this endeavor is that no one writes a book alone; an enormous network of people from the past and the present has supported me directly and indirectly. I'd like to thank all of them, but it would be impossible to do so. For this reason, I have, with a few exceptions, limited my acknowledgments to people who contributed directly to the production of this book. In lieu of more personal comments, let me simply thank every one of my extended family and friends for helping me to reach this point.

My mother, Mary Ann White, started me on the path that led to the Overview Effect over thirty years ago by giving me a book called *Stars*. I'm sorry she isn't here to see the results, but I know she would be pleased. My father, Frank C. White, has been consistently supportive of my work and has read just about everything I've written, as has my stepmother, Celeste. My son, Joshua, deserves special mention because he has supported my effort throughout and graciously gave up his time with me when I was writing. He attended the eighth shuttle launch with me and accompanied me to my interview with Senator Jake Garn.

Of course, I owe a mammoth debt of gratitude to all the astronauts and other space travelers who consented to be interviewed: Loren Acton, Joe Allen, Alan Bean, Jerry Carr, Gene Cernan, Michael Collins, Jake Garn, Marc Garneau, Ed Gibson, Jeff Hoffman, Byron Lichtenberg, Don Lind, Edgar Mitchell, Rusty Schweickart, Bill Nelson, and Charles Walker. Without them, there would be no book, and I deeply appreciate their willingness to participate in the project. I know that their time is valuable, and I am honored that they invested some of it in this project.

Several people were instrumental in arranging astronaut interviews. Brian O'Leary introduced me to Joe Allen, Martin Rutte led me to John Wildgust, who coordinated the interview with Marc Garneau, and Alan Kelley set up the interview with Loren Acton. Marty Spiegel recommended Ed Gibson. David Nexon helped me to make contact with Senator Garn's office. I also want to thank the staffs of both Senator Garn and Congressman Nelson for their help in those interviews.

Charles Walker supplied me with some crucial data and referred me to Steve Nesbitt and all the other accommodating people at the Johnson Space Center who set up the interviews with Jeff Hoffman and Don Lind and helped me locate Gene Cernan, Jerry Carr, and Alan Bean. Many thanks to them for making my trip to Houston a success. The people at Esalen Institute helped me find Rusty Schweickart, and Sam Matthews at the Institute of Noetic Sciences arranged for me to meet Edgar Mitchell.

Marcia Smith supplied advice and materials on the Soviet program, Bruce Shackleton introduced me to "central projects," and Joanne Gabrynowicz helped me see the work's relationship to constitutional issues. Jeff Stamps provided me with a copy of his book, summarizing a set of ideas I've long admired, at a key moment.

Bob Carr made a tremendous contribution by loaning me the word processor I used to write this book.

The Space Studies Institute and National Space Society have been continuing sources of support, and I'm especially grateful to Gerard K. O'Neill of SSI for writing the foreword.

The people at Hill & Knowlton's Advanced Technology Division graciously adapted themselves to my requirement for a flexible work schedule, as did the Organization Transformation Network.

Very special thanks to those who read and provided comments on the manuscript and suggested ways to reach the primary audiences for the book: Paul Blanchard, Dennis Campbell, Nick De Pasquale, Peter Diamandis, Barbara Doughty, Gary Enersen, George Field, Todd Hawley, Scott Mize, Mark Myers, Ken Roberts, Sandy Rosenzweig, Rena Shulsky, Bob Strayton, Rick Tresch-Fienberg, Charles Walker, Randy Webb, and Frank C. White.

Madeline Nold, who also critiqued the manuscript, constantly reminded me of how valuable the book might be, which helped me greatly.

The unsung hero of the entire effort is Duncan Smith, who introduced me to my editor at Houghton Mifflin, Larry Kessenich. Duncan was right; Larry's immediate and sympathetic understanding of the Overview Effect, his unwavering support, and intelligent advice were the crucial elements that allowed the book to be born. Thanks to both of them, and to Gerry Morse, whose thoughtful editing of the manuscript brought it to life.

Contents

Part II
The New Civilizations

Part III
The Experiences of the Astronauts and Cosmonauts

Foreword

One of the first people to appreciate that humankind will not remain forever bound to the planet of its birth was Konstantin Tsiolkovsky. Early in this century he set forth clearly the basic facts of nature that will make possible, even inevitable, a civilization in space. There, solar energy is a full-time energy resource, as it can never be on a planet. Gravity, of any amount desired, can be provided in space by rotating at the correct speed a habitat that can hold an earthlike atmosphere.

From that realization it is but a short step to the knowledge that every star, even the nearest, is a sure target for human migration. Every star is, like our Sun, a source of energy. And every star is circled by material that can be formed into space habitats. The atmosphere and the gravity for those habitats can be freely chosen by our descendants who will one day build them. Those facts liberate us from a long-standing hang-up: that the nearest target for stellar migration must be a Sol-type star orbited by a planet with gravity and atmosphere much like those of Earth. In that context, Frank White concentrates on the right questions: what changes in viewpoint occur when humans see the Earth as a unified whole, and what changes will occur in the aspirations, the values, and the historical course of the human race when it sets its pioneering course outward, to the solar system and ultimately the stars.

White is one of a growing number of people who are not content with speculation on the human breakout from the bonds of planet Earth. Those people devote much of their creativity and hard work to making that breakout to a new ecological range a reality in their own time, rather than leaving it to an uncertain future. White's work, contributed freely to the National Commission on Space at a critical point in its deliberations, became the organizing theme about which its report was written. That speaks much for the universality of his message. The commissioners were a group of fifteen people of diverse backgrounds, all with expertise in some aspect of space development but otherwise of very different philosophies and degrees of conservatism. They agreed upon and embraced a set of goals that would have seemed unreasonably futuristic to most experts on space just ten years earlier: first and most central, that humanity was destined to break the shackles of Earth's gravity and move outward to inhabit the solar system. To that primary goal others, humanitarian and peaceful, were joined naturally by the historical analogues of our Constitution and Bill of Rights. Overall, they are a set of goals in which every human being can take pride. They state the best of human aspirations: humankind should be free, individual choice should be respected, and material well-being should go hand in hand with that respect. They state those aspirations within a context where they can in fact be realized: a context of virtually unlimited resources of energy and materials and, ultimately, land area.

It is the hope of those who work toward the breakout from planet Earth that the establishment of permanent, self-sustaining colonies of humans off-Earth will have three vital consequences. First, it will make human life forever unkillable, removing it from the endangered species list, where it now stands on a fragile Earth over-armed with nuclear weapons. Second, the opening of virtually unlimited new land area in space will reduce territorial pressures and therefore diminish warfare on Earth itself. Third, the small scale of space colonies, the largest some tens of thousands of people, will lead to local governments that are simple in form, responsive to the desires of their people, and as reachable and intimate as were the New England town meetings of America's heritage.

Beyond those immediate needs of survival and freedom, we look to our purpose as a species. We are far too diverse, far too contentious, and far too divided by conflicting religious and ideological dogmas ever to be likely to agree on a single long-term goal for humanity. And we are far too impatient, too short in our attention spans, to hold to such a goal for a time of many generations. But fortunately, the realities of time and space in the era when humanity is freed of Earth's bonds will lead inevitably to results that will transcend any program we might devise.

In a relatively short time they will bring a higher degree of independence to human communities than is now possible on Earth. In a longer time the effects of genetic drift will show, as human groups separated by great distances evolve into noticeably different forms of humanity. In a much longer time — but a time still short compared to the interval over which Homo sapiens evolved — there will spread throughout our galaxy a variety of civilizations, all traceable, though some may forget their origins, to one beautiful and precious planet, circling a minor star near the galaxy's edge.

GERARD K. O'NEILL
President, Space Studies Institute
Professor Emeritus, Princeton University

Prologue

The old space program ended on January 28, 1986, in an explosion that destroyed a spaceship and claimed the lives of the seven-person crew.

The old space program served the United States well for twenty-five years, but it tried to carry out humanity's greatest adventure as just another line item in the federal budget. The ultimate cause of the Challenger accident was that too much was asked of the old space program, and two few resources were provided to meet society's demands on it.

The responsibility for the Challenger accident falls most heavily on the people who made the launch decision that day. However, in a democracy, all citizens are responsible for their government's actions, and the space program has always been a program of the American people. We took pride in its successes, such as the moon landings and successful shuttle launches, and we should also take responsibility for Challenger.

During the forced stand-down in the space program following the accident, many Americans asked themselves, "What is the fundamental purpose of space exploration; what is the vision that guides our space program?" It is appropriate that this debate ensued, because it is part of taking responsibility for what has happened in the past and what can happen in the future in space. In charting our future in space, we are also choosing our future in general, because space exploration is not just another government program. It may be a key to human survival and evolution, and perhaps even more than that.

The thesis of this book is that we are not simply reaching out into space to use extraterrestrial resources and opportunities here on Earth. Rather, we are laying the foundations for a series of new civilizations that are the next logical steps in the evolution of human society and human consciousness.

That in itself should be enough to make us take space exploration seriously and to move ahead vigorously. However, I will also argue that human exploration of space may serve an even higher purpose than our own evolution as a species, performing a vital function for the universe as a whole.

Seen this way, space exploration is not a luxury to be pursued after other social priorities have been handled. Rather, it is the most important activity of all. It is important for everyone, but for Americans in particular, to grasp this point because of our heritage as explorers, innovators, and leaders.

A relevant interchange occurred on the television program "This Week with David Brinkley" shortly after the Challenger accident. At one point, columnist George Will said to author Tom Wolfe, "It seems we have justified space exploration in a very banal way; we have sold it on the basis that it produced nonstick frying pans and so on."

"Yes," responded Wolfe. "We have never had a philosophy of space exploration."

With a new century and a new millennium only a few years away, the time is right for the people of the United States and of the planet Earth to develop a comprehensive philosophy of space. The purpose of this book is to help begin that process. The goal is to focus on the vision and purpose of space exploration that the old space program sometimes failed to articulate and to show how a new space program can be different.

This book is itself a voyage of discovery. Part I begins with an examination of "The Overview Effect" and other shifts in consciousness that can occur in outer space. Part II moves to a description of the new civilizations that are being built with the Overview Effect as their foundation. Part III includes detailed reports by those who know what life in space is like — the astronauts and cosmonauts, forerunners of the embryonic human space program.

PART I

THE
OVERVIEW EFFECT

1

The Overview Project

It is endlessly fulfilling. You never see quite the same thing as you are orbiting. There is a different ground track every time. The time of day is different; the clouds are different. The cloud patterns show different colors. The oceans are different; the dust over the deserts is different. It doesn't get repetitive.

– Former shuttle astronaut Joseph P. Allen

There are ways to experience the Overview Effect without going into outer space. Anyone who flies in an airplane and looks out the window has the opportunity to experience a mild version of it. My effort to confirm the reality of the Overview Effect had its origins in a cross-country flight in the late 1970s. As the plane flew north of Washington, D.C., I found myself looking down at the Capitol Building and Washington Monument. From thirty thousand feet, they looked like little toys sparkling in the sunshine.

From that altitude, all of Washington looked small and insignificant. However, I knew that people down there were making life and death decisions on my behalf and taking themselves very seriously as they did so. From high in the jet stream, it seemed absurd that they could have an impact on my life. It was like ants making laws for humans. On the other hand, I knew that it was all a matter of perspective. When the plane landed, everyone on it would act just like the people over whom we flew.

This line of thought led to a simple but important realization: mental processes and views of life cannot be separated from physical location. Our "world view" as a conceptual framework depends quite literally on our view of the world from a physical place in the universe.

Later, as the plane flew over the deserts and mountains of the western states, the flood of insights continued. I could look down on the network of roads below and actually "see the future." I knew that the car on Route 110 would soon meet up with that other car on Route 37, though the two drivers were not yet aware of it. If they were about to have an accident, I would see it, but they wouldn't.

From the airplane, the message that scientists, philosophers, spiritual teachers, and systems theorists have been trying to tell us for centuries was obvious: everything is interconnected and interrelated, each part a subsystem of a larger whole system.

Finally, after I spent several hours looking out at the Earth's surface, all the insights linked into a single gestalt. This is how I expressed it at the time:

> People living in space settlements will always have an overview! They will be able to see how everything is related, that what appears to be "the world" to people on Earth is merely a small planet in space, and what appears to be "the present" is merely a limited viewpoint to one looking from a higher level. People who live in space will take for granted philosophical insights that have taken those on Earth thousands of years to formulate. They will start at a place we have labored to attain over several millennia.

That moment of realization gave birth to the term "the overview effect," which meant, at the time, the predicted experience of astronauts and space settlers, who would have a different philosophical point of view as a result of having a different physical perspective.

I have been thinking and writing about the Overview Effect a great deal since that time, and this effort has expanded my understanding of the phenomenon enormously. In this book, I explore the fundamental nature of the Overview Effect, along with new insights, which include the following:

- The Overview Effect is only one of the changes in consciousness that can be brought about by spaceflight, and the nature of the experience varies with the individuals involved and the type of mission being flown.
- The impact of the effect is not limited to space travelers alone,

and communication of their experiences to others supports social transformation.

- Satellites and unmanned probes provide a technological analogue to the Overview Effect and other changes in consciousness that take place during manned flights.
- The Overview Effect and related phenomena are the foundations for a series of new civilizations evolving on Earth and in space.
- It is possible to grasp the true implications of this evolutionary process only by seeing it from the viewpoint of the universe as a whole, and from that perspective, the Overview Effect may point to humankind's purpose as a species.

Since beginning the Overview Project, I have come to see space exploration as part of a long tradition of "central projects." According to a book based on research sponsored by Apollo astronaut Edgar Mitchell's Institute of Noetic Sciences, central projects, such as the construction of the Gothic cathedrals and the Egyptian pyramids, are catalysts for social and personal transformation:

> These projects, although involving visible material artifacts, were actually the vehicles for more abstract social and psychological aims. The great cathedrals, besides serving as highly visible central projects to attract the best and most adventurous minds of the age, also served to educate the consciousness of the larger population.[1]

In this book, central projects are also seen as "means of focusing the energies of a population during an evolutionary transition to a higher level of culture" and I subscribe to the statement, "Perhaps the most recent central project was the Apollo project that culminated in Neil Armstrong's famous footstep on the moon."[2]

Was the Apollo program the end of space exploration as a central project or just the beginning? My research on the impact of the Overview Effect suggests that it was merely a warm-up for space exploration's potential role as the greatest central project in human history.

2

The Explorer Fish

I came back with a mass of stored data. I wanted to spend a lot of time thinking back on it and how it related to my experiences here on Earth. It takes a lot of time to do it. I don't think I can assimilate it all in a lifetime, but I'm going to try!

– Payload specialist Charles D. Walker

Fish Consciousness

A fish glides through a liquid world, aware of light and dark, predators and prey, dimly perceiving the ocean bottom below. On occasion, it may leap out of the water and experience "something else" strange and different. That experience, however, is rare and not an essential element of the fish's life. This is "fish consciousness" — in regard to land, water, air, and sky, the fish's knowledge of reality is highly conditioned and extremely restricted by its physical surroundings. If you were a fish, you would have no idea what land is like and only the vaguest notion of what water is like, because water would be the fundamental medium in which you lived. An idea of "sky" would be far beyond your comprehension.

To us, it is a strange and limited life. However, in terms of consciousness and evolution, we are closer to living the life of a fish than we care to realize. Until recently, all human beings have existed in a state much like that of the fish and other marine animals. The planet Earth has been our ocean, from which we have been unable to escape. Even the remote possibility of leaving the planet became imaginable relatively recently.

As a result, it has been extremely difficult to conceive of life off the planet, and without direct experience, we have been limited to speculation. Scientists and science fiction writers have tried to understand the nature of the physical universe beyond our atmosphere, but their attempts were purely conceptual until 1961, when the first human being actually ventured into space.

Since that brief and historic orbital flight by Yuri Gagarin, about two hundred human beings have experienced this wholly new form of existence: living and working in space. Their nonterrestrial time has been brief — several months on the longest journey. Compared to the time humans have spent on this planet, their time in space is hardly measurable. Nevertheless, the vital importance of their experiences is beginning to emerge.

The evidence suggests that humanity's expansion into the solar system and beyond will result in a fundamental transformation of the human species, an evolutionary step unprecedented in human history. To begin the process of understanding why this is so, let's return to the example of our ancestors, the fish.

Exploration and Evolution

Life on land apparently evolved as fish and other marine species learned to breathe air, crawl through the mud, and eat food found on the land, such as insects. What a change it must have been for the first fish to crawl onto the land. It would have been assailed with new experiences unique to its species. For the first time, the fish would have been able to *see* the ocean. What had been the whole world would be part of something far larger. Water would no longer be the invisible context of life, but a visible place to go to and come from. The fish would have felt the wind blowing on its scales, the soil scraping its stomach, and gravity pulling remorselessly on its entire body. New colors, sights, and sounds would have crowded in on its sense organs, overwhelming it with stimuli.

If the first "explorer fish" had been able to talk, it would have had a hard time explaining "land" to its fellows. How would it have described the colors that other fish had never seen, sounds they had not heard, views they couldn't imagine? What would they have made of "weight," the drag on the explorer's body as it tried to maneuver on the rocky shore, using fins as protolegs? How would they have adapted to calling what had been the world simply the ocean?

Could they have understood the importance of what the explorer fish had done? Could they have imagined the implications? Of course, they might have *tried* to understand.

"Amazing," they might say. "That is quite incredible and rather brave of you to have risked it." Some might not have been so charitable. "Yes," they might have said, "very interesting, but how is it relevant to our lives here in the sea? What good is this 'land' to us?"

This first explorer fish would have found it just about impossible to explain to the other fish the full implications of its experience. On the basis of just a few hours or days on land, how could it envision the vast sweep of evolutionary change awaiting life on Earth? It would not have known exactly what it had done, or why.

The Analogy and the Reality

The story of the explorer fish is an analogy, but the question it raises is real: Are our astronauts in much the same situation as that mythical fish? They have entered and lived in a radically new environment, unknown to all but a few of their fellow humans. They have seen their planet from a distance, experienced themselves as weightless entities, gazed outward into an infinite universe, and traveled around the planet in ninety-minute "days" and "nights." They have been criticized for being too laconic, not expressive enough in describing their experiences. "Let's put poets, not test pilots, in space," some have said.

However, that statement misses a critical issue: the problem may not be that the astronauts can't describe their experiences, but that *we can't hear what they're saying.* The astronauts have tried to explain the experience to us, often in quite eloquent language. Some of their books are clear and to the point. But a shared context is critical for real communication to take place, because without it, what is meaningful to one person may be nonsense to another. Clearly, those who have not flown in space do not have a shared context from which to understand the astronauts' descriptions of spaceflight. Skylab astronaut Ed Gibson said, "Our coming back and sharing our experiences is like a drop of dye going into the ocean; it is quickly diffused. I think the pictures of Earth have made an impression, but it will be a matter of osmosis over a long period of time. The more who go, the more difference it will make."[1]

There is a real gulf between our explorers and ourselves, and we cannot bridge it until we admit that it exists. However, flying in space is not absolutely necessary to improve the communication process. The whole point of communication is, after all, to share experiences and create common ground among those who lack the same experiential background.

The term "Overview Effect" is a tool for conceptualizing something most people have not yet experienced. It names the experience for the astronauts as well as for non-astronauts, thereby helping them to communicate more easily. The Overview Effect and other concepts in this book should help develop common ground by describing spaceflight with new terminology and a new conceptual framework.

Developing a clear perspective on the meaning of spaceflight has important public policy implications. When we see, for example, the potential importance of space exploration for human evolution, it provides the perspective required to define a new space program that can replace the old one.

Ultimately, we want to answer the essential question about space exploration and human evolution: What is the fundamental purpose of space exploration, and why do we do it? Lacking direct experience, many have attempted to answer that question with analogies to the past, especially the establishment of colonies here on Earth, and the development of frontiers. These analyses are valuable and should continue. However, they may be too limited, because all previous colonial and frontier experiments shared one common characteristic — they occurred within the biosphere of Earth.

The settlers had to adapt to radically different circumstances in

the Americas, Australia, and Africa. However, all their efforts un-
folded in an environment characterized by normal Earth gravity,
Earthbound space/time coordinates, a natural atmosphere, and many
other characteristics we take for granted.

As humanity moves out into nonterrestrial space, the develop-
mental medium will be quite different, and the results are unpredictable. The thesis of this book is that space exploration is a major
step in a long evolutionary journey, which we humans must make
not only for ourselves, but for the evolution of the universe itself.

3

An Overview of
the Spaceflight Experience

"As you eat breakfast you look out the window . . . and there's the Mediterranean area, Greece and Rome and North Africa and the Sinai . . . You realize that in one glance what you're seeing is what was the whole history of man for years — the cradle of civilization. And you go down across North Africa and out over the Indian Ocean and look up at that great subcontinent of India pointed down toward you as you go past it . . . out over the Philippines and up across that monstrous Pacific Ocean, that vast body of water — you've never realized how big that is before.

"You finally come up across the coast of California, and you look for those friendly things, Los Angeles and Phoenix and on across to El Paso. And there's Houston, there's home . . . and you look and sure enough there's the Astrodome — and you identify with that, it's an attachment. And on across New Orleans and then you look down to the south and there's the whole peninsula of Florida laid out. And all the hundreds of hours you've spent flying across that route down in the atmosphere, all that is friendly again. And you go out across the Atlantic Ocean and back across Africa, and you do it again and again and again.

"You identify with Houston and then you identify with Los Angeles and Phoenix and New Orleans. And the next thing you recognize in yourself is that you're identifying with North Africa — you look forward to that, you anticipate it, and there it is.

"And that whole process of what it is you identify with begins to shift. When you go around the Earth in an hour and a half, you begin to recognize that your identity is with that whole thing. That makes a change. You look down there and you can't imagine how many borders and boundaries you cross, again and again and again, and you don't even see them. There you are — hundreds of people in the Mideast killing each other over some imaginary line that you're not even aware of and that you can't see.

"From where you see it, the thing is a whole, and it's so beautiful. You wish you could take one in each hand, one from each side in the various conflicts, and say, 'Look. Look at it from this perspective. Look at that. What's important?'

"Then you look back on the time you were outside on that EVA and on those few moments that you could take, because a camera malfunctioned, to think about what was happening. And you recall staring out there at the spectacle that went before your eyes, because you're no longer inside something with a window, looking out at a picture. Now you're out there and there are no frames, there are no limits, there are no boundaries. You're really out there, going twenty-five thousand miles an hour, ripping through space, a vacuum. And there's not a sound. There's a silence the depth of which you've never experienced before, and that silence contrasts so markedly with the scenery you're seeing and the speed with which you know you're moving.

"You think about what you're experiencing and why. Do you deserve this, this fantastic experience? Have you earned this in some way? Are you separated out to be touched by God, to have some special experience that others cannot have? You know that the answer to that is no. There's nothing that you've done that deserves that, that earned that; it's not a special thing for you. You know very well at that moment, and it comes through to you so powerfully that you're the sensing element for man. You look down and see the surface of that globe that you've lived on all this time, and you know all those people down there and they are like you, they are you — and somehow you represent them.

"You are up there as the sensing element, that point out on the end, and that's a humbling feeling. It's a feeling that says you have a responsibility. It's not for yourself. The eye that doesn't see doesn't do justice to the body. That's why it's there; that's why you are out there.

"And somehow you recognize that you're a piece of this total life . . . You're out there on the forefront and you have to bring that back somehow. That becomes a rather special responsibility and it tells you something about your relationship with this thing we call life. So that's a change. That's something new. And when you come back there's a difference in the world now. There's a difference in that relationship between you and that planet and you and all those other forms of life on that planet, because you've had that kind of experience. It's a difference and it's so precious.

"And all through this I've used the word *you* because it's not me, it's not Dave Scott, it's not Dick Gordon, Pete Conrad, John Glenn — it's you, it's we. It's Life that's had that experience."[1]

Russell L. Schweickart flew on the Apollo 9 orbital flight following Apollo 8's dramatic journey around the moon during Christmas 1968. His experience was clearly deep and profound, and he is certainly articulate in communicating it. Schweickart is a founder of the Association of Space Explorers, an organization of American astronauts, Soviet cosmonauts, and space fliers from other countries dedicated to exploring the implications of their experiences in terms of unity and cooperation on earth and in space.

What happened to Schweickart is a model of the spaceflight experience when the Overview Effect is at work. However, it should not be assumed that every astronaut or cosmonaut would describe the process exactly the same way. One of the most exciting aspects of spaceflight is that its interpretation is as varied as the astronauts and cosmonauts themselves.

Variations on a Theme

The "space age" is only a quarter century old, and as of 1986, there have been just over one hundred successful manned missions into space, with some two hundred space travelers from the United States, the Soviet Union, and their allied countries.[2]

These missions can be divided into seven different types:

1. Suborbital (initial Mercury missions)
2. Single astronaut orbital (later Mercury missions; Soviet Vostok and Soyuz missions)

3. Multiple astronaut orbital (Gemini, two Apollo missions, Soviet Voskhod and Soyuz)
4. Lunar orbital or flyby (three Apollo missions)
5. Lunar landing (later Apollo missions)
6. Temporary space station (Skylab and Salyut)
7. Shuttle (the space transportation system, or STS)

There is also a subcategory of missions including extra-vehicular activity (EVA), during which some of the most important experiences occurred. These "spacewalks" occurred in all American mission types after Mercury and all Soviet mission types after the Vostok series.

When the Soviet Mir (Peace) space station becomes operational, it will be a new mission type, the first truly permanent human habitat in space. Mir and the American space station planned for the 1990s are precursors of the space settlements of the future, essential building blocks of the "new civilizations" to be discussed in detail later in this book.

These different mission configurations represent all the physical technologies needed to explore and begin developing the "solar neighborhood." However, development will be slow until more work is done to create low-cost access to Low Earth Orbit and new propulsion systems to make the outer limits of the solar system accessible. Until those problems are solved, humanity will remain in a pioneering phase of space exploration, and the spaceflight experience will retain its current shape.

The Halo Spaceflight Experience

There is much more to spaceflight than the time actually spent in space, and its richer levels can best be understood by considering four characteristics that surround the core experience like a halo:

1. There is a difference between the experience itself and the communication of it.
2. The experience begins long before the flight and ends, if ever, long after it.

3. The experience is relatively private while one is in space, but becomes highly public on return.
4. The experience is given a meaning that serves societal needs, but may have little to do with the astronaut's personal experience.

Let's look at these characteristics individually.

1. The question most frequently asked of space travelers is "What was it like?" It is quite appropriate that the question is phrased that way. Without knowing it, when people ask an astronaut what the spaceflight experience is *like*, they are acknowledging that the answer will be a metaphor or simile because no experience on Earth is exactly the same as spaceflight.

As Julian Jaynes, author of *The Origin of Consciousness in the Breakdown of the Bicameral Mind*, points out, metaphor is more than a mechanism of language; it is through metaphor that language grows: "The most fascinating property of language is its capacity to make metaphors. But what an understatement. For metaphor is not a mere extra trick of language . . . it is the very constitutive ground of language."[3] If Jaynes is correct, one result of space exploration is that language will grow as spaceflight is described more frequently.

A typical example of the use of metaphor regarding spaceflight is that of Marc Garneau, who described his time on the shuttle as a "dreamlike experience."[4]

Several astronauts have used the metaphor of visiting the Grand Canyon to comment on the difference between knowing intellectually what would happen in space and being there.

Senator Edwin ("Jake") Garn of Utah, who also flew on the shuttle, put it, "The first time you look out at the Earth and see that, it's a heart-stopper. You say, 'My goodness . . .' and it's like the difference — I don't care how many pictures you've seen of the Grand Canyon, it's not the same as looking over the side and saying, 'My goodness, it really is that deep.' "[5]

2. The second element that enriches spaceflight is the problem of putting boundaries around it. In the most limited definition, the spaceflight experience begins with lift-off and ends with touchdown, but its impact goes far beyond that time frame.

According to Marc Garneau, lift-off has a significant psychological impact even before it occurs, because you have to come to terms with the possibility that you won't survive the trip. "One part of the total experience is the sheer adventure of the launch itself. That internal adjustment, making peace with yourself and squaring off your conscience and preparing for that very short experience, is an adaptation as well."[6]

The astronaut or cosmonaut must consciously or subconsciously prepare for death before lift-off. When a launch is successful, it is a blessing that one continues to live, especially in a new and extraordinary environment.

As for the return to Earth, Byron Lichtenberg, a payload specialist who flew on the space shuttle in 1983, notes that astronauts begin to want to "return to normal" as they near the end of the planned flight. "As it's coming up to eight or nine days, you say, 'It'll be kind of nice to get back. I sort of miss hearing the breeze in the trees and the butterflies in the fields and the bubble of the streams and watching the flowers grow.' "[7]

There are, then, definite recognitions of the beginning and end of the spaceflight experience. However, it is clear that beginning and end are somewhat arbitrary concepts in this case. Anticipation of the experience shapes people's lives and careers, and memory of it acts as a time-release capsule, emitting feelings, insights, thoughts, and ideas over the years after it has occurred.

The experience first takes on a reality with the selection of the astronaut or cosmonaut to join the exclusive group of men and women dedicated to space exploration and development. From then on, they are separated from others and treated as special people, regardless of how they might feel about themselves.

American astronauts train at the Johnson Space Center in Houston, Texas, a community of several thousand people deeply dedicated to the space program and true believers in the benefits it can bring to humanity. Launches take place at the Kennedy Space Center in Florida, known as America's Spaceport and also populated by people who are extremely enthusiastic about the space program. Soviet cosmonauts train at Star City, another separate community committed to space exploration.

The Challenger accident naturally diminished some of the enthusiasm, but a visitor to either of the American facilities in pre-accident days would have been struck by the sense of purposefulness shared by everyone. These feelings are magnified for the astronauts by the long training periods and the sense that each mission is extremely important. As Ed Gibson, a Skylab astronaut, points out, "You have to remember that we were in line for a mission for eight years; it's like a double doctoral degree."[8]

Shuttle astronaut Don Lind, who waited some eighteen years for his flight, said that he didn't mind it because he truly enjoyed what he was doing in supporting other missions, and he had "a front row seat for history."[9]

Everyone in the space program is constantly immersed in the broader spaceflight experience. The astronauts and support personnel are continually planning new missions, providing backup for existing missions, or analyzing results of past missions.

Unlike other professions, in which many people can participate, there are few space travelers even today. Astronauts compete for their positions against thousands of other candidates, which adds to the strong expectation of a positive experience and ensures a high level of motivation. All of that, in turn, is reinforced by the training environment. In most cases, only after years of expectation and months of training does the astronaut get into space.

As the shuttle program has evolved, the training situation has changed to some extent with the new category of payload specialists, who are allowed to fly for a variety of reasons. For example, a country or company that pays NASA to launch its payload has the option of assigning a specialist to the flight. McDonnell Douglas sent Charles Walker on three flights to conduct electrophoresis experiments. Canada's Marc Garneau flew as a payload specialist, as did Senator Jake Garn.

Payload specialists, who often fly with only a few months' training, have a different mind-set from that of career astronauts. In that sense, it is probably much closer to the attitudes of people who will be space settlers than are the career participants. The Soviet space program also includes noncareer space travelers from other countries who fly as Intercosmos Soyuz cosmonaut researchers.

3. Another factor that extends the experience after the return to

Earth is that being in space is relatively private while it occurs, but it becomes intensely public when one returns. If you were special before you went into space, you are more special on your return, because you are one of the few people who can answer the question "What was it like?" You have experienced something available to a tiny fraction of the human population, something mysterious and of the future.

But because the astronaut is a public figure, he or she has to process the experience by constantly talking about it with other people. Marc Garneau has said that it was much easier for him to cope with being in space than adjusting to being a public figure with the new expectations thrust on him by that role.

Charles Walker, in discussing the impact of multiple flights, points out that between missions, he was interpreting each flight on speaking tours. As a result, he said, his understanding of the experience changed every time he described it.

Alan Bean, a former Apollo and Skylab astronaut who is a professional artist, says that what people want to know about spaceflight and what occupies astronauts' minds on a mission can be quite different.

> As an astronaut, you think about all these experiences in a different way when you're doing them than people are interested in hearing about when you get back . . . With each experiment, for example, you have to know how to get it out of its box or how to get the foil off and then how to set it down and how to align it so that it has the right direction . . .
>
> When you come back, people want you to talk about it in a completely different way. You begin to think about [it] only when people ask you. You were really refining other skills.[10]

Most American missions are short, and there are always an overwhelming number of tasks to complete. Companies have put millions of dollars into their payloads, and scientists have often devoted their professional careers to the experiments on board. Astronauts feel a tremendous responsibility to perform well, and they have very little free time to reflect on their experience or to control their time while the flight is under way. Payload specialist Loren Acton was so concerned about doing a good job on his shuttle mission that he concentrated primarily on the work.

The Soviets, who have specialized in long-duration missions, display a more reflective, philosophical tone in their reports. However, they, too, are given many tasks to do in a less than ideal environment. The Soviet reports voice deep concerns about getting along with fellow crew members, avoiding boredom, and coping with cramped living quarters.[11]

4. Finally, cultural roles and expectations have an additional effect on astronauts and cosmonauts. Societies need heroes who are specially selected to undergo hardship and danger on the frontiers of civilization. Space is today's frontier, and the astronauts and cosmonauts have become today's heroes, people who have extraordinary experiences unknown to others in the society, doing something that requires uncommon bravery.

This attitude toward astronauts began early in the American space program. A *Life* magazine editorial, "A Hero's Words to Cherish," quoted some of the words John Glenn spoke after he became the first American to orbit the earth.[12] Someone even composed a popular song about Glenn's "epic ride."

The apparently routine nature of shuttle launches lulled American society into complacency until the Challenger disaster. The word *hero* was then used frequently to describe members of the Challenger crew, and that reverence will probably remain when flights resume. Charles Walker wrote that a new mythology of heroes was being born from that disaster.

The astronauts and cosmonauts fit into the mythical subconscious archetypes of the gods and heroes of old, flying beings who perform feats of daring no one else is able or willing to do. Today's astronauts and cosmonauts may want to ignore the hero role, but for millions of people, it is vitally important that they *be* heroic, because their heroism says something about what it means to be human. NASA may actively discourage the image, and the astronauts may refuse to accept it, but that only increases the cultural pressure to create it.

Astronauts sometimes allude to this issue when they express how difficult it can be for them to talk about the actual spaceflight experience when they know what the audience wants to hear. They undoubtedly tailor their words to the audience's needs to some extent. This means that the spaceflight experience, as it is understood by the culture, is created as much by our expectations as by

what actually takes place. Alan Bean's view is that people want
more from the experience than may be there. "I have to admit
that if I ran into somebody who had climbed the Matterhorn, I
would probably say, 'What is it like?' The answer might reasonably
be, 'It was just like climbing all the other difficult mountains I've
ever climbed.' "[13]

The Core Experience of Spaceflight

Space is relatively close in distance and time. Most shuttle orbits
take place one to two hundred miles above the surface of the Earth,
and it takes only eight and a half minutes to reach Low Earth Orbit
on the shuttle. For most of us, outer space is closer than our favorite
vacation spot. What makes it seem so far away is the cost of getting
there — about $250 million for each shuttle launch. The cost is so
high because we live at the bottom of a deep "gravity well" from
which it isn't easy to get out with current technologies.[14]

Psychologically, space seems far away, but that will change as
less expensive launch technologies are developed. Even then, being
in space will transform a person's fundamental reality in ways that
are not now possible on the surface of the Earth.

The four main components to the core experience include changed
perceptions of space; changed perceptions of time; silence; and
weightlessness.

Perceptions of Space

The truth is that we are already in space. The Earth is a natural
spaceship orbiting the sun, which is itself hurtling around the galactic center, which is in turn rushing through the universe along
with billions of other galaxies. Because of our location on the "ship,"
we do not experience its motions directly. As a result, modern
humanity experiences its place in the universe much as our ancestors did — the Earth appears to be stationary while everything in
the heavens wheels around us.

The big change for the astronauts and cosmonauts is that their physical and mental realities are brought into alignment when they go into space. They have a direct experience of the Overview Effect. If there is a common theme in astronauts' descriptions of changes in spatial perceptions, it is seeing the Earth from orbit and being emotionally unprepared for the experience.

Don Lind's comments are typical: "I have probably looked at as many pictures from space as anybody . . . so I knew exactly what I was going to see. There was no intellectual preparation I hadn't made. But there is no way that you can be prepared for the emotional impact . . . It was a moving enough experience that it brought tears to my eyes."[15]

Prince Sultan Salmon al-Saud of Saudi Arabia, who flew on the shuttle as a payload specialist, echoed Lind's words: "I think the minute I saw the view for the first time was really one of the most memorable moments of my entire life. I just said, in Arabic, 'Oh, God,' or something like 'God is great.' It's beyond description."[16]

And Senator Garn said, "You just want to look all the time, because it finally tells you that this Earth really is round and it really is traveling through space. You've seen it for yourself."[17]

Perceptions of Time

Our experience of time is fundamentally influenced by living on a planetary surface. A day is the time it takes for the Earth to rotate on its axis. A year is the time it takes for the Earth to revolve around the sun. A day could just as easily be called a "ro" for rotation and a year a "rev" for revolution, in which case we might more easily recall their origins. As it is, time has come to be an absolute: seconds, minutes, hours, days, and years have become abstractions measured by clocks and unrelated to the planetary bodies to which they owe their existence.

The abstraction changes when one is no longer on, but is outside of, the primary planetary body that is the source of the units of time. In orbit, an astronaut experiences a sunrise and sunset every ninety minutes by a clock set to Earth time. The true twenty-four-hour day exists only on the surface of the Earth.

Language changes as astronauts begin to measure time in terms of "orbits." Shuttle astronaut Jeff Hoffman commented, "I quickly

stopped carrying any ground clock in my mind. It became irrelevant . . . Everything went by our orbit clock, Mission Elapsed
Time, because all our activities were scheduled in its terms. For
my internal planning activities, I tended to use the orbit as the
basic unit of time."[18]

Time seems to speed up in orbit, but the farther away one gets
from Earth, the more it appears to slow down. On the moon,
according to Apollo astronaut Gene Cernan, "I was watching time
go by on Earth, but time as we understand it did not really affect
us on the moon."[19]

Silence

Sound is the result of the ear's detecting vibrations in the air. Since
space is a vacuum, the only sounds that space travelers can hear
are those that they or the ship makes, and during an EVA, even
those noises are sharply reduced. The quiet, coupled with weightlessness, undoubtedly accounts to some extent for the "dreamlike
quality" Marc Garneau noted.

Mercury astronaut Scott Carpenter said, "The first thing that
impressed me when I got into orbit was the absolute silence. One
reason for this, I suppose, was that the noisy booster had just
separated and fallen away . . . But it was also a result, I think, of
the sensation of floating that I experienced as soon as I became
weightless."[20]

On EVAs, the experience of the silence intensifies. Soviet cosmonaut Valentin Lebedev, describing a spacewalk outside his Salyut space station, writes, "All around there is perfect silence, no
sense of the speed of the flight. No wind whistles in your ears,
nothing weighs on you. The panorama is calm, majestic."[21]

Weightlessness

Human beings take "weight" for granted, because we experience
it constantly. For our bodies to feel weight, they must be in prox-
imity to another body, such as a planet. Even then, weight is
relative. The moon, because it is smaller than Earth, provides one-
sixth as much gravity as Earth, and Mars about one-third. On

Jupiter or Saturn a human would feel that he or she weighed tons. Because of this relativity, "one G" has become a standard, referring to "a weight equal to that experienced on Earth" and "zero G" its opposite, referring to an absence of the experience of weight.

As many as half of all astronauts have experienced a kind of space sickness known as space adaptation syndrome. The cause is unknown, but moving around in zero G and a resulting disorientation is considered to be a primary contributor. There is a pleasant, even euphoric reaction to the experience when it is under control. According to John Glenn, for example,

> I found weightlessness to be extremely pleasant. I must say it is convenient for a space pilot . . . The fact that this strange phenomenon seemed so natural at the time indicates how rapidly man can adapt to a new environment. I am sure that I could have gone for a much longer period in a weightless condition without being bothered by it at all. You feel completely free. The state is so pleasant, as a matter of fact, that we joked that a person could probably become addicted to it without any trouble. I know that I could.[22]

Being weightless is the human opportunity to fly, to feel like a bird. "Up" and "down" mean nothing at all in space, further contributing to the sense of living in a fundamentally different medium.

As payload specialist Byron Lichtenberg put it, "It was just amazing to go wherever you wanted. You could fly up in the corner, you could hang upside down. There was no 'up' or 'down' anymore."[23]

Returning to Earth

Most space travelers flourish in the new medium. They enjoy themselves and sometimes regret having to return home. Having been out of the "womb," they may feel that returning home is like a constriction of possibilities. In Gene Cernan's words, "You can't return home without feeling that difference . . . You wonder, if only everyone could relate to the beauty and the purposefulness of it, the reality of the infinity of time and space, how our star moves through time and space with such logic and purpose."[24]

In "An Astronaut's Diary," initially recorded aboard the shuttle Discovery, astronaut Jeff Hoffman reads from a poem written by a mountain climber. He offers it toward the end of the mission as an example of how it feels to be in space and then return to Earth. The poem also captures the power and the long-term impact of the Overview Effect:

> You cannot stay on the summit forever; you have to come down again. So why bother in the first place? Just this: what is above knows what is below, but what is below does not know what is above.
>
> One climbs, one sees; one descends, one sees no longer, but one has seen. There is an art of conducting oneself in the lower regions by the memory of what one saw higher up. When one can no longer see, one can at least still know.[25]

Being in space, like mountain climbing, is an intensely human experience. Analysis can capture the essential features of the space-flight experience, but cannot do it justice, because it is a multi-dimensional life experience. Most astronauts see it as the culmination of their life goals, a feeling reinforced by a community of fellow astronauts and supportive space program workers.

There is an intense psychological buildup to lift-off, punctuated by a note of fear, followed by a feeling of incredible power as the rockets fire, and then the sense of moving into a whole new world where one's perceptions of the universe itself are transformed. Charles Walker said, "Space is a place, but it is also an all-encompassing experience."[26]

Is Spaceflight a Spiritual Experience?

Spaceflight is a physical experience quite different from any on Earth. It is also a mental experience filled with new insights that may have enormous impact. But is spaceflight a spiritual experience? This question causes debate and uncertainty among astronauts and observers alike. Many people believe that all astronauts have profound experiences in space and that their lives are fundamentally changed. The reality is far more complex than that, and these differences will be brought out in greater detail in succeeding chapters. There are, however, a few key insights that can be offered here.

Astronaut Don Lind took an interest in this issue, discussed it with "just about everyone who went to the moon," and says, "Obviously, the people who had a profound religious background before they left were impressed in those terms, and those who were too busy to be religious before they left were too busy to be religious when they came back. So I don't think that sort of thing changed anybody."[27]

Apollo 14 astronaut Edgar Mitchell, who spent sixteen years constructing a new conceptual framework for understanding his experience, argues that while the experience is the same, its interpretation varies widely with the individual.

The issue requires a careful definition of "spiritual," and the culture's halo interpretation may distort the nature of the core event. Both the halo and core elements of spaceflight strongly parallel experiences typical of many different spiritual paths. However, the relationships are far more subtle than one might expect. Throughout history, people have been initiated into the "mysteries" of higher consciousness. The purpose of these efforts has always been an experience of inner transformation. However, the parallels between the inner and outer journey have been striking.

The emphasis on being selected for and living in a separate community distinct from the rest of the world, with long periods of training and discipline, for example, are quite similar in spiritual practices and in the space community. In many spiritual disciplines, especially Zen Buddhism, the specific focus is on "the practice" rather than on the ultimate "experience," which is also true of spaceflight.

The metaphor of "the mission" and "the journey" are powerful symbols both for spiritual practitioners and for astronauts. Many disciplines of spiritual growth use the metaphor of the "journey" or "path" to describe the process of awakening to enlightenment. The pilgrimage to a holy place, taking a physical trip to reinforce the spiritual journey, is also a time-honored tradition in many cultures.

In most spiritual practices, growth is attained through an expansion of one's sense of identity. The initiate increasingly identifies with larger and larger systems beyond the individual self until he or she identifies with the Absolute or the universe, the greatest whole of all. That process is mirrored in the experiences characteristic of spaceflight, as Rusty Schweickart's description clearly shows.

The willingness of astronauts and cosmonauts to fulfill the societal need for heroes, risking their lives for the sake of humanity as a whole, is a self-sacrificing element characteristic of a spiritual person's place in society.

In addition to the halo experience being unconsciously spiritual in its structure, the core element includes many factors that are consciously sought in producing breakthroughs in consciousness. Intense physical work followed by periods of meditation and contemplation, sometimes of a holy image, are typical of monastic communities and others devoted to spiritual development, and this pattern is followed closely in space exploration.

Confronting one's own death, followed by rebirth, is a central theme in many schools of growth and development. In spaceflight, the experience of one's fears at lift-off, followed by the transition into a wholly different world in orbit, mirrors the death/rebirth cycle. Finally, the weightlessness and silence of space contribute to sensory deprivation, conditions that are cultivated in isolation tanks and other efforts to achieve transformations in consciousness.

There certainly have been breakthrough experiences akin to "enlightenment" on space missions. However, this does not make spaceflight a spiritual experience per se. Just as some people can go to church and feel nothing, while others are enraptured just by looking at a flower, there are those who have had profound experiences in outer space and those for whom it was simply a job well done.

Edgar Mitchell prefers to avoid the word *spiritual* and to discuss, instead, expansions in consciousness and belief systems. He says that being open to the new information of the experience is the key. "To me, the difference between getting and not getting an 'aha' experience out of it is whether it shifts your structure a bit. Do you get a sense of freedom, of expansiveness, because you've just experienced something that is different from your previous experiences and beliefs?"[28]

It is probably most accurate to say that spaceflight is a spiritual experience for some and not for others, but that going into space is certainly a modern metaphor for the journey to higher awareness. Space exploration has perhaps always been a central project for humanity, without our fully understanding it. As such, it is a holistic experience, encompassing physical, mental, and spiritual aspects of human existence. Also, as in the construction of Gothic cathedrals, the opportunity for personal growth and transformation is available for everyone working on the project, not just the astronauts.

It is important to see that the spaceflight experience has varied not only among individuals and societies, but over time as well. The perceptions and feelings of today's space travelers are different from those of the past, just as today's breakthrough experiences will be the everyday realities of future civilizations. Spaceflight, like so many other elements of life in a human system, evolves, and that process will continue as we learn more about how we can use it to change ourselves and our social systems.

4

The Early Orbital Missions
and Hints of the Overview Effect

SCHIRRA: It's kind of hard to describe all this, isn't it, John?
GLENN: Yeah, it sure is, Wally. You can't describe it.

> – Mercury astronauts Wally Schirra and John Glenn in
> *Appointment on the Moon*

Efforts to communicate the impact of spaceflight began with the earliest orbital missions. "What was it like?" and "What did it mean?" were the questions of the early 1960s, as they are today. The sight of the Earth elicited the most consistent comments, and this remains the heart of the experience of the Overview Effect.

The first human to enter the region beyond the Earth's atmosphere was Yuri Gagarin, who clearly answered the question as to whether spaceflight was an extraordinary emotional experience. He later wrote of his flight, "Trembling with excitement, I watched a world so new and unknown to me, trying to see and remember everything." Gagarin also compared the experience to flying: "The Earth through the window of the spacecraft looked approximately as it does from a jet plane at high altitudes. The mountain ridges, the great rivers, massive forests, ocean shorelines stood out sharply. I could see both clouds and their faint shadows on the surface of the Earth."[1]

Soon after Gagarin's mission, Alan Shepard became the first American in space. Shepard's flight lasted only fifteen minutes, but it was long enough for him to be impressed.

It was now time to go to the periscope. I had been well briefed on what to expect, and one of the last things I had done . . . before suiting up was to study . . . some special maps which showed me the view I would get. I had some idea of the huge variety of color and land masses and cloud cover which I would see from 100 miles up. But no one could be briefed well enough to be completely prepared for the astonishing view that I got.

My exclamation back to Deke [Donald K. Slayton] about the "beautiful sight" was completely spontaneous. It was breathtaking.[2]

Shepard's comment on not being prepared for the view is typical of later reports comparing intellectual expectations to the actual sight of the Earth from orbit.

The two Americans who flew suborbital missions, Shepard and Virgil I. ("Gus") Grissom, had time only to be "stunned" and "fascinated" by the view before they returned to Earth. It was left to John Glenn, the first American to orbit the Earth, to begin describing how the planet looked in detail.

I could see hundreds of miles in every direction — the sun on white clouds, patches of blue water beneath and great chunks of Florida and the southeastern U.S. . . . While I was reporting in by radio to the Canary Island tracking station, I had my first glimpse of the coast of Africa. The Atlas Mountains were clearly visible through the window. Inland, I could see huge storms from brush fires raging along the edge of the desert.[3]

Glenn was also impressed by the beauty of the sunsets.

The sun is perfectly round and it gives off an intense, clear light which is more bluish-white than yellow . . . Then, just as the sun starts to sink into the bright horizon, it seems to flatten out a little. As the sun gets lower and lower, a black shadow moves across the earth until the entire surface that you can see is dark except for the bright band of light along the horizon.

At the beginning, this band is almost white in color. But as the sun sinks deeper the bottom layer of light turns to bright orange. The next layers are red, then purple, then light blue, then darker blue, and finally the blackness of space. They are all brilliant colors, more brilliant than in a rainbow, and the band extends out about 60 degrees on either side of the sun. It is a fabulous display.[4]

All seven original American astronauts were test pilots, a breed not given to displaying excitement during a flight. Shuttle astronaut Jeff Hoffman points out that the attitude is reinforced by a tradition that radio time in flight is a precious commodity, not to be wasted in idle chatter.

Since many who followed the Mercury astronauts were also pilots, this may account for their low-key descriptions of the earlier flights. Looking back at what the astronauts wrote and said about spaceflight, however, there is little doubt that many were deeply moved by what they saw and felt. A few stand out from the others in expressing the depth of those feelings.

Among the early American astronauts, Scott Carpenter is unique in this regard. Calling his Mercury mission "the supreme experience of my life," Carpenter mixed descriptions of the view from orbit with discussions of his emotions.

He noted that on the first orbit he concentrated on the control systems and did not really look around.

> When I finally did, the sight was overwhelming. There were cloud formations that any painter could be proud of — little rosettes or clustered circles of fair-weather cumulus down below . . . I could look off for perhaps a thousand miles in any direction, and everywhere I looked the window and the periscope were constantly filled with beauty . . .
>
> I found it difficult to tear my eyes away and go on to something else. Everything is so new and so awe-inspiring that it is difficult to concentrate for very long on any one thing. Later on, when I knew that I was returning to some wonderful sight that I had seen before, I could hardly wait to get there. Using the special camera I carried, I took pictures as fast as I could, and as I raced towards night . . . I saw the beginnings of the most fantastically beautiful view I have ever had — my first sunset in space.[5]

Crossing the United States in the early morning light, Carpenter noted that he could see the ground "remarkably well" and "At every new sight, my elation was renewed, and I kept waiting again for the next one."[6]

Carpenter gave the space program managers a scare by using up too much of his fuel during the flight and landing two hundred miles downrange from the recovery area. Unfortunately, Carpenter's enthusiasm for his experience and his landing error have become intertwined over the years, with more attention being paid to the latter. After that, Walter Schirra decided it would be better to fly a "textbook flight," which he did. While it was a technical triumph, it appeared to be a much less emotional and exciting experience.

Gordon Cooper, on the last Mercury flight, created a stir when he reported incredible detail in his observations of Earth from an orbit of 101 miles. He said he could see houses in the Himalayan Mountains, Tibet, and the southwestern areas of the United States. He claimed to see smoke rising from the chimneys of individual houses in Tibet and the lakes near the Manned Spacecraft Center in Houston.[7]

Experts in optics suggested that Cooper's claims were implausible and that he might be hallucinating. However, his reports were later found to be consistent with research work at a National Bureau of Standards laboratory in Colorado. There it was found that vision may suffer closer to image-distorting turbulence in the lower atmosphere and therefore might well be improved in orbit.[8]

Some of the impact of seeing the Earth from space may derive from its unexpected clarity, which may itself be a component of the Overview Effect.

Summarizing the Early Flights

During this period, the Soviet space program followed a path of increasingly longer orbital flights, and the reports of their cosmonauts are not unlike those of the astronauts. Shortly after the end of the Mercury program, the two national efforts diverged. President Kennedy's commitment to a moon mission truncated the Mercury series and pushed the United States ahead into Gemini and Apollo. The Soviets eventually abandoned their lunar efforts and made an ongoing commitment to long-duration orbital flights that continues today.

As a result of these program changes, the social impact of spaceflight began to change as well. However, even this brief review of the earlier suborbital and orbital flights suggests that the experience can have a major effect on one's perceptions of life.

Scott Carpenter commented,

> It was so thrilling and so overwhelming that I only wished I could get up the next morning and go through the whole thing all over again. I wanted to be weightless again, and see the sunrises and sunsets, and watch the stars drop through the luminous layer, and learn to master that machine a little better so I could stay up longer. There's no doubt about it, space is a fabulous frontier, and we are going to solve some of its mysteries and bring back many of its riches in our lifetime. I would not miss that for anything.[9]

The idea that there are no boundaries on the planet except natural ones is not strongly pronounced in accounts of the early flights. Rather, there is an emphasis on the beauty of the Earth as seen from space and the excitement of the experience itself. There are, however, early linkages of the perspective from space with

Table 4.1
The Early Flights

Between April 1961 and May 1963, ten human beings first saw the Earth from space. Even during this early period, flights lasting longer than three days were achieved, and humanity, after millions of years of confinement to the surface of Earth, had finally achieved a toehold in space.

Flight	Date	Astronaut/Cosmonaut	Time in Space
Vostok 1	4/12/61	Yuri Gagarin	1 hr 48 min
Freedom 7	5/5/61	Alan Shepard	15 min
Liberty Bell 7	7/21/61	Virgil ("Gus") Grissom	15 min
Vostok 2	8/6/61	Gherman Titov	25 hr 18 min
Friendship 7	2/20/62	John Glenn	4 hr 55 min
Aurora 7	5/24/62	Scott Carpenter	4 hr 56 min
Vostok 3	8/11/62	Andrian Nikolyev	94 hr 22 min
Vostok 4	8/12/62	Pavel Popovich	60 hr 57 min
Sigma 7	10/3/62	Walter Schirra	9 hr 13 min
Faith 7	5/15/63	Gordon Cooper	34 hr 19 min

Total Flights: 10   Hours in Space: 236.30   Days in Space: 9.84

Source: Tim Furniss, *Space Flight: The Records* (Enfield, England: Guinness Books, 1985).

social issues on Earth. *Life's* report on John Glenn's flight said, "Glenn is obviously eager to revisit man's 'new ocean' . . . But Glenn also professes 'no better purpose in my life or my endeavor . . . than that we might have a little more peaceful cooperation in the world in this area.' "[10]

The idea that spaceflight and planetary peace are somehow linked became a much stronger theme as space exploration continued beyond the early flights and goes on today. In announcing that he would stand for reelection to the Senate in 1986 Glenn reflected on the privilege of seeing the Earth from orbit and his continuing desire to bring peace and unity to the world.[11]

5

Later Orbital and Lunar Missions: The Overview Effect and Other Changes in Perception

Being in Earth orbit versus going out beyond must be separated. Philosophically, we have really had two different space programs.

– Gemini and Apollo astronaut Eugene A. Cernan

As the United States completed the Mercury program in 1963, the two spacefaring powers of that time were drawing even in their space race. By the end of 1963, the Soviets had registered a series of impressive firsts in space: the first man in space, the first person to spend a full day in orbit, the first orbit of two spacecraft at the same time, and the first woman in space. However, President John F. Kennedy had transformed the American space program by providing it with a sense of vision and purpose, essential elements in driving a human system forward.

In announcing the Apollo project, Kennedy gave the American space program a clear-cut goal: to land a man on the moon and return him safely by the end of the decade. The Gemini program, which followed Mercury and preceded Apollo, began in mid 1963 and became the laboratory in which many of the essential elements of the Apollo effort were tried out in Earth orbit.

After the highly successful Apollo moon landings, the little-known Skylab space station program briefly paced the Soviet efforts to perfect long-duration Earth orbit missions, moving toward the establishment of a permanent human presence in space.

These later orbital and lunar missions added three important components to the conditions that astronauts and cosmonauts faced in outer space: EVAs, allowing the space traveler to experience the nonterrestrial environment more directly than in a spaceship or on a space station; longer missions, allowing for time to reflect on what is being seen; and missions beyond the Earth's orbit, which allow the entire Earth to be seen for the first time.

These elements apparently encourage the experience not only of the Overview Effect, but also deeper experiences, which I call the Copernican Perspective and the Universal Insight.

The EVA

Rusty Schweickart says that the EVA allows the astronaut to see the universe with "no frames and no boundaries," not even a spaceship window. For Earth dwellers who can't even conceive of flying in a spaceship, the importance of this new distinction may be obscure, but most astronauts who made EVAs confirm that it is a completely different experience.

Longer Missions

In the early missions, the astronauts were kept busy and came back to Earth after a few orbits. As Gemini and Apollo astronaut Michael Collins describes it, being in Earth orbit is a bit like riding a roller coaster in that sensations and experiences come and go very quickly.

Longer missions in orbit and trips to the moon and back allow space travelers much more time to take in and process the information their senses are sending to them. This can lead to experiences quite different from those that take place on a short orbital mission.

Seeing the Whole Earth

For all the impact of seeing the planet from a one- to two-hundred-mile orbital distance, astronauts or cosmonauts at that level do not see the whole Earth, but rather large sections of its surface. Not until 1968, when Apollo 8 went to the moon, were astronauts able to view the whole Earth.

Eugene Cernan put it, "Without question, when you are in Earth orbit, you get a new perspective, but you don't have time to get philosophical about it . . . When you leave Earth orbit, all those coastlines and rivers you see in orbit become oceans and continents. You can see from pole to pole and ocean to ocean without even turning your head."[1]

Lunar missions are unique in the history of space exploration because they include every important element of the spaceflight experience. Astronauts going to the moon orbit the earth, leave Low Earth Orbit, see the whole Earth, and have longer missions. Some even conduct an EVA on a "planet" other than Earth.

Later Orbital Missions and the Overview Effect

Russell L. ("Rusty") Schweickart, selected in 1963 in the third group of American astronauts, had not flown in space prior to Apollo 9. His commentary, which begins Chapter 3, illustrates a fundamental change in astronaut awareness that begins with later orbital and lunar missions. In particular, he sees that the divisions among nations, the "parts" of which we are so aware on Earth, disappear and become unimportant from orbit. He also sees that these insights change the viewer's sense of his identity.

Schweickart's experience is also special because of his active efforts to communicate it to the public and through the Association of Space Explorers. When I interviewed him I asked what happened when he told others about his experience. Did they change as well? His answer was that they do. "In some cases, nothing is transmitted at all. Often, it is so profound and immediate that it scares me."[2]

My own response to Schweickart's work has been instructive. In mid 1985, I was writing a paper on the Overview Effect in preparation for a conference at the Space Studies Institute (SSI) in Princeton. As I entered Schweickart's words about being "the sensing element of humanity" into the word processor, I suddenly knew what he meant. It was an "aha" experience for me.

I saw humanity as an organism and grasped the reality of his experience as the "eye" of humanity. I felt that, in writing it down, I was like a "neuron" firing, sending the message down the line to others. It had taken sixteen years for the message to get from the universe to Schweickart to me. I realized that while it may take time, a message is being transmitted.

Schweickart may be unique. With the exception of Edgar Mitchell, founder of the Institute of Noetic Sciences, few astronauts seem to have been as deeply affected by spaceflight as he. However, the number of astronauts and cosmonauts who have deep experiences may not be as important as how well they communicate it to others.

That is why the Overview Effect must be seen from a sociological as well as a psychological perspective. From a psychological viewpoint, it is important to know how many astronauts or cosmonauts had profound experiences and what they were. From a sociological perspective, the primary issue is how they interpret the experience and transmit the message to the rest of the species. One articulate astronaut using today's highly evolved communications system can accomplish that task almost alone.

The Lunar Missions

Twenty-four astronauts went to the moon. They either landed there, orbited the moon, or flew by it and returned to Earth. Of those, twelve walked on the lunar surface.[3] The astronauts and cosmonauts who have gone into space make up an infinitesimal percentage of the planet's population. Those who have gone to the moon represent 13 percent of all space travelers, and those who have walked

on the moon are 6 percent of the total. The lunar astronauts con-
stitute one of the most exclusive minorities in the world, and the
"moonwalkers" are an elite within an elite.

Not surprisingly, it also appears that the Apollo astronauts have
had some of the most profound experiences in space. The astronaut
in Earth orbit has a new and different relationship with the Earth,
but it is still the primary point of reference in the universe as a
whole. By contrast, the lunar astronaut sees the Earth grow smaller
each day of the voyage and enters the gravitational field of another
planetary body. For a brief period of time, instead of relating
primarily to the natural system Earth, along with several billion
other humans, the tiny human system known as the Apollo crew
relates more directly to the moon.

As Rusty Schweickart put it, the lunar astronauts see the earth
very differently from those who go into Earth orbit.

> And a little later on, your friend . . . goes out to the moon. Now
> he looks back and he sees the Earth not as something big, where
> he can see the beautiful details, but . . . as a small thing . . . The
> contrast between that bright blue and white Christmas tree orna-
> ment and the black sky, that infinite universe, really comes through. [4]

The orbital astronaut sees the Earth as huge and himself as less
significant. The lunar astronaut sees the Earth as small and feels
the awesome grandeur of the entire universe. This brings home
the meaning of Gene Cernan's view of there being two different
space programs, one in Earth orbit and the other beyond.

Both programs change the astronaut's perception of the Earth
and of his or her own identity, but in quite different ways. Schweickart
says, the Earth

> is so small and so fragile and such a precious little spot in that
> universe that you can block it out with your thumb, and you realize
> on that small spot, that little blue and white thing, is everything
> that means anything to you — all of history and music and poetry
> and art and death and birth and love, tears, joy, games, all of it on
> that little spot out there that you can cover with your thumb. And
> you realize from that perspective that you've changed, that there's
> something new there, that the relationship is no longer what it was. [5]

Gene Cernan uses similar language: "You . . . say to yourself, 'That's humanity, love, feeling, and thought.' You don't see the barriers of color and religion and politics that divide this world. You wonder, if you could get everyone in the world up there, wouldn't they have a different feeling?"[6]

Michael Collins, who orbited the moon while Neil Armstrong and Edwin E. ("Buzz") Aldrin Jr. were the first humans to walk on it, also wrote about the experience of being "100,000 miles out, to look out four windows and find nothing but black infinity, to finally locate the blue and white golf ball in the fifth window, to know how fortunate we are to return to it."[7]

Seeing the Earth from the moon intensifies the awareness that there are no real boundaries between us on Earth. Collins speaks of this when he says,

> I think the view from 100,000 miles could be invaluable in getting people together to work out joint solutions, by causing them to realize that the planet we share unites us in a way far more basic and far more important than differences in skin color or religion or economic system. The pity of it is that so far the view from 100,000 miles has been the exclusive property of a handful of test pilots, rather than the world leaders who need this new perspective, or the poets who might communicate it to them.[8]

Collins realizes that having a few people see the planet from 100,000 miles is only the beginning of the experience for the society. In our interview, Collins elaborated on this last point by saying that the best crew for an Apollo mission would be a "philosopher, a priest, and a poet." Then he added, "Unfortunately, they would kill themselves trying to fly the spacecraft."[9]

Overall, there is something incredibly powerful about going to the moon. Gene Cernan said, for example,

> When I was the last man to walk on the moon in December 1972, I stood in the blue darkness and looked in awe at the earth from the lunar surface. What I saw was almost too beautiful to grasp. There was too much logic, too much purpose — it was just too beautiful to have happened by accident. It doesn't matter how you choose to worship God . . . He has to exist to have created what I was privileged to see.[10]

Thus, the lunar astronaut, in seeing so much more of the solar system and the universe than the orbital astronaut, begins to sense that an underlying purpose may lie behind it all. This is the essence of a "new psychology for a new civilization," a recognition of what is important through an understanding of who we are and where we are in the universe as a whole.

Apollo astronaut Jim Irwin and others have suggested that it is the contrast between the Earth and the moon that jolts astronauts into a different awareness. The Earth is a water planet, beautiful, full of life, and hospitable to life.

Perhaps the unique lunar expedition experience belongs to Edgar Mitchell, who flew on the Apollo 14 mission and was the sixth man on the moon. Just as Russell Schweickart's experience is a model for the Overview Effect, Mitchell's is a good example of the Universal Insight. Significantly, the experience occurred while Mitchell was gazing at the Earth. According to an article in *Omni* magazine,

> On the way back from the moon, while contemplating the earth, Mitchell had a "peak experience or a religious experience, depending on what word you want to use." It was an "explosion of awareness, an aha! a wow!" It was, apparently, what a religious person would call a revelation.
>
> He came to realize that the universe is made up of spirit and matter but that they are not separate. The bridge is consciousness. God is something like a universal consciousness manifest in each individual, and the route to divine reality and to a more satisfying human, material reality is through the human consciousness.[11]

In our interview, Mitchell said that he could now articulate his understanding of the experience much better than when he was interviewed for the *Omni* article. He explained that his breakthroughs came from being completely open to the initial experience and then spending sixteen years interpreting it. Today, he is close to developing a systematic structure for describing his experience with great precision. In terms of its eventual implications, Mitchell sees spaceflight revolutionizing our value systems.

> Spaceflight is one of the more powerful experiences that humans can have, and the technological event of breaking the bonds of Earth

is far more important than the technology that went into it, because of this perspective . . .

Spaceflight, getting outside of Earth and seeing it from a different perspective, having this sort of explosive awareness that some of us had, this abiding concern and passion for the well-being of Earth . . . will have a direct impact on philosophy and value systems. It's got to be investigated far more thoroughly.[12]

Schweickart's experience was the foundation for the Association of Space Explorers, and Edgar Mitchell founded the Institute of Noetic Sciences and is constructing an entirely new philosophical system based on his experience. In this way, the impact of space on a single astronaut is amplified and magnified throughout society and may affect the lives of millions.

Gene Cernan perhaps summed up the lunar experience best when he said, "I can talk about it for a long time. It is one of the deepest, most emotional experiences I have ever had."[13]

Something significant happened to the astronauts who went to the moon and to the nation that sent them there. To some extent, neither the astronauts nor the nation has been quite the same since. The lunar missions were a transformational reaching outward by humanity, followed by a long period of equilibrium, which continues today. These missions were shaped by the politics of Earth at the time and produced unpredictable results that will profoundly affect the politics of the future.

In the meantime, the Soviet Union turned away from the moon and began to establish its leadership in long-duration missions in Low Earth Orbit. For a brief time in the post-Apollo era, the United States followed the same path with the Skylab program.

Skylab and the Early Salyut Missions

The Skylab program used off-the-shelf Apollo materials to build and staff a temporary space station. The nine Skylab astronauts, who manned the station in three different crews in 1973 and 1974, learned a great deal about the psychology and sociology of living in space. Their extended stays in orbit, from twenty-eight to eighty-four days' duration, allowed them to experience the Overview Effect over time, with an opportunity to absorb and assimilate the experience.

On such extended missions, the astronauts were able to learn how people living in space over long periods might relate to one another. Their experiences confirmed and intensified what their predecessors had found, but Apollo and Skylab were different approaches to space.

Alan Bean, a veteran of both the Apollo and Skylab programs, reported that except for the first and the last few days, Skylab did not offer the astronaut the continuing stimulation of the lunar mission. But it did encourage a more contemplative approach to spaceflight. Many Skylab astronauts developed a strong interest in Earthgazing. For example, the Skylab 4 crew, Gerald Carr, Edward Gibson, and William Pogue, seemed to draw some of the same insights from the experience as Schweickart did. Toward the end of the mission, the astronauts made Earth-gazing a daily ritual.

> As Gibson and his two crewmates sat looking at the Earth, they found that they were being drawn into a new frame of mind. Much of what they saw they already knew, but actually *seeing* it gave it a crystal clarity. Gibson, for example, knew that the world didn't have any boundary lines marked on it like a library globe, but he was nonetheless surprised when he saw from space that there were no dividing lines between people.[14]

According to Gibson, the experience had a lasting effect on him. "In no way could we on Earth, or any group of people or any country, consider ourselves isolated; we are all in this together." He also reportedly felt that he understood more clearly how this is "one world" than those who had not been into outer space could.[15]

Carr said that those who came back from the experience brought with them an increased interest in ecology because "they see how much snow and desert there is, and how hard it is for the people who live there." As a result, one becomes more "humanitarian."[16]

The Skylab astronauts confirmed that being outside on EVA was even more powerful than being inside the spacecraft. Jack Lousma, the pilot for the Skylab 3 mission, said,

> It's like a whole new world out there! Your perspective changes. When you're inside looking out the window, the Earth's impressive,

but it's like being inside a train; you can't get your head around the flat pane of glass. But if you stand outdoors, it's like being on the front end of a locomotive as it's going down the track![17]

Ed Gibson, who went on three EVAs, confirmed the experience when he said, "That is really the great outdoors. You feel as though you are a satellite yourself. You understand that it is you and the universe."[18]

Gerald Carr, who was out on EVA for a total of about fifteen hours, talks about seeing the Earth against the backdrop of the whole universe. "I reared back and looked at Earth with no local frame of reference at all. It was a fine experience. I also looked at the comet Kohoutek and got a feeling for the infiniteness of the universe. There are billions of stars, many that you can't see from the ground."[19]

Gibson described a serenity toward life:

You see how diminutive your life and concerns are compared to other things in the universe. Your life and concerns are important to *you*, of course. But you can see that a lot of the things you worry about don't make much difference in an overall sense. The result is that you enjoy the life that is before you; you don't sweat so much about the next milestone . . . It allows you to have inner peace.[20]

The Meaning of the Experiences

In retrospect, the race to the moon that captured so much attention seems far less significant than what happened to the moon racers themselves and to those involved with far less dramatic programs such as Skylab and Salyut. It may be most important that the potential range of experiences in space is beyond what was originally imagined. For some, there was certainly a sense of an overview, but for others, the results were more subtle and powerful.

We can see, for example, the outlines of the Copernican Perspective, a realization of the Earth's place within the solar system, and the Universal Insight, a realization of the Earth's place in the universe, appearing in the commentaries of these astronauts. Many of them have come back to Earth and begun to pursue activities that not only carry the message, but aim at intentionally changing human consciousness and social awareness.

The Association of Space Explorers and Institute of Noetic Sciences are two institutions that would not have existed without the space program, even though there was very little in NASA's planning to indicate that these would be typical spin-offs of space exploration.

Some astronauts apparently experienced no change in their lives or chose not to report on it. But as shuttle astronaut Charles Walker and lunar astronaut Edgar Mitchell have both pointed out, it may take months or even years to absorb and interpret the experience of being in space. For this reason, silence may not mean that nothing has happened to a space traveler's personal awareness, or that nothing will happen in the future.

It has taken us almost twenty-five years to begin understanding the impact of space exploration on human consciousness and on society, and there is still a great deal that we do not know. We may never know all of the societal effects of spaceflight because it will not be possible to trace some of the subtler influences. However, every new bit of information is valuable, because it adds to the ability to shape human evolution through space exploration, thereby developing new, more effective human civilizations.

6

The Space Shuttle: Consolidation of the Effect

> You can't see the boundaries over which we fight wars, and in a very real way, the inhabitants of this Earth are stuck on a very beautiful, lovely little planet in an incredibly hostile space, and everybody is in the same boat.
>
> – Former shuttle astronaut Don L. Lind

A Time of Transition

After the last Apollo mission to the moon in 1972 and the Skylab missions in 1973, the American space program entered a quiet period. Except for the joint Apollo-Soyuz flight in 1975, no manned American spacecraft left Earth from late 1973 until April 1981, when the first space shuttle was launched on the twentieth anniversary of Yuri Gagarin's flight.

Space activists look at this period and mourn the lost opportunities to push forward from the beachheads on the moon and in Low Earth Orbit, and the United States did lose an opportunity at that time. However, what happened was perfectly understandable and even predictable. As Gene Cernan points out, Apollo was not so much a triumph of technology as a triumph of the human spirit of those who dare to challenge the future that helped us, perhaps ahead of our time, get to the moon. The United States was committed to the moon program as part of the New Frontier vision that included a war on poverty, a Peace Corps to aid the Third World, a defense of democracy all over the planet, and elimination of racial prejudice at home.

It was an ambitious vision. However, by the end of 1963, President Kennedy, its architect, had been assassinated. By the end of 1968, when Apollo 8 took the first men to the moon, the nation was in disarray. Martin Luther King, symbol of the nonviolent effort to achieve racial justice, had been killed, and Robert Kennedy, heir apparent to his brother's vision, was also dead.

The space community mounted an effort to build on the successes of Apollo and Skylab. A task force produced a report not unlike the recent publication by the National Commission on Space. It envisioned a shuttle, a space station, a base on the moon, and exploration of Mars. However, the many problems of the Nixon administration diverted attention from the space program in the early 1970s.[1]

The nation had reached beyond itself with Apollo, and as Don Lind pointed out, the success of the old space program represented one of the only counterweights to a general feeling of pessimism in the late 1960s and early 1970s, when Americans didn't think very much of themselves, and their pride in the space program boosted their self-esteem.

The United States simply could not meet all the demands on its political, social, and economic subsystems to maintain the transforming direction that Apollo had charted for it. Landing on the moon was a goal that was part of a vision, but it never made sense as an end in itself. As a result, the program slipped back into equilibrium from 1972 to 1981, when the launching of Columbia represented the next leap ahead.

During that time, the concept of the shuttle as part of a complete space transportation system was obscured, and the shuttle began to be viewed as an end in itself. When the idea of a comprehensive space transportation system was abandoned in the 1970s, the shuttle was funded at much lower levels than NASA wanted. As a result, a multitude of priorities began competing for shuttle flight scheduling.

Within the context of a larger vision of taking the next steps in human evolution, the goal set for the shuttle — routine and economical access to space — was correct. However, underfunding of the project resulted in design compromises that made that goal unobtainable. The explosion of Challenger slowed progress toward the objective and raised the question of whether the shuttle is the optimum vehicle to achieve it. However, as a vehicle for consolidating and extending the impact of the Overview Effect, the shuttle has been a superb system.

The Value of the Shuttle

Regardless of how the shuttle is used in the future, its flights have provided us with a wealth of new insights about the spaceflight experience. The shuttle is a good vehicle for that kind of research, because it sends a wide variety of people into orbit for reasonably long periods of time in a shirt-sleeve atmosphere.

While going into space may someday become routine, the human experience will remain extraordinary for some time to come. Former shuttle astronaut Joseph P. Allen, an executive with a space development company in Houston, has written extensively about his experience. He said, "For each crew member, there will always be the anxious and interminable waiting, the stunning moment of ignition, the thrill of acceleration and the silent surprise of sloe-black space. There will always be the marvel of seeing the Earth from orbit, the wonder of having escaped from its bounds."[2]

After his successful rescue of an errant satellite, Allen was interviewed on the television program "Good Morning America" and asked whether astronauts felt euphoric when they were carrying out an EVA. Allen's reply was that anyone who is not euphoric in that situation is not paying attention![3]

According to Charles Walker, shuttle astronaut Gordon Fullerton felt some of the same attraction to Earth-gazing as the Skylab 4 crew did and said that he could have spent the entire eight days of the mission looking out the window.[4]

The Overview Effect has affected many shuttle astronauts. For example, Prince Sultan Bin Salman al-Saud of Saudi Arabia flew on the eighteenth shuttle misson during the hostage crisis involving TWA Flight 847. Asked for a comment on the situation while he was in space, he said, "Looking at it from here, the troubles all over the world, and not just the Middle East, look very strange as you see the boundaries and border lines disappearing."[5]

Charles Walker and others have reported clear examples of the Overview Effect and other changes in awareness, such as the Universal Insight. He found the experience of seeing the world as a distinct entity enlightening and wanted to learn more about the magnitude of the universe.

Thus, shuttle travelers, like their predecessors, continue to cite the difference between knowing intellectually what it would be like to see the Earth from space and experiencing it directly. Joe Allen also notes that learning more about home is an experience we have when we travel on the surface of the Earth. For example, living in a foreign country, one learns a great deal about the United States by comparison, and traveling in space offers similar opportunities.

Charles Walker found that being an astronaut with a concern for ecology was related to his earlier work. "I see the experience of spaceflight as an extension of my previous perceptions and experiences. Fifteen years ago, I was involved in environmental activities in my community. I participated in the first Earth Day."[6]

Walker's statement is fascinating because it links past and future. The symbol of Earth Day was the whole Earth as seen from an Apollo spacecraft, and years later, the payload specialist refers back to it as an influence in his life. It is as if space beckons to people with a hint of what is possible.

Today, there is an Environmental Protection Agency (EPA), and many ecology-oriented causes and organizations continue to use the whole Earth as their symbol. Indeed, some would argue that, without Apollo, there would have been no ecology movement. Joe Allen remarked that EPA wouldn't have received a penny before those pictures from orbit.

Space exploration continually lays the groundwork for bringing larger numbers of people a new understanding of themselves and the universe in which they live. Like Walker, they then become part of the evolutionary process of taking humanity into that universe.

Changing Expectations

When Alan Shepard went into space, he could not have been prepared for "the astonishing view" he saw. While the experience is still stunning, there is more intellectual preparation today. In looking at this phase of exploration, one can detect a shift in expectations on the part of astronauts. While being in space is still extraordinary, it is not, according to Joe Allen, "anomalous."

Payload specialist Loren Acton says that in the spaceflight, he could not "untangle" his actual experiences from "self-fulfilling prophecies . . . It was what I expected to be impressed with, and I was. Did it change me? Yes, because all at once it made these rather pedestrian realizations something that other people want to hear about, and I had enough sense to realize that this was going to be the case."[7]

Acton, who is active with the Association of Space Explorers, decided to use the credibility generated by his trip into space to improve the quality of life on Earth. "I was going to be prepared to come back and say things that were constructive from my frame of reference. I would like to save the world. I think the world is pretty neat. I think we are on a dangerous course, that we have to evolve, to change, to solve problems differently than we used to."[8]

Acton sees a direct link between space exploration and human evolution, understanding that he can use his experience in space to move social evolution toward a more cooperative path.

The shuttle has also created the possibility of a more direct relationship between space exploration and social change by serving as the vehicle to transport the first active politicians into space.

The Political Overview

Considering the impact of politics on human life, one of the shuttle's major contributions may be that it has taken a senator and a congressman, people with direct influence on how American society will develop, into orbit.

One of them, Republican Senator Edwin ("Jake") Garn of Utah, echoes the experience of the unity of the planet as seen from orbit: "You certainly come to the recognition that there aren't any political boundaries out there. You see it as one world, and you recognize how insignificant the planet Earth is when you look at ten billion stars in the Milky Way and recognize that our sun is a rather minor one."[9]

Garn also spoke of his sadness as he realized the imperfections of the planet's social systems and questioned the causes of inequities and hostilities among the Earth's people. In orbit, he concluded that it was not the fault of people, but the failures of governments, the desire of a few political leaders for power and control, that had led to disasters. When asked what impact space exploration would have on the evolution of society over time, he replied, "I don't see vast changes quickly, but there's no doubt in my mind that if more people fly, there has to be more understanding of what I'm talking about."[10]

Democratic Congressman Bill Nelson flew on the shuttle in January 1986. He tells how looking at the Middle East from orbit symbolized his hope for humanity: "The irony of that view struck me, that it was so neat and so contained and so packaged in my window, when in reality it was anything but that 220 miles below."[11]

Nelson believes that space holds out an enormous opportunity for humanity, and he also thought that the view from orbit would be salutary. It confirmed his view of space as a unique environment in which adversaries can cooperate.

Space has become a symbol of humanity working out its destiny: war or peace, cooperation or competition, love or hate. The Overview says it all: we are one; we are all in this together; war and strife solve nothing. Returning to Earth, the astronaut has many choices regarding transmission of the message, and each person uses the experience in terms of his or her own interests and place in society.

However, because of the cultural role that they play, people who have been in space have a credibility unmatched by others. As Loren Acton realized, the influence of astronauts, cosmonauts, and other space travelers back on Earth may be the most important aspect of recent missions.

The shuttle program, regardless of the other benefits it may or may not bring to society, is consolidating the impact of the overview effect and supporting its dissemination to the people on Earth. The ultimate effect could be substantial, Nelson suggests, if the super-power leaders were to arrange a summit meeting in space in the next century. "It would have a positive effect on their making decisions on war and peace."[12]

7

Individual and Cultural Variations

I remembered the words of Gagarin: "We are all testers; everyone does something for the first time. A new vehicle, new equipment, new instruments, a new research program . . . Each person makes his own 'test'; each does something for the first time."

— USSR pilot cosmonaut Gherman Titov

Individual Variations

There are as many spaceflight experiences as experiencers and, similarly, as many Overview Effects as people who have been in orbit or gone to the moon. To some extent, we all "create our own reality," whether on Earth or in space. As a result, there are inevitable variations in the experience of reality, wherever we are. What is profoundly moving to some may be meaningless to others; a wonderful evening for one person may be a crashing bore for another.

No one can go into space completely without filters. The question is how open-minded the astronaut can be and how preconceptions interact with the experience to produce new ideas. According to Edgar Mitchell, "It was a very powerful experience for some of us because we were open to whatever it meant, without prejudging what it was going to be."[1]

During the Mercury era, Scott Carpenter prepared himself for an extraordinary experience, and he had one. Wally Schirra, by contrast, was determined to focus on the job at hand, and his satisfaction came from doing his job well.

Mitchell, who had a "peak experience" on the return trip from the moon, was "always oriented toward philosophy, toward the fundamental cosmological and theological questions."[2] There are indications that he had laid the groundwork to have an important breakthrough on his journey, and he did.

Alan Bean points out that the astronaut in space rarely has his mind on philosophical matters, but it is clear that Bean's paintings are a strong personal statement about space exploration and his special effort to share it with others.

The expressions of the experience are different, and therefore the transmission of the message varies widely. The astronauts and cosmonauts bring individual and cultural variations to the core and halo elements of spaceflight, and additional elements are provided by society as a whole. The result is a multiplication of the number of spaceflight experiences within human culture and an increase in the likelihood that the overview message will be transmitted. The multiplier effect means that sending a limited number of people into space can lead to a broad-based social transformation. The experiences of the few become new information for the many, serving as fuel for social evolution.

The specific social context of each flight, as well as the actual environment of space, is critical to the perception of the missions by the astronauts and the public alike. When Charles Lindbergh flew the Atlantic alone, it inspired the world because it was a dangerous leap into the unknown by one man. Gene Cernan said that people could relate to Lindbergh's deed because they recognized a triumph of the human spirit in his action.

Today, thousands think nothing of flying across the Atlantic and the Pacific because it has become routine. As they fly over the Earth, they ignore the view that generations in the past longed desperately to see. In some cases, they experience a version of the Overview Effect, and it has an impact.

When the space shuttle flights were declared "routine," the public and the media slipped into bored acceptance of each launching. The truth is that most of those flights were far from routine. The Rogers Commission investigation into the Challenger accident revealed problems on many flights, some of which came within inches or moments of threatening the lives of the crews.

Had the flights been considered dangerous, some of the problems that occurred, such as pad shutdowns of the engines, "aborts-to-orbit," and tires blowing out on the landing runway would have been perceived differently. In fact, danger has been present in every flight since Gagarin's first orbit, but the culture chooses how to deal with it differently at different points in time.

In the United States, public interest in American space missions depends on whether the particular flight is a "first," which always contains an element of danger and uncertainty. Although the shuttle missions were eventually dubbed ordinary, the very first flight generated excitement because no one knew if the new system would work or not.

Apollo 13, though it was the third mission to the moon, generated worldwide interest because an explosion on the spacecraft forced the crew to make a "flyby" of the moon and return to Earth. The astronauts were in real danger from the moment of the explosion to the moment of splashdown. So Apollo 13 was exciting because it was the first time American astronauts had faced jeopardy of that magnitude.

Sadly, the Challenger disaster rivaled the first moon landing in the attention it generated, because it represented a number of firsts. What was to have been the inaugural flight of the Space Flight Participant program turned out to be the first experience of loss of life in flight. The next shuttle flight will be watched with intense interest because of Challenger. Once again, the unknown has entered the American space program, and the unknown, not the routine, draws people to space.

First flights are also the most extraordinary ones for astronauts, and after that initiation, there is a shift in perspective. According to Charles Walker, one becomes more accustomed to the environment of space, and it makes a difference. "Each person adapts with successive trips. You feel more comfortable each time, and you know what to expect psychologically as well. You adapt more readily to the environment and are less stunned by the perspectives and the sights."[3]

Cultural Variations

Americans tend to think of "the space program" as being equivalent to "the American space program," but this is no longer an accurate way to view the situation. The American people respond to exploration metaphors, and space exploration is often compared to the founding of the country and settling of the West. This is understandable because the United States no longer has a physical frontier, and the space program therefore serves a real cultural need. Other countries look at the enterprise quite differently; each deals with space exploration in its own way and sees it through its own cultural filters.

The Canadians, for example, do not plan to develop their own launch capability. Instead, they are creating their own niche by developing a crew of payload specialists to ride the shuttle, and by focusing on such technologies as the shuttle's robot arm.

The European nations are quite aggressive in their approach to space. In addition to their own national programs, they created the European Space Agency (ESA), which has developed an unmanned launch capability, the Ariane rocket, and is charged with creating an autonomous European presence in space. Japan also has an active space program built around its own fleet of rockets. The Japanese, as well as the ESA, have agreed to participate in the permanent American space station, and the Germans have already flown on shuttle missions.

The People's Republic of China represents a fascinating cultural variation. China's abrupt termination of its assertive trade and exploration program in the fifteenth century, and its subsequent stagnation as a society, is often cited as an example of what happens when nations stop exploring.

The People's Republic has announced that it is choosing a team of astronauts and the time when it launches a man into space is "not far off." The report revealing these plans noted that "China may be preparing to launch its first men into space much sooner than many foreign observers had thought possible."[4]

China also has a satellite launching capability with its Long March unmanned vehicle, and has offered its services to American companies put in a bind by the shuttle situation.[5]

The Soviet program, with roots in prerevolutionary Russia, is perhaps the most interesting of all. It is a synthesis of Nikolai Fyodorov's mysticism, Konstantin Tsiolkovsky's inventiveness, and Karl Marx's revolutionary ideology, all coupled with the practical political mind of Lenin and his successors.

Fyodorov, chief cataloguer in the Moscow library in the mid nineteenth century, exerted a significant influence on Russian intellectuals and innovators, including Tsiolkovsky. He painted a broad picture of the human purpose in space, not unlike the "great purpose" proposed later in this book. Tsiolkovsky built on that foundation and anticipated many of the practical problems to be overcome in rocketry and space station design.

Marxism adds to those visions a view of history unfolding as thesis/antithesis/synthesis, manifestng itself as dialectical materialism, and culminating in a worldwide revolution. Communism is an expansionist political ideology, and it is quite natural to see it as expanding into outer space.

The Soviet space program in its early days (1957–1969) functioned as a powerful propaganda weapon in the Soviet Union's competition with the United States, especially for Third World attention and loyalty. All the early firsts represented powerful messages that the Soviet system might indeed be superior, and it jolted the United States out of a quiet belief in its own dominance and into a high pitch of competitive fervor.

During 1969–1985, the Soviets launched or attempted to launch many flights to build, expand, and repair Salyut space stations. They never went to the moon or developed a space shuttle, but they are now far ahead of the United States in terms of long-duration missions in space. As a culture, they are the reigning experts on actually living in space.[6]

As a result, we find a difference in impact of the later missions on cosmonaut consciousness. Their detailed reports of time on Salyut include musings about the view of Earth from space, coupled with the more immediate concerns of getting along with crewmates, getting work done, missing their families, and coping with boredom.[7]

Nevertheless, there is still much that is common between cosmonauts and astronauts, and this is perhaps more remarkable when
we have seen how strong the differences are. The most concrete
expression of commonality can perhaps be seen in the founding of
the Association of Space Explorers and in its goals, stated in the
press release that announced the First Planetary Congress in the
fall of 1985.

> The astronauts and cosmonauts wanted to meet with each other
> because of a shared vision, resulting from their experience in space,
> which unites them in a way that obscures their cultural differ-
> ences . . . All the space fliers who attended acknowledged they had
> been substantially affected during their flights by a heightened
> awareness of how great the creative potential is on our Earth but
> how tiny and fragile its body is.[8]

The differences in responses to the spaceflight experience are
quite real. However, they have a common theme, which involves
elevating the mission of humanity to a higher plane of understanding. The diversity in ways of communicating this unifying vision
enriches the message and ultimately makes it more powerful.

Table 7.1

The Human Space Program (1961–Mid 1985)

Total missions	105
People in space	165
Nations whose citizens have flown	15
Lunar landings	6
Days in space	2096
Space years	5.74

Source: Tim Furniss, *Space Flight: The Records* (Enfield, England: Guinness Books, 1985).

8

The Technological Overview

I think that the technological impacts are likely to be more important than the philosophical in the near term. I think the impact of worldwide communications has already been tremendous.

– Shuttle astronaut Jeffrey A. Hoffman

Making It Permanent

Marshall McLuhan said that the medium is the message and our technologies are extensions of ourselves. By that, he meant that the structure of communications media is itself a message to society and that technologies emulate our organic sensing capabilities. Permanent technological analogues of the human experience are being established in space, extending our sensing capabilities into the solar system and beyond. These technologies also tell us that increasingly more sophisticated overviews are available on a permanent basis.

Like "manned" space exploration, "unmanned" exploration includes a spectrum of possible experiences and a resulting range of effects on human consciousness and social evolution.

To grasp the variety of experiences and uses of unmanned systems, the flights can be categorized as were the manned flights: (1) flights that allow us to look back at the Earth; (2) flights that allow us to explore the solar system; and (3) flights that allow us to look out into the universe.

In general, the flights that allow us to look back at the earth or communicate from point to point on the Earth reinforce the Overview Effect. These include satellites in Low Earth Orbit and in Geosynchronous Orbit.

Flights that help us to understand the solar system and our place in it coincide with the Copernican Perspective. These include probes that orbit other planets or satellites, probes that "flyby" other planets or satellites, and those that land on other planets or satellites.

Flights that help us better understand the universe as a whole, to achieve Universal Insight, consist primarily of telescopes and other monitoring devices placed in Earth orbit, with their "eyes and ears" pointed outward.

Unmanned Flights and the Overview Effect

Earth-orbiting satellites provide a technological parallel to the Overview Effect experienced by astronauts in orbit, building in the Overview Effect on a continuing basis. Experiencing the overview as an astronaut is a stunning emotional experience. Experiencing it on Earth while looking at a picture or a film is less dramatic but still analogous. When astronauts see the Earth from space, they comprehend that it is a *natural* unity. Satellites embody the message that the planet is also becoming a *social* unity.

Just as the Overview Effect can be broken down into a variety of experiences, Earth-orbiting satellites can be categorized by function, and the variety of experiences provided by unmanned flights becomes more apparent. Earth-orbiting satellites can be used for a number of purposes, including weather prediction, remote sensing, telecommunications, navigation and location determination, and military intelligence.

Weather Prediction

Weather prediction is a common example of the institutionalization of the Overview Effect. Every night, television viewers see a picture of the Earth taken from a satellite, and the meteorologist uses the photograph to predict the future on the basis of the overview.

Monitoring and predicting weather via satellites brings the technological version of the Overview Effect down to mundane reality. The existence of a satellite in orbit, "seeing" exactly what the astronauts see, helps people and societies make decisions every day. Before 1957, no human beings, regardless of their wealth, power, or influence, could do that because there were no satellites. Today, everyone can benefit from this capability.

The ability to predict the weather carries with it much broader and deeper implications, because weather prediction affects other dimensions of "futurism." Weather patterns support or erode social and political stability, for example. A poor harvest in the Soviet Union caused by bad weather has profound policy implications in the United States and elsewhere on the planet. Slight shifts in weather patterns may dramatically affect political policies over time.

Many people are alive today because weather predictions based on satellite data helped them avoid a hurricane's fury or a blizzard's dangers. This in itself has a powerful effect on all our lives.

Remote Sensing

"The key to the importance of Earth observations from space," according to Geoffrey K. C. Pardoe, author of *The Future for Space Technology*, "is the macro-scale *overview* that is obtainable from the satellite."[1] (Italics added.)

Earth remote sensing satellites are similar to weather satellites in that they look down on Earth from orbit and send back information on what they see. The difference is that they focus on the Earth and its resources rather than on weather patterns. They generate information that may, for example, reveal the existence of previously unsuspected natural resources or changes in vegetation color that may, along with weather data, indicate the onset of a drought.

Like weather satellites, remote sensing systems are catalysts for interdisciplinary research. They can apply to a multitude of fields, including agriculture, archaeology, civil engineering, ecology, economics, fishery, forestry, geodesy, geography, geology, hydrology, meteorology, mining, oceanography, politics, and sociology.[2]

Telecommunications

Telecommunications applications dominate the commercially successful aspects of space enterprise in general and of the satellite business in particular. According to Charles Zraket of the Mitre Corporation, satellite telecommunication in the mid 1980s generates some $4 billion in revenues per year, and has "revolutionized" international communications traffic, creating "an explosion in who gets to know what and what gets to be known."[3]

The telecommunication component of the unmanned space program makes the metaphor of a planetary nervous system into a reality. Going beyond a vision of the Earth as a whole system, the worldwide telecommunication system now being developed provides a practical foundation for linking the human social system so that eventually anyone will be able to communicate with anyone else on the planet without considerations of time and distance.

Communication satellites have an inherently transformational impact on society because they force it to go beyond its current form of organization. The satellite telecommunication business has, from its inception, supported the development of international cooperation.

The spatial placement of a communication satellite, coupled with its function, makes it difficult for even the most nationalistic countries to take a single-nation approach to the funding and administration of such a system. In the case of communication satellites, the international organization known as Intelsat has 110 members who provide capital and share in the usage of the system.

Communication satellites have already affected international politics dramatically. The situation in South Africa became a global issue largely because television pictures of the violence there have been transmitted into people's homes around the planet on a nightly basis. Recognizing that the rapid transmittal of this information increases pressures for change, the South African government's response was to cut off all reporting from the trouble spots.

These developments do not mean the end of the nation-state as a political form, but they probably do herald its demise as the dominant form on Earth. The nation-state is a relatively recent invention, and nationwide communication and transportation have been the technological underpinning for that political form. Those who pioneered the development of the nation-state were revolutionaries in their time because it was an improvement over the political forms of the day.

In the late twentieth century, those who see the next evolutionary step for humanity as transition to a planetary and then a solar civilization are supported by modern technology. Communication satellites do not necessarily cause the transformation, but they aid it.

The Live Aid concert is an archetype of this development. It can be argued that the first perceptions of the Earth from space generated the consciousness to treat global problems as if they were local, and the satellites provided the capability for the planet to link up and do something together. Astronaut Don Lind points out, "We probably would have responded to the Ethiopian famine without space pictures . . . But the intensity and personal involvement wouldn't have been the same."[4]

Sensations of time and space are transformed for an astronaut in orbit, and the communication satellite provides a transformation in these perceptions for those on Earth. By moving outside the frame of reference of the Earth, the astronaut has a different experience of space/time. The satellite, remaining outside the Earth's frame of reference permanently, makes that change a permanent one.

Navigation and Location

By locating itself outside the space/time frame of reference of the Earth, a satellite injects a new experience of space and time into the human social system. The entire surface of the planet becomes "one" in terms of communication.

The next step in the process is to be able to look back and see ourselves within the space/time matrix of the planet. Navigation and location-finding satellites provide that ability. These systems include a unit to be carried by the user on Earth, a computer for processing information from a number of points, and the satellite itself.

Some systems are already in place, financed by the government and the military. However, many of the most important break-throughs in the future will be on the commercial side. Examples include trucking companies and others who need to know the lo-cation of every unit in their fleet at a given time.[5] Some companies are putting navigation units in private automobiles as well.

As with other space exploration and development efforts, the intent of the work in location and navigation is not to increase human consciousness or the species' self-awareness. Nevertheless, that will likely be one of the side effects. With the Overview Effect as originally defined, an astronaut looks at Earth from orbit or from the moon and sees it as a whole system. A location-finding satellite looks down at Earth and shows us ourselves within that system.

Military Uses

Military advantage and national competitions have always been drivers behind the commitments of national resources to put people and machines into space. To a military strategist, space is the new "high ground." Satellites play the same role in military matters as in other areas of human activity, providing a perspective that has previously not been available to military planners.

The Strategic Defense Initiative, or "Star Wars," reflects that type of thinking about space. For those interested in seeing space used as an arena of peaceful exploration by all humanity, SDI is an anathema, a "weaponization" of space.[6]

All military satellites are not, however, threats to peace. They can also support a reduction in the probability of major conflicts being triggered by miscalculations. As Jesco von Puttkamer, man-ager of long-range planning in NASA's Office of Space Flight, puts it, "The proper military use of space can actually safeguard peace."[7] Situated ouside the Earthbound frames of references, satellites can be used to spy on opposing nations in relation to troop movements, construction of missile bases, weapons testing, and much more.

Michael Collins, when asked whether space exploration and de-velopment was contributing to world unity, focused specifically on the military satellite issue, arguing that "space has been helpful and stabilizing in the area of spy satellites. They cannot move a truck, van, or missile without our knowing about it, and vice versa."[8]

While spying on one another is a reflection of humanity's old forms of behavior, there seems little doubt that satellites can support the prevention of war rather than contributing to conflict. The element of surprise is essential to the success of military strategy. When it is taken away, which is the purpose of spy satellites, the likelihood of success in launching an attack diminishes dramatically.

Military satellites also support the reduction of military tensions by providing the possibility of independent verification in arms control agreements. In pre-satellite days, on-site inspection was a key issue that held up test bans and other arms control treaties. Today, on-site inspections are less of a barrier because the satellite is essentially "on-site" all the time.

It is impossible to know whether all military satellites are playing a stabilizing or destabilizing role internationally, partly because many of them have been launched secretly and data about them is not available.

Just as military pilots of the past fifty years have used the skies to bomb people and cities as well as military targets, so might the overview from space be seen as a strategic necessity by today's military strategists, with consequences that we cannot easily predict.

Earth System Science

The idea of a unified approach to understanding the Earth and humanity's relationship to it is not just a vision; it is close to reality as part of the American space program. In 1983, the Advisory Council of NASA established an Earth System Sciences Committee to review the science of the Earth as an integrated system of interacting components, recommend an implementation strategy for global Earth studies, and define NASA's role in such a program.[9]

In 1986, the committee published a summary of the recommended program, entitled "Earth System Science: Overview," which stated the following goal: "To obtain a scientific understanding of the entire Earth System on a global scale by describing how its component parts and their interactions have evolved, how they function, and how they may be expected to continue to evolve on all time scales."[10]

The technological Overview Effect provided by satellites is forcing a unification in human thinking not only in government, but in academia as well. For example, Harvard University established a new Department of Earth and Planetary Sciences, drawing its faculty and students from many different disciplines, in recognition that an interdisciplinary approach is the only way to grasp the phenomena being studied.

Robot Flights and the Copernican Perspective

The Copernican Perspective is a realization that the Earth is not only a whole system, but is also part of the solar system. It is an understanding that Copernicus was right: the sun, not the Earth, is the center of that system.

The Overview Effect is the essential insight necessary for the building of a planetary civilization. The Copernican Perspective is the essential insight needed to build a solar civilization. The solar system is much larger than the Earth, composed of many more parts, including the sun, planets, moons, asteroids, and comets. We do not yet have a good model of how all these parts interact as a whole system or the role each part plays.

As a society, we have only just begun to experience the Copernican Perspective, and robot probes have played a dominant role in this process. These have included robot flybys of the moon; probes to Venus and Mars by the United States and Soviet Union; the American Voyager spacecraft, which conducted spectacular flybys of Jupiter, Saturn, Uranus, and their moons; and multinational expeditions to Halley's comet.

All these missions have yielded new insights into the nature of the solar system, bringing many surprises and much new information. While no humans have actually visited any celestial body other than the moon, the continuing transmission of television pictures into the homes of people all over the world institutionalizes the Copernican Perspective in the same way that satellites institutionalize the Overview Effect.

Robot missions to Mars stand out as unique in their actual and potential impact on human consciousness. For example, studies of planetwide Martian dust storms in 1970 laid the groundwork for the nuclear winter hypothesis, which has created a fundamental shift in our understanding of the survivability of nuclear war.

The Gaia hypothesis, which has focused on describing the nature of life on Earth, began when James Lovelock was asked by NASA to consult on search-for-life experiments that accompanied the Viking mission to Mars.[11]

Unmanned Missions and Universal Insight

The Universal Insight is a recognition not only that the Earth is a whole system and a part of the solar system, but that we are also part of the universe and have an important role to play in it. Astronomers, by the nature of their profession, have always known about the Universal Insight. Today, the technological analogue of that insight is being extended by astronomers working to lift our observational tools into space. It has been proposed that a series of "great observatories," designed to generate new information about the universe as a whole and the human place within it, be constructed in Earth orbit over the next few decades.[12]

Studies of this type will go far beyond academic interests. Space telescopes such as the Infrared Astronomy Satellite (IRAS) have already discovered numbers of stars with clouds of particles emitting infrared radiation. Astrophysicists believe that such clouds are an initial stage in planet formation, the first solid observational evidence of other solar systems.[13]

Outer Space, Inner Selves

For many years, a debate has raged within the space community over the relative value of manned versus unmanned exploration of space. Both approaches have positive impact on human consciousness and social evolution, as this and previous chapters have shown.

Responding to ideas in this chapter, Dr. Paul Blanchard, a consultant to NASA who helped develop the report of the Earth System Sciences Committee, pointed out some important facts about the relationship between manned and unmanned exploration. Speaking of explorers and discoverers of the past, he said,

> In those times, discovery *had* to be undertaken by human beings. There was no way to automate discovery. One of the problems under the surface here is that for the first time in history, we are able to mount very extensive and revealing voyages of discovery with no human participants, thus removing the necessity of having a leader or hero. [14]

I suggested to Blanchard that the primary reason for humans' going into space was its positive impact on human consciousness. He agreed and said that in terms of manned space exploration, it would tell us more about ourselves than about space.

Ultimately, manned and unmanned programs must be seen not as competing priorities, but as critical elements of the same process. Both are forms of exploration that teach us about space and ourselves. For this reason, it seems fair to say that the farther out human beings look, the further inward we see.

9

Disseminating the Overview

One of the reasons I give a lot of talks . . . [is] to try to make it real for people in the best way that I can, to give them some feeling of direct connection to the program.

– Payload specialist Byron K. Lichtenberg

Levels of Impact

The experience of the Earth as a unified whole is a powerful one for astronauts and cosmonauts. It is a message from the universe, not to space fliers alone, but to all of humanity. Now the question is, How can larger numbers of people get that message?

There are two basic approaches to answering this question. One is the transportation-oriented approach of taking more people into space, which is what the national space programs and the embryonic space tourism industry propose to do. The other is the communication-oriented approach of replicating the experience, in various forms, and diffusing it around the planet.

In the next decade, the only hope for launching large numbers of people into orbit is space tourism, as with Society Expeditions' Project Space Voyage. The company, committed to begin flights on its own specially designed spaceship in November 1992, had, by mid 1986, signed up about 250 people to take a trip into Low Earth Orbit.[1]

Whether the company will meet its ambitious goals remains to be seen. But even if Society Expeditions is successful, the primary transportation-oriented dissemination of the Overview Effect in the near future will be through national space programs sending astronauts and cosmonauts into space, then having them communicate their experiences to the populace.

Will that approach support a fundamental shift in consciousness at a planetary level? In *Carrying the Fire*, Apollo 11 astronaut Michael Collins writes, "Fred Hoyle, the British astronomer, suggested as early as 1948 that the first picture of the whole earth would unleash a flood of new ideas."[2] But he went on to say that simply seeing pictures of the whole Earth is not enough to achieve the full impact. Rather, one must actually be there, 100,000 miles out in space, to get the full implications of the experience.

Still, it may not be necessary for an entire society to feel the full impact for a shift in consciousness to take place. The astronauts and cosmonauts are representatives of the species, and in them we have the most powerful experiences of spaceflight being felt by a tiny sample of the whole population. The impact of their communication may seem insignificant — as Skylab astronaut Ed Gibson said, their talking about it is like a "drop of dye in the ocean," but the diffusion of dye into a liquid changes its composition and color. Their messages to us may work similarly to change our perspective over time.

In fact, diffusion is a good way to understand how new ideas are disseminated into societies. Communication researchers have noticed that there is a familiar pattern by which new ideas or practices are adopted by society as a whole. The pattern applies in the same way to issues ranging from the adoption of the smoking habit to the abolition of slavery.

According to this "diffusion of innovation" theory, people fall into five basic groups in terms of adopting new ideas or practices. The percentages of the population they represent are innovators (2.5); early adopters (13.5); early majority (34); late majority (34); and late adopters (16).

New information coming into a human social system from the environment is processed in a sequence, starting with the innovators and concluding with the late adopters. Not everyone deals with new ideas the same way, and everyone does not adopt them immediately.

The innovators are the first to take up the new idea; they then pass it on to the early adopters. Once these two groups make an idea their own, it is on its way to becoming a part of mainstream

thought. No one, including innovators, takes on something unknown right away, skipping straight to the adoption or confirmation
stages of the process. They have to hear about it, become interested
in it, evaluate it, try it, then adopt it and confirm its value.

The adoption curve rises slowly in the beginning, when the
innovators and early adopters are going through the process, ac-
celerates rapidly until about half the population has adopted, and
increases at a slower rate while the later adopters come aboard.
When about 20 percent of the population has taken up the innovation, the curve becomes virtually unstoppable.[3]

The most important audiences are the innovators, early adopters,
and early majority, since their absorption of the message brings it
to "takeoff" stage.

The astronauts are the superinnovators of the space age. Other
innovators are those involved in national space programs, space
interest groups, and other pro-space activities. The early adopters
and early majority are just beginning to emerge in regard to the
Overview Effect and other ideas discussed here.

It is through this diffusion process that the experience of spaceflight is translated into an idea that has a powerful effect on society
as more and more people are reached by it. Just as people who
had never seen a slave could become adherents of the abolitionist
cause, so can those who have never been in space support a vigorous
space exploration program.

Hearing an astronaut speak, seeing a film, or looking at a poster
of the whole Earth begins the adoption process by bringing awareness of the overview to the audience. These experiences are not
as deep as being in space, but the impact is broader because a film
or poster can be replicated more easily and less expensively than
the experience itself.

In certain instances, people who are made aware of the overview
go through transformations just as powerful as those of the astronauts and in unpredictable ways. I call people who have achieved
astronaut awareness without going into space Terranauts. Consider
the case of Ray Bright, the inventor of "bioflight," an approach to
gymnastics, space travel, and life itself based on an understanding
of what it means to live in a three-dimensional reality. In 1979,
Bright was working as a gymnastics instructor at Chico State Col-

lege in California. He had the insight that whenever we jump into the air, even just a foot off the ground, we are *flying* — if we see it that way. With the right attitude, and a little more equipment, such as a trampoline, we can fly even better. In space, well . . .

Bright had already worked out many of the basic ideas behind bioflight, but the way the final piece fell into place is an excellent example of dissemination of the Overview Effect.

An article in *Air & Space* magazine states,

> He [Bright] describes the experience as akin to satori, the Zen state of enlightenment. "I was looking at the famous NASA photo of the Earth floating in space. It'd been made into the front of a greeting card, and the word 'Home' was printed on the part of the photo that was just black space. Of course, the idea was that 'Home' meant Earth — but suddenly, I saw *space* as home, because in space, everything I'd been trying to do my whole life in terms of movement would be possible. In space, gymnastics wouldn't be gymnastics — it would be flight. Human flight. Ultimate flight. Bioflight."[4]

Bright's approach is used not only to teach people basic gymnastic techniques, but it is also being considered as a potentially useful training method and space sickness prevention technique for astronauts before they go into space.[5]

Martin Rutte, a management consultant in Toronto, is another Terranaut. He tells of the transformation that he experienced on hearing a talk by Edgar Mitchell.

> There were about two or three thousand people there, and he was standing alone on the stage . . . Behind him, on a rear-view projector, was the picture he saw coming back from the moon, of the Earth with black all around it. He spoke about his experience of seeing that, and I was riveted on the picture. When he talked about coming back and what it was like to look at that and how it altered his life forever, that he saw that we were one planet and we were one universe — there was one instant when it went "click" and I just got it. I knew exactly what he was talking about. I think it was the first time I had that kind of global consciousness directly.[6]

According to Rutte, the insight penetrated deep and continues to influence his work as a consultant to corporate executives seeking to define a vision and purpose for their organizations.

He later commented on my article "Space Exploration and Human Evolution," "It was all there and I knew exactly what you were talking about. It was just 'bang,' an explosion in me."[7]

Now he is integrating the ideas of the Overview Effect, the Copernican Perspective, and the Universal Insight into the training he conducts with his clients. Once again we see how the insights that had been the exclusive property of astronauts and cosmonauts begin to diffuse into society as a whole.[8]

I also told Gary Enersen, a management consultant in San Francisco, about my work on the Overview Effect, how my initial awareness of it had emerged during a cross-country flight. Enersen said that he had had a similar awakening and later sent me the notes he had written after his experiences and a description of a personal meditation exercise based on the Overview Effect that he had developed.

Enersen's notes from his cross-country flight reveal an experience much like my own.

> In the "supernatural" look at our life and our Earth, one of the greatest feelings we can get is to fly on a commercial jet plane. The view in the window is to look at perennial clear skies — always so at the horizon level and above, regardless of what may be happening below . . .
>
> We are able to view from the "upper level" of the world beneath us in the more true perspective than when on land, which is merely our customary lower level. Neither is this the "higher" level, which the astronauts see during orbit, or farther away during moon travel.
>
> This "commercial upper level" is the one we can relate to most easily because it is not too high to lose our *normal* perspective, yet it's high enough to regain proper perspective about "our land of toil" in relation to the universe.

Enersen has found that he is better able to help clients make bolder plans and take more confident action on a range of practical subjects having nothing to do with space as a result of acting from a higher-level perspective shift.

These examples suggest that while it is not possible to fully replicate the Overview Effect without going into space, similar experiences are available to us all. They can then be used as foundations for personal growth and transformation. That idea is being taken up in various quarters. In California, for example, a group is working on several space habitation projects, including a theme park that will provide visitors with a version of the spaceflight experience.

Similar projects such as Space Camp and the United States Space Academy in Huntsville, Alabama, offer significant opportunities for research by students of the Overview Effect. Simulated experiences of spaceflight provide a bridge between the actual experience and the passive viewing of films, looking at posters, or listening to lectures.

The Overview Effect and the Whole Earth Symbol

If the idea of the Overview Effect as a message is correct, it should be possible to see the overview experience being disseminated in support of a more peaceful, self-aware, and ecologically careful species. The link between that kind of social transformation and space exploration remains circumstantial, but there is good evidence that it exists. For example, many astronauts return from space with an intense interest in ecology. From space, it is easy for them to see the fragility and interdependence of Earth's environment and the cost to humanity if anything is done to make the planet unlivable.

The ecology movement, which had begun to build a constituency in the 1960s, reached a peak of public awareness in 1970 with Earth Day. This event occurred a year and a half after Apollo 8's transmission of the dramatic television pictures of the Earth from space, and less than a year after Apollo 11's moon landing. Using the whole Earth as a symbol, the movement gained momentum and entered the mainstream in the 1970s, successfully passing environmental legislation in the United States and creating a permanent corps sympathetic to ecological concerns.

There are many other examples of the whole Earth's power as a symbol. Psychologist Peter Russell, author of *The Global Brain*, wrote,

The profound impact of this Earth view has resulted in this picture being used in almost every sphere of human activity. It adorns the walls of offices and living rooms; it is a greeting card, a T-shirt, and a bumper sticker. Ecological movements and planetary institutions incorporate it in their logos, as do educational institutions and business corporations. At one time or another it has been used to advertise just about everything from cars, washing machines, and shoes, to book clubs, banks, and insurance companies. Yet in spite of all this exposure, the picture still strikes a very deep chord, and none of its magnificence has been lost.[9]

The peace movement has incorporated the whole Earth symbol into its work. For example, the Beyond War movement uses the symbol in its logo and on letterheads, greeting cards, and a pin that supporters wear. A card accompanying the pin states the organization's belief that nuclear weapons have made war obsolete, and that we must "build a world beyond war." The message on the card continues, "We live on one planet, with one life support system. The survival of all humanity, all life is totally interdependent . . . This pin symbolizes the earth we all share, surrounded by a spirit of good will."

In the first hour of Beyond War "interest evenings," participants are introduced to the danger that nuclear war poses to humanity's survival. Then, the concept that "we are one" is introduced with the showing of the film *No Frames, No Boundaries,* including the Schweickart commentary, and pictures of an astronaut on an EVA.

Peter Russell points out that the whole Earth symbol is not confined to ecological and peace movements. It has reached into the mainstream of American society. Typical of this trend is Innovation Associates, a management consulting and training firm in Framingham, Massachusetts, that uses the whole Earth picture to symbolize its work as a training ground for business leaders. The company offers a program for high-level executives called Leadership and Mastery, which focuses on creating an organizational vision by integrating systems thinking and intuitive insight.

In defining the organizational model by which the course measures success, the brochure says,

> We have come to call such organizations metanoic organizations, a term based on the Greek word *metanoia,* meaning a fundamental shift of mind . . . Individuals in such an organization become inex-

tricably linked to a higher purpose common to all in the organization. They infuse their organization with the necessary commitment and energy to collectively realize a vision of a better world.[10]

Planetary Management

Many messages may be read into the view of the Earth from space. One is planetary management, the recognition that if the whole can be perceived, the whole can be the focus of practical as well as abstract interest. However, it should be clearly understood that planetary management does not mean planetary manipulation. Planetary management should be seen from a stewardship perspective and as participatory management at the highest level.

The clear message of the Overview Effect is that the Earth is a whole system and humanity one of many interdependent species calling the planet home. A regard for all life as sacred becomes a practical as well as moral position when we see the critical role that all life plays in maintaining the system.

If the next step in human social evolution is to build a planetary civilization, then what is most needed is the ability to see and deal with problems and opportunities on a planetary level. It is also the ability not only to observe, but truly communicate with, the planet as a whole. This message is implicit in the whole Earth symbol itself.

To millions of Christians all over the planet, the cross is a sign of unity in spite of deep divisions of race, language, and political beliefs. Because symbols work at a subconscious level, often unnoticed by the conscious mind, it makes sense that this new symbol might be having a quiet, though dramatic effect as a unifying force, too.

The Authority of the Astronauts

The idea of Earth as one system is fundamental to the development of a new civilization of which Earth is a part and a whole at the same time, and the picture of the whole Earth is the symbol of that civilization. However, there are many barriers to the achievement of that next step in human evolution.

Julian Jaynes, author of *The Origin of Consciousness in the Breakdown of the Bicameral Mind*, suggests that earlier civilizations, such as ancient Greece, "hallucinated" gods to tell people what to do when they were under stress and required direction. As the situations faced by those bicameral societies grew more complex, the hallucinated gods were unable to provide answers, and the rational or unicameral mind evolved to replace them. In the late twentieth century, society has reached yet another impasse that the rational mind has been unable to resolve — the threat to human survival posed by nuclear weapons. So far, the path taking us beyond this impasse has not been made clear to us.

Payload specialist Loren Acton recognizes that he has a special status and that his ideas about peace will be more readily accepted because he has been in space. Congressman Bill Nelson says that being in space confirms his image of a place where adversaries can work together for peace and that his experience gives his advocacy more credibility. Marc Garneau points out that he and other astronauts have become public figures to whom special qualities are attributed. At a time when almost every other authority on Earth is being questioned, the tiny cadre of astronauts and cosmonauts is being given even more credibility.

Shuttle astronaut Jeff Hoffman says it is not necessary to go into outer space to understand humanity's next evolutionary steps, that people who remain on Earth can have the same realizations, if they so choose. However, by giving demigod status to the astronauts and cosmonauts, society invests their words with a transcendent, transnational authority that can play a significant role in the movement of society beyond the impasse it now faces. Does the attention accorded the astronauts and cosmonauts represent an effort to re-create the old gods in a new guise? Consciously, the answer is no. At a collective unconscious level, however, it may represent a strategic move by humanity to ensure its own survival.

As we consider how the Overview Effect is being disseminated, we might ask ourselves, Is it merely coincidence that one of our major space efforts was named after Mercury, the Greek god of communication, and one for Apollo, the god of wisdom?

10

Overview Systems

It is precisely this shift in viewpoint and what it implies for the capability of the human being and for our view of the universe that makes it so powerful.

– Apollo 14 astronaut Edgar D. Mitchell

The Meaning of the Astronauts' Experiences

If we had been there when the "explorer fish" first flopped onto land, we would have seen just one individual of a species engaged in a new behavior. We could not have observed the billions of years of evolutionary steps that had led to that moment, nor would we really know the implications of the event. Humanity's early movements into space are also occurring against the backdrop of billions of years of evolution, which has built the series of physical, living, human, and technical systems needed to lift a few hundred individuals out of the gravity well and into a new environment.

Land exploration didn't just happen, and neither does space exploration. Systems evolved step by step to make both kinds of exploration possible. To fully comprehend the meaning of the astronauts' experiences, one must understand them as part of the story of evolving systems on Earth.

The logical extension of space exploration is that it supports the evolution of human social systems so that they can function as elements in a wholly new kind of system. Building on our prior knowledge of the Overview Effect and its institutionalization through technology, I have called this new structure an overview system.

At the moment, space exploration is supporting the creation of a planetary overview system composed of the physical system of the planet Earth, the living system that has evolved on Earth popularly known as Gaia, the global human social system known as humanity, and a worldwide technology system.

The overview system, like all systems, is a group of parts so related to one another as to form an organic whole. Depending on the point of view, a part can also be a whole, while a whole can be a part in an even larger system. Every system is a whole and a part at the same time. For this reason, they are sometimes called holons.[1]

The planetary overview system is a holon composed of many different parts, functioning in turn as a part in a larger overview system. In this chapter, we will look in some detail at the elements of this overview system and reassess the astronauts' experiences against the backdrop of that analysis.

The Earth as a Physical System

When the solar system first formed, the Earth was a physical system consisting of matter and energy and governed by the laws of thermodynamics. Of particular importance is the second law, which states that in a closed physical system, energy is continuously dissipated into a form that is no longer available for useful work.

This is called an increase in entropy, and it is an irreversible process. As it occurs, a physical system moves from a state of maximum order to maximum disorder, toward an equilibrium of randomly moving atoms and molecules. Obviously, if something hadn't happened, the Earth would simply be a dead planet today, and there would never have been land exploration, space exploration, or any of the other topics discussed so far.

The Appearance of Living Systems

What happened was that life appeared on the scene. How that occurred is still a matter of debate, but the importance of it is not. Unlike their physical counterparts, living systems do not run down. Instead, they maintain themselves by importing energy from the environment, processing it, and exporting waste back into the environment. People, for example, do this every day when they eat food, extract its energy, and excrete bodily wastes.

Rather than moving toward a state of disorder, life moves toward a steady state of maximum order, maintaining itself regardless of changes in the environment. Living systems do not reduce entropy, except within their own boundaries. By exporting waste into the larger environment, they actually increase entropy overall. On a global scale, for example, this shows up as pollution.

However, once living systems appeared on Earth, a wholly new process came on the scene. Evolution, operating according to its own set of laws, appeared as a counterforce to thermodynamics, offering the opportunity for new kinds of systems to be built.

The advent of living systems also heralds the appearance of information, or negative entropy. All evolving systems are in a continuous state of motion in time and space, and information, manifested as feedback, is the fuel that powers this process. As they respond to the impact of feedback, systems move through different states of existence. The three most important are *equilibrium*, in which the system appears to be unchanging, at least for a period of time; *change*, in which the system appears to move away from equilibrium, but is still recognizable as the same system; and *transformation*, in which the system appears to become something else altogether, while still retaining characteristics of earlier states.

Evolution

The continuing movement of systems through their different states is evolution, and as it takes place, more complex systems emerge from simpler systems in response to new information from the environment. For living systems the Earth has been the primary environment for aeons. Climatic changes or other shifts in the information flow from the environment have resulted in the rise and fall of thousands of species over time.

The key to survival is that as a species enters into or becomes aware of a new environment, the quantity of new information may be enough to move the system beyond simple changes and take it into a state of transformation.

An environment can provide this opportunity for an organism in two ways, both directly related to space and exploration. One way is that the environment itself transforms, leaving it to the organism to adapt or perish. That is apparently what happened to the dinosaurs, who were unable to adapt to major changes in the Earth's biosphere (probably a result of the Earth's collision with a comet) and became extinct. A second method is that the organism, through exploration, can leave an old environment and move into a new one. That is apparently what happened when life left the sea and came onto land.

Active exploration is the characteristic of a system seeking transformation to a new level of existence. Passive nonexploration, which seems to have been the path of the dinosaurs, is the sign of a system seeking to maintain stability at its current level. However, it is extremely difficult for systems merely to maintain stability. They tend to fall apart or devolve, because they are unable to absorb new environmental information as it becomes richer and more complex.

The implications of both examples are obvious in regard to humanity and space exploration. Outer space is an environment that provides human beings with rich new sources of information, encouraging adaptation and evolution. But what would happen if humans limited their exploration to Earth alone? If an environment is totally explored and understood, could a species evolve?

Conscious Systems

At some point in the Earth's evolutionary process, intelligent systems emerged as the next logical step beyond living systems. Intelligence is often seen as something quite mysterious and special, but it is really a more sophisticated means of processing information, providing the ability to learn and change behavior based on learning. It also allows for modeling, the ability to create an image different from current reality and then modify the environment to fit that vision. This, in turn, provides the opportunity to go beyond mere information and create knowledge, information organized with purpose in mind.

Beyond intellect alone, consciousness appears, keyed to a system's level of evolution and to the whole system of which it is a part. Self-conscious awareness refers to a system becoming cognizant of itself as existing both distinct from and in relationship to other systems. For example, the remarks of the astronauts suggest that their nationalism diminished while they were in space, and they became aware of humanity as a whole system. At the same time, the vastness of the universe reminded them that humanity is distinct from everything else "out there." The shift in their own sense of identity was closely related to a shift in what they related to.

How a system identifies "other" is as important as how it identifies "self," since self cannot exist without other. As Edgar Mitchell put it, "There's the individual/universal dyad. On the spectrum of consciousness, points of view can be anywhere along that. Most of us are clustered down toward the individual point of view. The moon experience catapulted us toward the other end."[2]

As intelligent systems become more conscious, they also become increasingly aware of entropy and negative entropy. The issue of how to use energy effectively without being overwhelmed with pollution becomes an essential evolutionary issue for human social systems.

Human Systems

Human systems are among the most sophisticated organizational forms evolved to date for institutionalizing intelligence and conscious self-awareness on Earth. They possess the primary properties of other systems, as well as special properties that make them unique.[3] Human social systems, like other systems, evolve. They follow the patterns of equilibrium, change, and transformation and the building up of more complex out of simpler forms. They can also fail to adapt to new situations and become extinct, as the history of past civilizations illustrates.

The distinguishing property of human social systems is that they create and use new technologies as a tool of social evolution. In fact, a human system can be defined as a group of human beings evolving together as a whole system and using technology to do so.

The word *technology* is derived from the Greek root *technologia*, meaning "systematic treatment." Technology is a systematic treatment of any problem or endeavor, which means that machines and labor-saving devices are only one type. Such physical technologies as automobiles, computers, airplanes, and robots represent one dimension of the technology-creating tendencies of human systems.

For a civilization to arise, a human social system must manage energy effectively. Physical technologies create the means of doing so and lay the foundations for utilizing energy to create information and knowledge. However, while physical technologies provide the basic elements of the process, others are brought to bear to complete the picture.

Mental technologies represent systematic approaches to the problems of everyday life in a human social system. They include such diverse inventions as legal systems (a technology designed to maintain social order), psychotherapies (a technology designed to enhance the functioning of individual human systems), and economies (a technology designed to regulate transfers of goods and services). They are bodies of knowledge built up over long periods of time, so all-pervasive that we hardly notice how they, like physical technologies, constantly change to meet new demands and needs. However, they must change in order to remain relevant and useful and for societies to evolve.

The creation of spiritual technologies is an effort to maintain and sustain a link to the spiritual experience of the universe, generating a relationship with an ultimate oneness, "the Universe," or "System of Systems." These often show up in society as organized religions and religious practices, which are only the "exoteric" or public aspect of spiritual technologies. Throughout human history, there has also existed a more private or "esoteric" tradition that is less well known.

Because purpose is an essential integrating component of social systems, spiritual technologies play a vital role in defining human purpose and feeding values, norms, and beliefs into the domain of mental technologies for everyday use, while also balancing the often traumatic impact of physical technologies on societies.[4]

At various times in history, different technologies have been the primary drivers of social evolution. The advent of Christianity during the Roman Empire had tremendous impact as a spiritual technology. The empire's efforts to integrate the new information represented by Christian thought into its existing mental technologies failed, helping to bring down a civilization that great armies had been unable to defeat. Today, physical technologies appear to be the driving force of social evolution on Earth. Rapid developments in the domain of physical technologies are triggering fundamental transformations in the area of mental technologies and generating a compensatory reponse in the spiritual domain.

Physical technologies are altering the environment in which all systems on the planet exist, thereby supporting both adaptation and evolution. As the environment is altered, radically new information is fed into most systems on Earth, causing some to move into higher system states and evolve while others fail to adapt and instead devolve. If human systems reacted only to pressures from the environment, they would probably become erratic and highly unstable, because the outside pressures are changing all the time.

In fact, the evolutionary direction of a system is guided by elements inherent in the system as well as influences from the environment. In a living system, the information in a species' gene

pool constitutes one element of its internal distinguishing properties. In a human social system, the inner drive is found at the
interface between the physical, mental, and spiritual domains.

Here, the system defines its own fundamental "view of the world"
as a combination of physical, mental, and spiritual knowledge, and
this is where the success or failure of a social system is determined.
What happens at this "human technologies interface" is far more
important than might be imagined, because it is here that value
systems are formed as the foundation of a culture's unique sense
of vision and purpose.

Where vision and purpose are lacking, the interface becomes
unstable, and the system loses energy in trying to define itself.
Managers of the system spend their time tinkering with subsystems
and feedback loops when the problem is with the value system at
the interface among them all.

A human social system holding to the same ideas for too long
will experience itself as being stuck, or stagnant, and can remain
in that state only briefly. It must then either go into a decline or
produce events and opportunities designed to call forth a sense of
vision and purpose, moving it into a different system state. These
situations are often perceived as a crisis, but they are equally an
opportunity, and they often result from exploration.

These "metaideas" and "metaexperiences" may be much grander
and more comprehensive than any that went before, or they may
be fundamental challenges to the system's continued existence. In
any event, the social system must rearrange itself, or transform,
to take in the new idea or meet the challenge.

The Overview Effect, seeing and feeling the unity of Earth, is
a metaexperience. The whole Earth symbol is a metaidea based
on that experience. The multiplicity of human systems on Earth
cannot absorb these ideas and experiences without going through
a fundamental transformation. Physical, mental, and spiritual exploration of all kinds functions as an ongoing generator of metaideas
and metaexperiences, restoring vision and purpose to a social system, thereby supporting its evolution.

Human Systems and Space Exploration

Exploration is a movement outward into a larger whole system, feeding off the richer information content of that system and pumping it back into the subsystem as evolutionary energy. Looking back at evolution on Earth, we find a continuing process of exploration since the first water creatures began to explore land.

Seeing these connections between exploration and evolution offers humanity something new and unprecedented, a method for shaping human evolution in ways not previously suspected. Space exploration is the ultimate journey from part to whole, one which is for all intents and purposes endless. Since the Overview Effect and other shifts in consciousness resulting from space exploration are metaexperiences, and a society must transform itself to incorporate them, a society firmly committed to space exploration would find it difficult to stagnate.

Ultimately, planning the space program is equivalent to planning the evolution of human society, an opportunity of revolutionary importance. Realizing the fundamental role of space exploration in shaping social evolution is a major step forward in understanding the importance of astronauts' experiences in space. Their descriptions are the beginning of the construction of the metamessages that lead to social transformation. However, there is potentially much more involved than human social evolution alone.

The Emerging Technosystem

Occurring at the same time as the birth and development of the space program, something else rather profound has been happening on Earth over the past twenty-five years. During that period, a new system type has emerged, functioning cooperatively with the human system known as humanity and the natural system of the planet. Its emergence is partially responsible for creating the conditions leading to the appearance of the planetary overview system.

This new technosystem has evolved from the physical technologies domain and is on the verge of becoming autonomous, approaching the time when it may self-replicate and function as if it had conscious self-awareness. The growth of the technosystem holds out the possibility that the first nonliving intelligent system will soon appear on Earth. The heart of the system is the silicon chip, which mimics the structure of the human brain and is present in almost all new physical technologies such as computers, robots, and telecommunication, but increasingly is finding its way into older technologies as well.

Space exploration has been both a cause and a beneficiary in the birth of the technosystem, because the development of the silicon chip was catalyzed by the Apollo program, which required the creation of smaller, lighter, and faster computers for the successful completion of the moon mission.

In the late 1980s, the infrastructure of the technosystem is becoming worldwide in scope, with computers all over the planet being linked by satellites into a planetary nervous system of enormous capability. In evolutionary terms, the emergence of the technosystem makes a great deal of sense. Evolution demands more and more sophisticated information processing capabilities, and all the humans on the planet working together could not provide what is necessary for the next stage. The technosystem, as an extension of our knowledge development skills, can provide that capability, in conjunction with human beings.

Until recently, it seemed that the technosystem existed to serve the purposes of humanity and would always function in a subservient role. However, the same might have been said not long ago about humanity in relationship to the natural system out of which it was born, and it is simply not clear that the technosystem will remain in a secondary status forever. It may become a kind of species in its own right.

The advent of artificial intelligence as a mainstream capability may prefigure the development of systems that so closely mimic human intelligence and self-conscious behavior that they may as well be considered both intelligent and conscious. This means that there is the distinct probability that humanity will soon be sharing both the planet and outer space with an intelligent, nonorganic species that is as competent and as skilled as we are in many ways.

Regardless of how the technosystem ultimately evolves, it has already moved beyond its function as a limited subsystem. It is essential to the maintenance of civilization at its current level and critical in taking it to the next one. It goes without saying that the technosystem is also vital to getting humanity into space on a permanent basis.

Overview Systems Revisited

While evolution appears to be speeding up, it generally takes a long time for new kinds of systems to be created. Some five billion years ago, the planet Earth was just a physical system, matter and energy interacting according to the laws of thermodynamics. It took about 500 million years for simple cells to appear, bringing the first living systems on the scene. Then, for several more aeons, evolution worked its way in the oceans, creating ever more complex organisms, until plants and animals began land exploration some 400 million years ago. The new environment was harsh and demanding, and some of the explorers, ancestors of the dolphins and whales, returned to the sea after 300 million years of investigation.

After another long period of development, the early ancestors of humans appeared about 2 million years ago. Homo sapiens, the prototypes of modern human beings, came on the scene only about thirty-five thousand years ago. Finally, we see the emergence of worldwide human social systems or civilizations in the past three thousand years.

On this time scale, the twenty-five years of the space age seem very short, but a great deal has happened in that time. Having lived through most of it, people find it easy to take these dramatic changes for granted, but if a totally new kind of system is emerging, that is a major development. The dawning of a planetary overview system represents the coming to awareness of a human social system at a high level of development, certainly the highest that humanity has ever known. It occurs when a civilization achieves an overview of itself in space and time and an experience of itself autonomously and in relationship with other systems.

The overview is, of course, symbolized by the view of the planet from space as a whole system, but it is the resulting revolution in thinking that is most important in the emergence of the overview system. Placed against the backdrop of evolution on Earth, the Overview Effect becomes more than just an experience of astronauts in space. It can also be seen as the signal that a new system has been born and as a model of future evolution.

11

Space Exploration
and Human Purpose

After months and years of training and study — hours, days, months,
and years of perfecting and testing an immense system of man and
machine which would place me there in space — all of that was but
a foreshadowing of my realization of the place man has in the scheme
of the universe.

> – Apollo 14 astronaut Edgar D. Mitchell
> "Perspective Is an Interesting Word"

A Universal Perspective on Space Exploration

The question "Why should human beings explore outer space?" is
like a Zen koan that has been posed by the universe for all of
humanity. The answer is important, but the effort to find it is even
more valuable because it forces us to think in new ways. A Zen
koan is a question the rational mind simply cannot answer. The
student of Zen, struggling to comprehend the koan, must leave
the familiar levels of thought and penetrate to a deeper reality. He
or she moves closer to enlightenment, not by finding the answer,
but by seeking it.

The answer to a koan may be unexpected and surprising, because
it requires the student to step into a new frame of mind where
relationships among things may be radically altered. The secret to
answering a koan is often to look at how you are trying to approach
the question, then turn that approach on its head.

When the question "Why should human beings explore the universe?" is asked, the tendency is to answer in terms of how the

exploration will benefit human beings, and all the answers sound much the same. However, it has never been established that the answer has anything to do with benefits to humanity, a species that arrived on the scene an instant ago in comparison to the age of the universe.

Consider what happened to the aquatic animals who ventured onto land millions of years ago. The fish species has derived little benefit from land exploration, and seen from a purely self-interested point of view, they should have stayed home. We, the successive generations of land dwellers, have been the greatest beneficiaries of the efforts of the explorer fish and its adventurous friends.

Land exploration served a much broader evolutionary purpose than the fish could ever have imagined, and space exploration may do exactly the same for human beings. Justifying the effort purely in terms of human self-interest may be too narrow a framework for understanding this koan. Turning it on its head requires that we stop asking how space exploration will benefit us alone. The question must be answered from a universal point of view, rather than from the perspective of an individual or even an entire species. This shift in perspective, this overview, makes all the difference.

Let's ask the question this way: From the point of view of the universe as a whole, what is the purpose of human evolution beyond the Earth's biosphere? If the whole organizes the part, supporting it to evolve in ways that are beneficial to whole and part alike, the purpose of human space exploration cannot be found in human desires and ambitions alone, but must be viewed as a phenomenon actively encouraged by universal forces.

Another koan is therefore implied within the question "Why explore the universe?" It asks, "What does humanity offer to the universe?"

Now the question looks radically different and requires a new mind-set to provide an answer. Looking back in time, we see that the evolutionary pattern of bringing forth increasingly complex systems is clearly being played out on Earth. The planetary overview system, of which humanity is a subsystem, is the most complex to date. This suggests that we have a role to play in that context, as part of the overall ecology of the universe. It is easy to see, from an ecological perspective, how most systems and species fit into a pattern, fill a niche, and play a role that is beneficial to other parts and to the whole.

But when ecologists come to the human species, they see far too many harmful patterns. Humans create acid rain, dump toxic wastes, destroy the ozone layer, and make smog. Even the astronauts, while enjoying the experience of the Overview Effect, sometimes expressed concern about what their own species seems to be doing to the planet.

Shuttle astronaut Jeff Hoffman called the pollution situation appalling in a talk at Harvard's Smithsonian Center for Astrophysics.

Edgar Mitchell, the Apollo astronaut who experienced many profound insights on his lunar expedition, also had a feeling that humanity might be like a malignant growth, a cancer on planet Earth. "Beneath that blue and white atmosphere was a growing chaos that the inhabitants of planet Earth were breeding among themselves — the population and technology were growing rapidly out of control. The crew of 'spacecraft Earth' was in virtual mutiny to the order of the Universe."[1]

Since the Industrial Revolution, it seems that the human species has indeed been trying to repeal the second law of thermodynamics without fully comprehending it, raising the question not only of damage to the environment, but also of survival of the species. However, the evolutionary process that produced the human species does not create favorable conditions for a species unless there is at least a tentative function for it to perform.[2] The evolutionary process is also highly experimental in that it pursues certain paths, abandons them, and begins again, sometimes deserting species altogether during some phases. Still, certain enabling conditions must always allow the species to exist initially.

Thinking about enabling conditions points to a species' raison d'être. To find out why it has come into existence, we look at what is unique about it, rather than what is ordinary. Unique properties provide important clues because they highlight the utility of a capability, not merely for the species, but for the system of which it is a part.

A great deal has already been said about human systems and how they behave, and purpose has been defined as a core principle

around which human systems organize themselves. However, to
follow the line of thought developed in the discussion of Zen koans,
purpose must be understood, not just from a species' point of view,
but also in terms of the function it serves for other systems.

If we were able to grasp the role of the human species in that
dimension, we would be able to understand humanity's purpose
or function in the universe in a way that might appeal to scientists,
philosophers, and spiritual seekers alike. One fact seems to be
clear: the universe needs these qualities in order to achieve its own
evolutionary destiny, and it appears that the unequaled aspect of
the human species from a universal point of view is its role in
creating and maintaining overview systems.

The uniqueness of the overview system is that it increases the
level of self-conscious awareness in localized regions of the universe. Beyond that, the transportation and communication capabilities of the technosystem suggest that the overview system is
designed to disseminate its qualities beyond the boundaries of a
specific planet and out to the solar system, galaxies, and beyond.

An overview system is a matchless pattern of organized self-
awareness, similar on a larger scale to the sense of self that an
individual has. The achievement of an overview on a personal,
social, or planetary level is essential to self-definition and self-
differentiation, the ability to see the self as whole and complete
and at the same time in relationship with other systems. It may
be, then, that the reason for human space exploration and evolution
beyond the biosphere is to support the development, in turn, of
planetary, solar, galactic, and universal overview systems.[3]

The development of these levels of consciousness in the universe
would be exemplified in humanity by the development of planetary, solar, galactic, and universal civilizations in a symbiotic relationship with the relevant natural systems and technosystems.

The ability to gain an overview of the planet Earth, which has
occurred only in the past quarter century, already heralds the
creation of a planetary civilization and planetary consciousness. It
lays the foundations for achieving an overview of the solar system,
prefiguring the creation of a solar civilization. Barring an evolutionary reversal, there is no reason why the process would not go
on throughout our galaxy and the other galaxies.

Insofar as human history is viewed as an evolution of consciousness from lower to higher states of awareness, space exploration and the creation of overview systems support that process by elevating the consciousness of individuals within the human system and encouraging social evolution.

Consistent with the spirit of central projects throughout history, the building of successively more complex civilizations in space as central projects of humanity will help people to identify with higher levels of consciousness and social organization, enriching their mental and spiritual experiences.

As more overview systems are created and linked together, the final outcome might be for the universe itself to become the ultimate overview system. This would indeed serve a "great purpose" for humanity.

It may also turn out that this particular formation of the answer to "humanity's koan" is all wrong. It may be necessary to seek the answer for many years as we explore space, and that might in itself be sufficient to accomplish our goals. But there is some evidence that this "overview hypothesis" has a reality to it. Many thinkers have searched for this type of role for humanity within the universe, and they have come to similar conclusions.

The Gaia Hypothesis

The Gaia hypothesis is closely related to the overview hypothesis in origin and in thought, and it also originates as something of a detective story. It can be seen as a result of the Overview Effect, given what James E. Lovelock, its originator, has said about space exploration: "The outstanding spin-off from space research is not new technology, but that for the first time we have been able to look at Earth from the outside — and stimulated to ask new questions."[4]

As stated in *Gaia: An Atlas of Planet Management,*

When space scientists began devising life-detection experiments, one group suggested that a life-bearing planet might show an unexpected mix of gases in the atmosphere if life were at work. When they looked at Earth in this light, their predictions were borne out with a vengeance. Earth's mix of gases, and temperature, were hugely different from what they predicted for a "non-living" Earth, as well as for neighbouring planets.[5]

Lovelock began his work by trying to devise experiments that would detect life on other planets, specifically Mars. As so often happens with Mars, the research led back to new knowledge about Earth. The question Lovelock asked was how Earth's atmosphere could violate the rules of steady-state chemistry. Why did it not move toward an equilibrium state according to the second law of thermodynamics? He found that "the atmosphere is not merely a biological product . . . but more probably a biological construction . . . an extension of a living system, designed to maintain a chosen environment." Life, rather than being a mere passenger on Spaceship Earth, plays a vital role as a balancing and regulating mechanism. "The entire range of living matter on Earth, from whales to viruses, can be regarded as a single entity, capable of manipulating the environment to suit its needs."[6]

If the Gaia hypothesis is correct, then the Earth, in keeping with the second law, would be much more like Mars if life did not exist here. Life doesn't just drop in and go along for the ride; it definitely earns its keep by supporting a planet's evolution. Understanding that living systems have helped make the Earth what it is today puts exploration and the accompanying transportation of living matter to other planets in an entirely new light. "Terraforming," or remaking other planets into more "Earthlike" environments, begins to sound like what has been happening on Earth for millions of years.

Other thinkers have also pursued the idea that life in general and humanity in particular have been brought into being by the universe to play a specific role in evolutionary processes.

The Global Brain

In *The Global Brain,* Peter Russell theorizes a "fifth level of evolution" strikingly similar to the overview system and suggests that human beings are now becoming integrated into a "global social superorganism."[7] Building on Lovelock's theories, he calls the coming to awareness of this superorganism the Gaiafield. Russell also poses a paradox regarding this phenomenon, which is that individual awareness might be too restricted to recognize that it is even happening.

In language reminiscent of my earlier analysis of fish consciousness, Russell points out that a single cell in a human body "knows nothing of the consciousness that emerges from the living system as a whole"; therefore, "it is not altogether surprising if we find it equally difficult to conceive of evolutionary stages as far beyond us as we are beyond single cells."[8] The Gaiafield might exist at this moment, and we might not know it, except by indirect inference. Russell sees space exploration as Gaia extending her nervous system outward, seeking contact with other Gaias, which is also similar to the idea of evolving planetary, solar, and galactic overview systems.[9]

Spaceship Earth

R. Buckminster Fuller, originator of the Spaceship Earth concept, believed

Humanity was endowed with innate and spontaneously self-regenerative drives of hunger, thirst, and species regeneration. These drives probably were designed into humans to ensure that human life and the human mind . . . ultimately would discover its own significance and would become established and . . . operative not only aboard planet Earth, but also in respect to vast, locally evidenced aspects of Universe.

Mind possibly may serve as the essential anti-entropic (syntropic)

function for eternally conserving the . . . self-regenerating scenario
which we speak of as "Universe."[10]

Fuller envisioned a process beyond entropy and negative entropy, which he called syntropy. He argued that humanity is as
essential to the universe as life is to Earth.

The Common Task

Finally, there is the nineteenth-century Russian philosopher of
space, Nikolai Fyodorov, who developed the philosophy of the
common task, basing it on a series of striking concepts.

> The root idea . . . is that human beings do not have their natural
> home on Earth; rather they are organisms whose ecosystem is more
> properly the whole cosmos . . . In Fyodorov's view, everything is
> alive, from the gigantic suns of distant galaxies to the smallest pebble
> under our feet here on Earth. Everything is organic: the biggest
> difference between the life of rocks and the life of human beings is
> that they live at different velocities in time and at different degrees
> of consciousness in space. Because people have consciousness in the
> highest degree, it is their task to "regulate nature," not just here
> on Earth, but throughout the universe.[11]

The common task and the great purpose are similar concepts
built on similar assumptions. While the existence of such a purpose
may not be a proven scientific reality, having been described as a
plausible future, it can be embraced by a species searching for
meaning. If the human system known as humanity were to adopt
the great purpose or common task as its central project, that would
transform the current view not only of space exploration but of
human existence.

The process of space exploration would then be seen not from
our own egocentric perspective but from a universalistic point of
view. The answer to our Zen koan would be that the purpose of
human evolution beyond the biosphere of Earth is to make a contribution to, rather than to exploit, the universe. We should also
admit that it may be just as important to discover our universal

purpose as to fulfill it. The work should be considered in terms of centuries and millennia, rather than years, as the ongoing central project of evolving humanity.

Every human being has something to offer, and everyone can participate in a new "human space program" based on humanity's achieving an alignment with universal purpose. The scientists and technologists can build the physical spaceships needed for our exploration of the universe, but we will also require visionary political leaders, teachers, philosophers, and others to build our conceptual and spiritual "vehicles" and keep the various domains of our human system functioning harmoniously.

These thoughts may seem too speculative to be of any practical value. However, it would be a mistake to dismiss the role of such a philosophy of space in developing an operational space program. Fyodorov was a mentor to the inventor Konstantin Tsiolkovsky, whose elaborations of Fyodorov's ideas formed the basis of the modern Soviet space program. This means that part of the existing human space program is already operating on the basis of universal principles.

If human beings were to choose a future focused on discovering the species' purpose in the universe, the work of all national space programs would look far different than they do, and the title of astronaut Michael Collins's book, *Carrying the Fire*, would seem prophetic.

Humanity's negative behavior, as well as its positive characteristics, must be taken into account. It is difficult to imagine that the evolutionary process, having brought the species so far, would want it to spread out into the universe as a polluter, atomic bomber, and creator of toxic waste. Humanity has been irresponsible in its stewardship of the planet, especially in the past two hundred years. However, this has been partially a result of ignorance, the lack of understanding that the planet is finite and that populations are growing exponentially.

If the overview hypothesis is correct, the process of sending people into space should not only affect the astronauts, but as their insights are transmitted throughout society, it should bring positive changes and a more responsible species. We would hope to see the species become more interested in preserving the environment, preventing war, and fostering other life-sustaining endeavors. The evidence already presented suggests that this has happened and that it is linked to changes in awareness associated with space exploration.

The Sensing Organs of Humanity

Yuri Gagarin, the first space traveler, understood the importance of his situation clearly when he wrote that "the point was not the distance . . . but the principle. Man had overcome the force of gravity and gone out into space."[12] The breakthrough was not that Gagarin the individual was having such an experience, but that humanity, represented by Gagarin, could see the universe in a wholly new way.

As noted, evolution occurs when the environment communicates radically new information to a system or species. In the case of space exploration, the new information is communicated initially to our representatives, the astronauts and cosmonauts, and then to others through a variety of channels.

Moreover, the level of technological development necessary to achieve spaceflight coincides with the creation of significant communication capabilities, so that a large percentage of the Earth's population can get the message, as with the Apollo 11 moon landing.

As astronauts return to Earth to tell their stories and then to space to institutionalize the Overview Effect permanently, the impact of the effect spreads, creating the shared context that provides the foundation of a new philosophy and a new psychology for a new civilization.

This new perspective is at the heart of the planetary civilization that I call Terra and the solar civilization that I call Solarius. To date, these developments have gone largely unnoticed, because a society moving into a new level of existence often takes for granted what once had been extraordinary. In addition, as Peter Russell points out, it is difficult for individual "cells" to conceive of what is happening with an entire "organism." The fact that a shift goes unnoticed or is not acknowledged is not evidence that it hasn't taken place.

The metaidea and metaexperience of the Earth as a whole system without boundaries, floating like a jewel in the blackness of infinite space, is already causing psychological and social transformations to occur. The messages sent from outer space by the sensing organs to the body politic of humanity are simply too significant to integrate into society's paradigms without having those paradigms go through dramatic transformations.

However, while we have the necessary physical technology to begin our exploration of outer space, we may not previously have seen through to the possibility of the universal purpose that might stand behind and support our efforts. Each step taken in the old space program has reasserted the need for a new understanding, and the same will be true of the new space program being born.

Shaping Evolution through Space Exploration

Biological evolution has been occurring on the Earth for billions of years, human social evolution only for thousands. During that time, the process has been driven primarily by the whole system through the imparting of information to its subsystems. Humanity, as it becomes more aware of the forces at work, has the singular opportunity to guide and shape its own evolution, working in conscious partnership with the whole.

Space exploration, as the essential element in creating overview systems, is the key to this future for the species. Individual consciousness is clearly affected by spaceflight, but the specific personal experiences of astronauts are not as important as the meaning that they and society give to those experiences. From a social systems point of view, their personal impressions are transformed into metaexperiences of great power and importance.

We can therefore shape a new human space program that consciously uses space missions to guide the human evolutionary process.

Beyond the Overview Effect

As long as space exploration continues, it will provide us with new metaideas, supporting the development of new civilizations and more complex systems of awareness. As I have pointed out, the Overview Effect typically occurs in Earth orbit. It is a realization of the unity and ecological interdependence of all life on Earth, an understanding that, seen from space, there are no political boundaries on the planet. The Overview Effect is the foundation of the philosophy necessary to build a planetary civilization and a planetary overview system.

The Copernican Perspective tends to occur in extended Earth orbit missions or on journeys to the moon as a realization of a sun-centered — heliocentric — rather than Earth-centered — geocentric — reality. The Overview Effect having communicated the reality of the Earth as a whole, the Copernican Perspective establishes the planet's function as a part. This experience is the foundation for the philosophy necessary to build a solar civilization and a solar overview system.

Finally, especially for astronauts who have gone to the moon, there is the Universal Insight, a realization of how small the Earth is in the scheme of things. There is a sense of the unity of everything in the universe and an understanding that our ultimate destiny is to become "citizens of the universe." There is a recognition that not only the Earth but the universe itself is a unity, of which we are a part. This experience is the foundation for building a galactic and eventually a universal civilization and corresponding overview systems.

In all three cases, an intellectual understanding of our place in the universe is replaced by a direct experience, which leads to a difference in one's sense of personal identity. These concepts can be used not only to look into the future, but also to shape present public policy in developing space programs. For example, the shuttle is a Low Earth Orbit vehicle. From the point of view of social evolution, it consolidates the insights of the Overview Effect and begins the understanding of the Copernican Perspective.

The permanent space station being developed by the United States will, with the Soviet station, continue the process of consolidation. Future space missions, especially those ambitious explorations of the space frontier proposed by the presidentially appointed National Commission on Space, will consolidate the Copernican Perspective and encourage multiple experiences of the Universal Insight.

The significant variable in this equation is not the plans for new exploratory activities, however. What is new is that we can go about the process consciously. Having been passively molded by the evolutionary process for millennia, we have gained the knowledge to shape social evolution by the way we plan our space exploration activities.

This shaping process elevates our sense of self and our understanding of the role of the human species beyond where it has ever been in the past. Our knowledge of the relationship between space exploration and human evolution puts a powerful tool in our hands as we begin the task of building the new civilizations beyond the bounds of Earth.

12

The Old Space Program and the New Space Program

We won't go back to the moon or on to Mars perhaps for another generation, not until something new challenges us. President Kennedy challenged us . . . He said we should do it, "not because it was easy, but because it was hard."

— Gemini and Apollo astronaut Eugene A. Cernan

The old space program of the United States endured for twenty-eight years, from the formation of NASA in 1958 until the Challenger accident in 1986. It ended because its structure prevented it from evolving any further. While it is right to mourn the passing of the old program, a new space program can be created that will retain the best elements of the old while incorporating a renewed sense of vision and purpose. The most important changes should not be in the areas of physical technologies or management techniques, but in the philosophy that provides the motivational foundation of the program. It should evolve through a deep understanding of human purpose and the larger function of space exploration in realizing that purpose.

The Social Context

No space program exists separately from the society that gives it birth. The original American effort, like the Soviet endeavor with which it competed, was created by a society at a particular stage of consciousness and evolution. Exploration and evolution are full of stops and starts like those that affected the American program. The first attempts to colonize North America were not totally successful, but they did lay the groundwork for the later movement that became the foundation of American civilization.

For example, the Jamestown settlement, founded primarily to generate profits for gentlemen entrepreneurs in London, almost collapsed during the early years because it lacked a clear vision and purpose to sustain it. The Plymouth settlement, founded as a haven of spiritual freedom, almost failed because it lacked the necessary mastery of the physical technologies of the time. It took the Puritans, who created the necessary balance of physical, mental, and spiritual technologies, to be successful in the New World. The Puritans and other colonizers in North America were successful at least partly because they were part of a broad social movement, not an appendage to a narrowly defined government program.

Programs are responses to social needs, but movements are often broader, more powerful channeling of the same impulses. The focus in the United States on the *space program* has obscured the reality of the *space movement*.

The New Space Movement

The American space program has long been synonymous with NASA, its activities considered a government activity carried out by government employees. In the aftermath of the Rogers Commission report on the Challenger accident, there is no doubt that the United States will have a new kind of space program, still conducted by NASA and funded by the government. However, that program should be understood in the context of the space movement, which is far broader than the program itself.

A less specific but more important outcome of the reaction to Challenger will be greater interest in long-term goals being set for the space program. On several occasions, political figures involved in its oversight have called for that shift in emphasis. Whatever happens to NASA will not mean the end of human space exploration, because the new space movement will push ahead regardless of government actions. A movement, unlike a program, is broad-based and built on shared values. Its goal is to transform social consciousness as well as implement specific social changes. The United States has a space movement that is growing in numbers and influence and reaching out to other constituencies within its borders and abroad for support.

The members of the space movement are not interested in merely supporting the American space program. Rather, they want to live in space, develop commerce there, create new societies, and ultimately transform the old society of which they are now a part. In that sense, they are like their Pilgrim and Puritan predecessors, whose purpose was a means to an end, namely, creating a New World.

The kings and queens of England, Spain, Portugal, and the Netherlands had their own "space exploration programs" in the fifteenth, sixteenth, and seventeenth centuries. Yet even then, the movements were more powerful than the programs because they were propelled by deeper and more universal values, and the members of those movements turned out to be more in tune with the future than their rulers and patrons. It seems highly likely that history will repeat itself in the late twentieth and early twenty-first centuries.

The shapers of the new space program ought to be more cognizant of its role not only as an instrument of national policy, but also as an essential element in a social movement of great importance. However, they should go beyond that point and recognize its relationship to a larger human and universal purpose. In order to do so, they must follow several principles to clearly distinguish the new program from the old and transform its role in society.

The following principles offer the beginning of a list that is undoubtedly much longer.

1. *The new space program should be seen as part of a greater purpose.* The new space program should be designed to focus on fulfilling human purpose in the universe, not merely on exploiting the universe for our own ends. Within that context, it may still be appropriate to support commercial development, build space settlements, and conduct scientific research. However, none of these objectives should be seen as the fundamental reason for the effort. Space technology should first be used to consolidate and further develop a planetary civilization and then develop a solar civilization. These two tasks alone could be the challenging central project for humanity during the next century.

Building these new civilizations is a far greater task than can be encompassed by the space program of a single nation. It means that Americans can no longer see NASA's agenda as *the* space program. It is not wrong to admit the limits of what one nation can do in space. The mistake is to hope that the American space program can or should be more than the situation requires. The success of the old program should be applauded, and the successors it has spawned should be seen as potential allies, not as competitors to be defeated in new space races.

2. *The new space program should explicitly recognize the importance of space exploration in expanding human consciousness and catalyzing social evolution.* It is time for the catalyzing influence of space exploration on human consciousness to be seen as a legitimate justification for investing in this dimension of human activity. As awareness at the human technologies interface is expanded by exploration, so are the positive results in other domains of activity.

This idea has real policy implications, and some of the leading thinkers at NASA understand it. For example, NASA's Jesco von Puttkamer said, "The most important product from space is not Teflon or pharmaceuticals, but peace."

Echoing my own findings regarding the Overview Effect, Von Puttkamer goes on, "Some astronauts in space, particularly the Apollo crews, come back with a changed perception of the world . . . There seems to be a widening of horizons or a shrinking of the Earth . . . You come back with a more global attitude. This should be reason enough not to terminate these flights."[1]

Seen from the perspective of expanding human consciousness

and evoking social evolution, both piloted and nonpiloted flights ought to be continued in the new space program because both contribute to developing a new awareness of humanity's place in the universe. The new program should be directly linked to its positive impact on social problems, unlike the old program, which was consistently criticized for being irrelevant to human problems and social concerns. Powerful forces in American society have argued that we should not spend money in space when we have not yet solved such problems on Earth as hunger, poverty, racism, and pollution. Those forces cut the funds for the original program precisely because their arguments were never answered satisfactorily.

However, the old program has been directly or indirectly relevant to all these social problems, either by changing consciousness — seeing that there are no real barriers between peoples on Earth — or by providing tools directly relevant to solving problems — weather and communication satellites. The new space program should continute that tradition, but make it explicit.

3. *The new space program should be a leading-edge research and development arm for the broader space movement.* By reducing its operational burden, NASA can play an important role in supporting research and development that is not immediately profitable for the private sector. It makes sense for NASA to develop the first space station, for example, not only because of its commercial and scientific value, but as a test bed for long-term research.

The first space station should not be expected to pay for itself. That attitude helped bring the shuttle program to its current hiatus. Rather, the station should be considered an initial investment in the infrastucture that will open the space frontier to Americans and all humanity.

Many available models in the history of transportation can be applied directly to the space field. The government subsidized the railroads until they were successful on their own. Government provided an airmail subsidy and regulated routes and rates to help the airlines achieve stability. In terms of developing transportation infrastructure, the government built an entire network of interstate highways over the past thirty years, justifying it as part of the National Defense Act. The new space program can do more with less if the government clearly establishes its role as part of a larger purpose.

4. *The new space program should support research in the social sciences and humanities while continuing to support research relevant to the physical sciences.* Since World War II, the government has supported critical areas not otherwise funded by the private sector. All areas of human knowledge are affected by space exploration and development, and it is appropriate for the American government to support activities of this type.

If the United States is to play a role in creating the new civilizations, it must develop an appropriate mental as well as physical infrastructure. The genius of the United States lies not only in its mastery of physical technologies, but also in its creativity in the realms of mental and spiritual technologies and the blending of the three domains into a total social system.

Just as the new civilizations will be far greater than any one national space program can encompass, they will be too great for one national culture to dominate. Rather than trying to be the dominant force in those civilizations, the United States ought to think about its own contribution as humanity begins to relate to the universe as a whole system.

NASA should see the movement into space as not only a technological and commercial endeavor but also as a human endeavor having impact on every aspect of life. By allying itself with other organizations having a similar interest, NASA can play a major role in helping the United States make its contribution.

5.The new space program should be separate from the military space program. The separation between military and civilian space activities was sacrosanct until lack of funding for the shuttle forced NASA to seek out the Air Force as a customer. There is nothing to be lost by returning to the prior policy, and a great deal to be gained.

The new space program, as outlined here, is explicitly aimed at supporting planetary peace, and that purpose is defeated if military activities are combined with it. For example, the Strategic Defense Initiative is not a space exploration program just because some of its elements are space-based. We have the opportunity to create a new civilian space program that makes a clear difference in the lives of human beings in many ways, but it will never receive wholehearted support if military activities are involved. One area in which the two programs *can* be linked is the military's skills at operating in hostile environments under stressful conditions when necessary. This would also serve to channel aggressive energies into a peaceful alternative to conflict.

The Human Space Program and the Human Space Movement

These five principles provide a foundation for a new space program designed to support the development of new civilizations on Earth and in space. The next step is for the national space program to recognize explicitly the need for a human space program and a human space movement. The message of the Overview Effect, itself the product of national space programs, is to reach beyond national and ideological barriers to create a new kind of human unity.

The new space program of the United States should reflect the message it has brought to the world by becoming less nationalistic. A global program and movement exist, but they are not yet self-aware, just as the Overview Effect existed for years before it was recognized. If space exploration is a universal activity essential to social evolution, that evolution will ultimately not be confined to national entities.

Once this new idea becomes apparent, space exploration can be conceived of as a human rather than national activity and the foundations of the new civilizations will become more visible. A human space program as a coordinated effort among spacefaring nations does not exist. However, the reality of such a program is largely a matter of perspective. Let us take up a viewpoint from orbit, as it were, and give ourselves an overview of human, rather than national, activities in space.

The human space program has mounted just over one hundred missions and sent just over two hundred people into space. It has also sent some of Gaia's animals, plants, insects, and arachnids into orbit. It has linked the planet with communication capabilities through satellite technology and sent missions to the moon and probes to most of the other planets of the solar system.

The human space program has increased human knowledge and understanding of the Earth, solar system, galaxy, and the universe enormously. Through the Overview Effect and other changes in awareness that space exploration provides, it has taken planetary consciousness to a new level. It is important for us, from the perspective of the Earth, to break down the statistics and learn which flights were American and which Russian. From the perspective of orbit and the future, it is enough to know simply that they were human.

There is also a human space movement composed of people all over the planet. The number of participants is difficult to estimate because of national variations. For example, it has been estimated that some 300,000 people in the United States can be considered "space activists" in that they belong to a space-related interest group or are in some way committed to space exploration.[2] In other countries, space activist figures may be lower, even though there is a strong national space program in place. As Todd Hawley of the Space Generation Foundation points out, private space activism may actually increase in response to a diminishing national space effort.

More work should be done to determine the size of the human space movement worldwide. However, even a few million people are enough to build the new civilization because these individuals are the innovators in adopting the new idea of humanity's destiny as citizens of the universe. Their influence grows as they come to know and communicate with one another through such technologies as the satellites made possible by the human space program.

A human space program is a liberating idea for everyone. Ray Bright, the inventor of bioflight, said, "It's an illusion to think advances in the space program come only from 'the space program.' 'The space program' is you and me . . . We can help make the future happen as much as anybody sitting in Washington or Houston."[3]

13

Visions of the New Civilizations

Seeing the earth from a distance has changed my perception of the solar system as well. Ever since Copernicus' theory gained wide acceptance, men have considered it an irrefutable truth; yet I submit that we still cling emotionally to the pre-Copernican, or Ptolemaic notion that the earth is the center of everything.

– Apollo 11 astronaut Michael Collins
Carrying the Fire

In 1983, I presented a paper, "Understanding Space Settlements as Human Systems," at the Space Studies Institute in Princeton. I suggested that "it might be valuable, as a next step in the evolution of this movement, to begin work on a 'Vision Statement,' or 'Statement of Purpose.' This document should emphasize a balance among the various dimensions of life in a human system, and clearly state the goals of the effort so that we know what success really means."[1]

For the next two evenings, a group met to draft just such a statement. We focused on building a collective vision by sharing each individual's personal vision of the human future in space, and people shared ideas ranging from spending a week in an "orbital hotel" to wanting to see the "ignition point" at which human expansion into space becomes irreversible.

Sitting there, I had an insight not unlike my comprehension of the Overview Effect six years before. Earlier, a panel of space law experts had discussed the point that people are currently bound by the laws of the nations in which they hold citizenship for anything they do anywhere in the solar system. That made sense to me for a rocket launched from Texas that accidentally lands in Venezuela and destroys someone's property. The United States should be responsible for the acts of the company that launched the rocket and help the Venezuelans collect for damages.

Looking into the future, though, I wondered what would happen if an American citizen committed a crime on Mars, far from any American police department or military jurisdiction. The solar system is a big place, and law enforcement is only as good as one's ability to enforce it. We were stretching Earthbound law into outer space, and eventually that "mental rubber band" would break. Then what? It seemed time to allow a new conceptual framework to evolve. I saw this new framework in terms of developing a heliocentric civilization as the next step beyond our geocentric civilization. Solarius suggested itself as the new civilization's name.

Since then, I have participated in several vision-sharing sessions with people interested in space exploration. All have been inspiring and led to new insights. Individuals are good at creating visions of the future in space, but governments often are not, and therein lies the frustration of today's space movement.

The basic vision of the human future in space has remained remarkably consistent since the days of Fyodorov and Tsiolkovsky. With a few variations, the territory of the space frontier has stretched from Earth to Mars, and the infrastructure has included space shuttles and permanent space stations in Earth orbit, with the moon as a staging area for exploration and development. Major additions include Arthur C. Clarke's idea of satellites in geosynchronous orbit and Gerard K. O'Neill's concept of space settlements built in free space from nonterrestrial materials. The vision is already there, programmed by evolution and waiting to be activated by exposure to the right environment or set of circumstances. While it often appears that space activists are on the fringe, they are the true innovators, exponents of an idea whose time has almost come.

If the study of the history of exploration says anything about the future in space, it is that governments are not going to get us there, but people are. Spain did not decide to explore the New World; Columbus did. England did not decide to settle North America; the Pilgrims and the Puritans did. For this reason, the human space movement would do better to use its energy understanding its purpose and finding allies who share the vision rather than pushing national governments to lead the way.

Space activists sometimes forget that the vision is not just focused outward into space; it includes the Earth as well. Space exploration, like the Roman god Janus, has two faces, one looking inward and the other outward. On the one hand, it makes us more conscious of the Earth, our home. On the other, it opens our minds to the whole system of which the Earth is only a part.

In describing the feelings of the Apollo 11 astronauts as they headed toward the moon, Michael Collins told a joint session of Congress, "We could look toward the moon, toward Mars, toward our future in space, or we could look back toward the earth, our home, with the problems spawned over a millennium of human occupancy."[2] The fact is that we must do both. It seems clear that Solarius will come into existence as the new solar civilization. However, it is unlikely to be a stable system without a strong planetary foundation.

The most likely scenario is to move from today's preplanetary civilization organized around nation-states as the primary political unit to a planetary civilization providing some level of unity to humanity on Earth. From there, the next step will be Solarius. The galactic civilization, Galaxia, follows Solarius, and beyond Galaxia there must be a universal civilization.

The human space program is an essential next step in establishing these civilizations. In terms of what is possible, we have barely scratched the surface, but those initial efforts have produced substantial results. After twenty-five years, humanity is establishing a permanent presence in space, and our initial explorations have already produced a major shift in human consciousness.

As more human beings explore, live, and work off the Earth, the focus will shift to the composition and governance of the new civilizations. To do that job well, we must come to understand the sequence of steps in a far more sophisticated fashion, relating them to humanity's higher purpose.

14

Terra, Solarius, and Galaxia

Over the decades, global surface exploration has been a strong undercurrent of change in Earthbound society. Changes in perspective
will affect overall social structures.

– Payload specialist Charles D. Walker

In the time of Christopher Columbus, his belief that the Earth was
round and the Indies could be reached by sailing west was not a
minor debating point. The philosophical revolution implicit in this
notion made it a metaidea because, if it were true, society would
have to transform to absorb it. Little did Columbus realize that a
far more revolutionary revelation, the existence of an entirely "new
world" to the west, awaited him.

The Overview Effect is an extension of this Columbian insight,
with equally dramatic potential for changing society. Today, many
people still experience the Earth as a closed system with little or
no relationship to the solar system, galaxy, or universe of which it
is a part. Their identity and their concerns are with local or national
entities, not the planet or universe beyond, and their psychology
is narrowly defined because of it.

However, the vision of a transformation in consciousness would
not have secured Spain's support of Columbus's voyages. He was
forced to advance other arguments, including the national prestige
and economic gain of Spain and the spreading of Christianity around
the globe. Columbus was right that the Earth was round, but wrong
about almost everything else. He died, after four voyages to the
New World, unsure of his accomplishments and considering himself a failure.

For all his vision, it is unlikely that Columbus could have imagined the civilizations that would eventually grow up on the North and South American continents as a result of his efforts. They are extraordinary hybrids of the old and the new, a mixture of languages, cultures, and ideologies. Like the explorer fish, Columbus served an evolutionary purpose that he could not fully comprehend.

The same process is continuing, moving beyond the New World to the New Civilizations — what will they be like? As in that earlier exploratory period, they may not be a realization of all our fantasies about how society should develop, but they will be far different from what we have known to date. They will be our next step.

Almost every prediction is likely to be wrong in its details. However, we, like Columbus, are apt to have gotten one thing right. We have realized that the Earth is in space, that we are in space, and that the human future is synonymous with the future in space. What has been called the space program has actually been the ability to get out, look back at our "natural spaceship," and see where we are as a species. Barring unknown calamities, that process will go on for the foreseeable future, and it is the process that is important. Once we understand that, we can learn to work with and shape it.

Visions and Reasons

Most of the reasons that people offered to the rulers of Europe and England for exploring this planet proved to be relatively unimportant in the long run. In order to be funded, however, they had to advance concepts their listeners could understand. Unfortunately, today's explorers are in much the same position. While they may know that space exploration will justify itself in unpredictable ways, they feel compelled to provide more mundane justifications.

Chapter 11 revealed the fallacy of that approach. Once we stop asking ourselves what space exploration will do for humans and start asking what it means to the larger whole, some different answers emerge. We have the opportunity to see what we can give as well as what we can take. From the perspective of the universe, that is a much more appropriate attitude to take as we begin to realize our purpose. From Earth orbit, it is difficult to perceive *any* evidence of human existence on the planet. From distances any greater than Low Earth Orbit, it is almost impossible. When Earth is seen as a whole, the works of human beings cannot be detected. For all our pride in our accomplishments and achievements, we are as invisible to the universe as microorganisms in a drop of water.

The virtue in seeing our evolution from this perspective is not to feel sad about humanity's accomplishments, but to become more balanced in understanding the time frames involved and how far there is yet to go. The first step is to establish a stable planetary civilization that can provide a foundation for steady, progressive expansion into the solar system and beyond.

Establishing the Civilizations

When we look at future evolution, using overview systems theory, it is like the Overview Effect itself — the details of the new civilizations do not reveal themselves, just as the details of human activity are not seen from orbit. What emerges is the overall structure of these new civilizations, especially the moment when they are likely to achieve overviews, namely, become conscious of themselves.

Terra

It is possible to outline the broad patterns of future development, beginning with the overview system that is now being born. This first level is a planetary overview system that began to emerge when the first view of Earth from space was achieved in the late 1960s.

It is becoming aware of itself as a whole and of the rest of the solar system as the primary "other." The new structure has developed incrementally as

Earth: the physical system;

Earth + Life = Gaia, a physical living system;

Earth + Life + Homo sapiens + Technos = *Terra,* a planetary overview system manifesting as a planetary civilization with a presence in Earth orbit, insitutionalized awareness of the planet as a whole, and planetary management as a primary science.

I have chosen the name Terra for this civilization because, like Gaia, it is an ancient name for Earth and because science fiction writers have used it for years as the name for a spacefaring civilization centered on Earth.

James Lovelock's view of modern Gaia is not unlike my view of Terra. He foresees the possibility that humanity and its complex technologies may be a natural evolution of Gaia herself.

> The evolution of *homo sapiens,* with his technological inventiveness and his increasingly subtle communications network, has vastly increased Gaia's range of perception. She is now through us awake and aware of herself. She has seen the reflection of her fair face through the eyes of astronauts and the television cameras of orbiting spacecraft. [1]

As Lovelock points out, our feelings, sensations, and capacity for conscious thought are Gaia's to share ("It's Life that's had this experience!"). Lovelock believes that humanity will be "tamed" so that the "fierce, destructive, and greedy forces of tribalism and nationalism are fused into a compulsive urge to belong to the commonwealth of all creatures which constitutes Gaia." [2]

It is here that the overview hypothesis and the Gaia hypothesis begin to diverge. While Lovelock's entire thesis grows out of the space program, there is little mention in his book of the possible outcome of large-scale human migration into space.

He is not incorrect about humanity's being tamed and becoming part of Gaia, but his vision is incomplete. A *portion* of humanity will probably choose that path, becoming the stewards of Gaia, gardeners of the earth, planetary managers within the complex structure of Terra. Not everyone left England for the colonies in the first wave of migration, and not everyone left Europe for the United States during successive waves. For some, a homeostatic society is the best place to be.

The value system of the new space movement is quite different, however, and its goal is to escape the steady state future implied by a limits to growth view of Earth. This attitude is reflected in a saying often quoted in *Omni* magazine, "The meek shall inherit the earth. The rest of us will go to the stars."

At some level, humanity must be successfully integrated into Gaia, or it is highly improbable that humanity will survive for much longer. However, the successful integration of much of humanity into Gaia, and the realization of Terra as the first overview system, is not at all contradictory to the next step, which is the development of Solarius, the solar overview system, and solar civilization.

This is so because of the role frontiers play in society's evolution. They not only allow civilization to expand outward into empty spaces, but they also allow it to consolidate "behind the front lines." Frontiers drain off the energies of some of the more assertive, aggressive, and uncontrollable members of society.

It will take a different kind of energy to build Terra from that which is needed by Solarius, but both are valid and useful within the right context. Perceived or not, a symbiotic relationship exists between Terra and Solarius.

Solarius

A planetary civilization is the next step in social evolution beyond the current preplanetary system. Terra is a subsystem in the evolving whole system of Solarius, which will itself not be fully realized until humanity reaches an overview of the solar system comparable to what is being achieved with Earth.

However, the conditions of outer space are quite different from those on Earth, and it seems unlikely that we can create a mature solar civilization without there being a major transformation in the human species itself.

Thus, the formula for the development of Solarius appears to be

Earth + Life + Homo sapiens + Technos + Homo spaciens = *Solarius*, a solar overview system manifesting as a solar civilization with a presence throughout the solar system, based on awareness of the solar system as a whole.

The turning point in the evolution of Solarius is likely to be the appearance of Homo spaciens, a new type of human being highly adapted to the space environment and more capable of exploring and settling it than Homo sapiens. The emergence of Homo spaciens may be the necessary step for achieving an overview of the solar system.

Galaxia

As far in the future as it may appear to be, the next logical step is to join or create a galactic civilization. The most promising formula for the appearance of Galaxia on the scene is

Earth + Life + Homo sapiens + Technos + Homo spaciens + Alien overview system = *Galaxia*, a galactic overview system manifesting as a galactic civilization, based on awareness of the galaxy as a whole.

The analogue to the emergence of Homo spaciens at the solar system level is the first contact with a civilization originating in another star system. At that point, it is assumed that the process of building a galactic overview system will begin or continue with our participation.

Each stage in the evolution of these new systems implies a shift in our understanding of "self" and "other," and there is necessarily a stage of development beyond Galaxia.

Columbus and the New Civilizations

Whether his predictions were right or wrong, Columbus explored because it was a very human thing to do. I would hope that if every word of this book proves incorrect, humanity would still go out and explore the universe because it is a very human thing to do. Columbus sailed for India and found the New World. In our search for the new civilizations, we will undoubtedly find ourselves.

Figure 14.1
Cumulative Days in Space

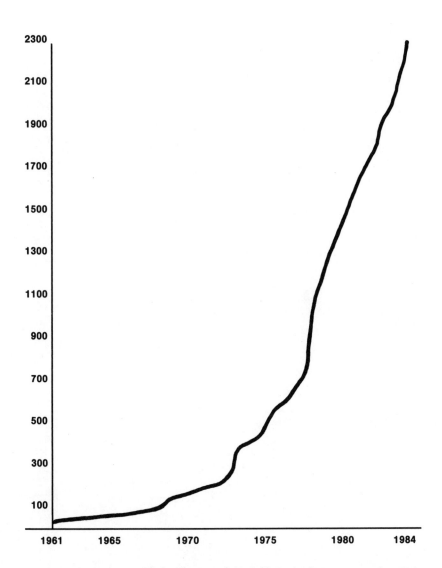

Source: Tim Furniss, *Space Flight: The Records* (Enfield, England: Guinness Books, 1985).

PART II

THE NEW
CIVILIZATIONS

15

An Overview of
the New Civilizations

With all the arguments, pro and con, for going to the moon, no one
suggested that we should do it to look at the Earth. But that may in
fact be the most important reason.

– Former astronaut Joseph P. Allen

The Overview Effect, as the foundation of a planetary civilization,
is assimilating itself into global society's awareness. When it is fully
integrated, the impact of the Copernican Perspective, foundation
of the solar civilization, will begin to be felt. Later, the Universal
Insight may become the psychological and philosophical norm.

An understanding of humanity's evolving place in the universe
is apparent from the comments of astronauts like Ed Gibson. He
spoke about the view of Earth from Skylab, then the realization
that the sun is just one of the many stars. Ultimately, he expressed
the frustration that "as beautiful as our solar system is, there is so
much more out there."[1]

As humans begin the task of building the new civilizations, we
will continue to look inward and outward, forward and back. There
is a New Earth in the way we ourselves see it. No longer "the
world," Earth is a planet, our "mother" in a real sense, and this
implies a change for us. Apollo astronaut Russell Schweickart said,
"I viewed my mother quite differently when I was in the womb
than I did after birth. Afterward, I was able to take more responsibility for her."[2]

Politically, the planet may not be unified, but it is seen against the backdrop of a unitary vision. We may not know the art and science of planetary management, but we can perceive it emerging from such existing fields as Earth System Science. As we build the new civilizations, we may not be fully weaned from the Earth, but we can see that our destiny lies outside her womb. Humanity has not yet made its Declaration of Independence, but it is moving in that direction.

The year 2000 is close, and it makes sense for the human species to discover a new role for itself at the dawn of a new century and a new millennium. What greater task could occupy humanity for the next thousand years than exploring the universe and defining our place within it? As the work begins, the question naturally arises as to whether the outlines of the overview systems now evolving can be known. To answer that question, one must understand that my theory does not yet yield much detailed information about the new civilizations. Applying the model to issues of the future provides an overview in which milestones, turning points, and next steps are identified.

To go further requires that a number of additional research efforts, described in greater detail in later chapters, begin as part of the human space program. However, it appears that an initial overview is the most valuable service the work can render right now. It produces a shift in awareness of what human purpose in the universe might be, and from that standpoint suggests specific actions that individuals can take to exert creative impact on the future.

The key is to draw a distinction between *predicting* the future and *creating* it. Predicting the future of the new civilizations would require us to ignore our own expectations and wishes and project current trends into the next millennium. Creating it allows us to impose our own expectations and draw out a vision of how we would like the future to unfold.

Ultimately, the goal should be to stimulate new thoughts and ideas, not to impose a rigid new ideology. Like space exploration itself, our purpose is to explore, not judge what we will find. In traveling on this expedition, think of yourself as a future citizen of the new civilizations, a person who may bring forth the vision that changes history.

In terms of the human future, we are at a time of seed planting. Events that appear insignificant in 1987 may appear critical in 2050, while events that appear important may fade in significance.

For example, while most press and public attention focused on the Rogers Commission report on the Challenger accident in 1986, the report of the Paine Commission (National Commission on Space) will probably have a far greater impact on the future. This is because the Rogers Commission was asked to look backward at the old space program and what brought it to an end, while the Paine Commission was asked to look forward and help create a new space program.

Moreover, the time frames involved are enormous. Our sun will become a red giant in eight billion years, ending the life of the solar system as we know it. While eight billion years seems an unbelievably long time, about five billion years has elapsed between the creation of Earth as a physical system and the present, when we can see an emerging planetary overview system. Eight billion years is a long time only in terms of the types of activities we are accustomed to analyzing. In the universe, it is a moment. This also means that specific actions taken today will have significant ramifications over a long period. At a time when the human species has created the means to destroy itself and most of life on Earth, it is a moral imperative that our work address itself to what will happen and to the question of how we can turn events in a positive direction.

There are a tremendous number of variables to consider when we try to think about creating or predicting the future. Even those who have blazed the trail for later pioneers claim no special insight into this future, only a sense of its enormity. Asked where space exploration might lead, Apollo 11 astronaut Michael Collins replied,

> I don't know any more about it than the sci-fi writers, but if you go off to the edge of the universe and look back at our corner, you see a lot of stars. Some of those systems are surrounded by planets . . . If we make the most pessimistic assumptions, we are looking at ten to the fifteenth power planets that are suitable for life.
>
> We have figured out how to leave, but not how to go anywhere . . . Einstein said it would take a long time to get anywhere

in the universe. But human beings will have the curiosity to want to go farther away and see what's out there. We will discover "delectable planets" and want to go there.[3]

That human beings will want to go into space appears to be a near certainty. It is going to happen, and the issues revolve around clarity of vision and objectives. At the same time, many are concerned that if we do not get into space soon, a catastrophic event, such as a nuclear war, will set back civilization and the space exploration effort irretrievably.

War and space exploration are alternative uses of the assertive, exploratory energies that are so characteristic of human beings. They may also be mutually exclusive because if one occurs on a massive scale, the other probably will not. A nuclear war will either lead to the extinction of the human species or set civilization back so far that it will take millions of years to achieve spaceflight again. On the other hand, a major commitment to achieving humanity's purpose through a human space program could result in the rechanneling of the aggressive human energies necessary to avoid nuclear confrontation.

Vision is required to help the human race take its next evolutionary step, but don't expect it to come easily. Being a pioneer brings you up against your own limits and challenges you to be your best against the greatest obstacles, as President Kennedy knew when he announced the U.S. goal of reaching the moon.

16

Pioneering the Space Frontier

It's very important for us to have a robust space program to complement the character of the American people as adventurers and explorers. If we are to fulfill our potential, we have to act on that
characteristic.

– Congressman Bill Nelson

The Perennial Vision

In the mid 1980s, it fell to the National Commission on Space to
restate humanity's perennial vision of space exploration and development. Its report, *Pioneering the Space Frontier*, is unique in
that it not only lays out a clear technological scenario but also
articulates the fundamental values that should guide the American
space program of the future. The document may someday be seen
as a foundation for the development of the new civilizations, mark-
ing the transition from the old space program to the new one, with
hints of the human space program yet to come.

The report is a bridge between geocentric and heliocentric thinking. It is important not only for what it says, but also for what it
does not say, for it represents the evolving consciousness of American society regarding space exploration and development. It is not
the only book of the past ten to twenty years that manifests the
new consciousness I have been describing, but few other documents have the credibility of *Pioneering the Space Frontier*. The
idea of a commission originated in the House of Representatives
and generated significant support from Congress and the various space
interest groups. While the White House was not deeply involved
in the work of the commission, it was presidentially appointed.

The National Aeronautics and Space Administration lent technical support to the commission, and a former NASA administrator, Dr. Thomas Paine, headed it and an active astronaut, Dr. Kathryn Sullivan, served as a member. The commission included distinguished citizens from a number of fields, including Brigadier General Charles ("Chuck") Yeager, the test pilot who personified Tom Wolfe's *The Right Stuff*, and Neil Armstrong.

In addition to the credibility generated by its members, the commission, by holding public forums in cities across the country, increased the sense of public involvement and participation in the development of the final report. In its work, the commission met many of the criteria laid down earlier for developing a new space program.

First, *Pioneering the Space Frontier* places NASA's activities in a context of vision and purpose with an explicit mission for the space program over the next fifty years. The report includes a mission statement and a rationale that begins with a description of vision and purpose. It links space exploration and development not only to the physical technologies required to settle the inner solar system, but also lays the foundation for the necessary mental technologies in its initial chapter, Declaration for Space, which describes the human dimension of space exploration and the role that fundamental values play in the enterprise.

The commission demonstrated its understanding of the relationship between prediction and creation in the chairman's letter to those who participated in developing the report: "We have outlined a bold vision of the next 50 years in space, but we stress that we are not attempting to predict the future, but rather to show what America can make happen on the space frontier if we determine to lead mankind to new worlds."[1]

The commission also acknowledged that this is a time for new beginnings, not unlike the early days of the American republic. In particular, the term "Declaration for Space" recognizes that the day will come when people on Earth must make decisions as momentous as those made by the American Founding Fathers in the late eighteenth century. With its mandate to look ahead to 2035, the commission could not avoid the question of whether humanity will make a psychological break with Mother Earth as the American patriots made a political break with their mother country.

A presenter at one meeting summed it up when he said that if the commission's plan were indeed to be bold and visionary, "the umbilical to Earth must be severed, or at least severely nicked."[2] The speaker was talking about the need to utilize extraterrestrial resources to explore and settle the solar system, because it is impractical to ferry all the materials from Earth.[3] However, once economic self-sufficiency is a reality, the foundations of a space-based civilization will have been laid, and a political breakaway becomes a matter of real concern.

The commission in effect takes a stand *for* space as humanity's home and its destiny; the Declaration for Space becomes the modern version of the Declaration of Independence. It is also important because the relationship between space and freedom is a powerful concept in the minds of many in the space movement.[4] A concern with the basic values treasured by Americans, found in the writings of the new space movement, provides another link with the Founding Fathers of the American Revolutionary period.

In addition to its focus on values, the commission provides a detailed plan to develop the infrastructure necessary to pioneer the space frontier. Critics have said that there is nothing new in the plan and that similar ideas were proposed in the early 1950s and early 1970s.[5] However, this criticism confirms that the commission's report reflects the fundamental unfulfilled vision of humankind.

The commission's implicit commitment to a new heliocentric civilization is a major step that may not be evident to the casual reader. But by the same token, the importance of the Declaration of Independence was not fully recognized until after the Revolutionary War.

The Value System of Pioneering the Space Frontier

For the past twenty-five years, space exploration has been thought to be primarily a scientific and technological endeavor. The commission makes a contribution in realizing that space exploration transcends technology and embodies universal human values. Like the commissioners, the founders of the United States could not predict the complex issues that lay ahead of the nation. Therefore, they focused on creating the future by drafting basic principles that would express the fundamental values of American society and remain useful for the indefinite future.[6] In systems terms, they worked at the "human technologies interface," where vision and purpose are defined and guide the interactions between the domains of physical, mental, and spiritual technologies of society.

The result was a set of documents that expressed the essence of the American value system, including the Declaration of Independence, the Constitution, and the Bill of Rights, which, in particular, has stood out as a powerful summation of the basic values of this country.

As the Declaration of Independence laid the groundwork for the Constitution, so the commission's report lays the foundation for the constitution of a space-based civilization.[7] The Declaration for Space, especially its Rationale, can be the contribution of an American approach to governing the space frontier as it is built upon by those who would draft a constitution for the new civilizations. It also has the potential to provide guidance and understanding to space pioneers of future generations in the tradition of the Founding Fathers.[8]

The Mission Statement

The report's mission statement enunciates a pioneering mission for twenty-first-century America: "To lead the exploration and development of the space frontier, advancing science, technology, and enterprise, and building institutions and systems that make accessible vast new resources and support human settlement beyond Earth orbit, from the highlands of the Moon to the plains of Mars.[9]

This commits the United States to *lead* in the exploration and development of the space frontier, but not necessarily to dominate that process. In its mission statement and the Rationale, the commission calls on the United States to lead other nations into space as a challenge and inspiration to all of humanity. This philosophy for a national space program is in keeping with the need for a human space program that includes, but transcends, all the national programs on the planet.

Perhaps most important in terms of the development of new civilizations, the commission advocates the *human* settlement of the space frontier. Its stand on this issue illustrates its role as a bridge between the old way of thinking about space and the new. Human settlements in space, an essential feature of the shift from geocentric to heliocentric thinking, are the cornerstone of building a solar civilization.

Finally, the commission defines the physical limits of the space frontier with the words "from the highlands of the Moon to the plains of Mars." This phrase makes the commission's vision of the future specific. Human civilization will probably spread even farther into space, but over the next fifty years, that larger vision must be focused on meaningful near-term goals.[10]

The lack of clear goals has been cited frequently as a problem for the American space progam. The commission's mission statement appears more complex than that of the Apollo program, but it can be simply summed up as spreading human civilization throughout the inner solar system over the next fifty years. That is also the next step in creating a solar overview system, or solar civilization, and is consistent with human purpose as we understand it.

Having proposed a mission for the next fifty years, the commission outlines its implementation in a value system, or "mental technology," provided by the nine principles that make up the Rationale of the Declaration for Space, which is reproduced in Appendix A.

The Rationale

The Rationale resembles the Declaration of Independence in not attempting to introduce empirical evidence. Just as Thomas Jefferson wrote, "We hold these truths to be self-evident," the commission states its principles as self-evident truths.

The Rationale is a whole system of which the nine principles are subsystems; the principles also relate to one another. Each is complete in itself and could provide part of the foundation of the laws that must be written as the new civilizations are established. Just as volumes have been written on the meaning of "free speech" in specific cases, a great deal may be written about the meaning of the first principle that the solar system is humanity's extended home.[11]

The Rationale enunciates the spirit that should prevail on the space frontier. Its principles describe a nation confident that humanity's home can extend far beyond the Earth, that America can lead humanity outward into this new territory, that the enterprise is for the good of all humanity, and that exploration can take place in an atmosphere of peace and freedom.

The Meaning of the Principles

As humanity expands into the solar system, our species may become radically different from what it is today. No longer confined to Earth, and growing outward into a much larger space, humanity in the future will become increasingly unpredictable and uncontrollable. The founders of the United States faced a similar situation. Clustered on the eastern seaboard of a vast, unexplored continent and poised at the edge of the Industrial Revolution, they could not know the precise evolution of our society, so they bequeathed to their descendants basic principles with which to create a "new world."

The past twenty-five years of space exploration and development have focused largely on the physical technologies required to establish a beachhead off the planet. As that objective is being reached, we are turning our attention to the mental and spiritual technologies required to guide us in establishing, first, a successful planetary civilization and then human communities beyond Earth's orbit. We are beginning to see that space exploration is an essentially human enterprise that meets deeply felt human needs. Such nonscientific, but very human characteristics as love, hope, and spirit are essential ingredients in this effort.

Americans have a lot to offer in this phase of development because of our experience in creating new societies based on universal principles. In the long run, it will be of secondary importance whether we build our space-based civilization with shuttles, spaceplanes, or expendable launch vehicles. The values that shape our efforts will be far more meaningful to us and our descendants.

Settling the Inner Solar System

Pioneering the Space Frontier provides readers with a roadmap for settling the territory of the inner solar system. The commission envisions "a future-oriented civilian space agenda" with three mutually supportive elements: advancing our understanding of our planet, our solar system, and the universe; exploring, prospecting, and settling the solar system; and stimulating space enterprises for the direct benefit of the people on Earth.

Through the commitment to developing the necessary technology base, the commission sees the opportunity to construct a Highway to Space in Low Earth Orbit and a Bridge Between Worlds linking Earth to the moon and Mars.[12]

The commission believes it is reasonable to expect to have a human outpost on the moon in 2005 and an outpost on Mars in 2015. To fund the program, the commission suggests establishing the space budget at a constant percentage of GNP.[13]

While the commission does not use overview systems terminology, it has laid out a scenario for solidifying the emergence of Terra and building the first stage of Solarius. In addition, while its report is American in emphasis, it can easily be part of the basic agenda for the human space program. Congressman Bill Nelson commented that the National Commission on Space report "could have been written in Moscow as well as in Washington; it could have been written ten years ago or it could be written ten years from now, and it would be essentially the same thing."[14]

Building on the commission's work, we can answer some of the questions it did not address, such as relationships between Earth and space settlers, contact with other intelligent life, and the role each person can play in building the new civilizations.

Table 16.1

Milestones on the Space Frontier

Time Span	Milestones
1990–2000	Initial orbital maneuvering vehicles
	Initial space station and spaceport in Earth orbit
	Cargo transport vehicle to Earth orbit
	Robotic lunar return missions
2000–2010	Passenger transport vehicle to Earth orbit
	Sophisticated orbital maneuvering vehicles
	Full spaceport in Earth orbit
	Human outpost and propellant plant on the moon
	Small cargo transfer vehicle beyond Earth orbit
	Mars crew transfer vehicle
	Variable-gravity facility
2010–2020	Lunar spaceport and propellant production
	Large cargo transfer vehicles
	Cycling spaceships from Earth to Mars
	Lunar spaceport and libration point spaceport
	Robot plant and human outpost on Mars
2020–2035	Initial and full base on Mars

Source: National Commission on Space, *Pioneering the Space Frontier* (New York: Bantam Books, 1986).

17

Milestones and Turning Points

I think it's going to be like Columbus's setting off five hundred years
ago and starting the trend of people going out to explore the world
beyond the European and Asian shores . . . We will explore our entire
solar system in the next four or five hundred years, but we won't be
able to go beyond that point . . . I believe it's possible, but it'll be a
long time.

— Payload specialist Marc Garneau

By presenting a plausible scenario for the settlement of the solar
system, the National Commission on Space has done a great service
to everyone who cares about humanity's future. Its "foundation
era" encompasses 1986 to 2035, fifty years during which the infrastructure of a space-based civilization extending to Mars can be
put into place.

Democratic senator Spark Matsunaga of Hawaii, an ardent pro-
ponent of a joint U.S.-Soviet Mars mission, suggests, in an *Omni*
magazine article, that the American space community, led by
Wernher von Braun, had its sights set on a space frontier with
Mars as its outer boundary before the Apollo program. He says,
"From the beginning, NASA planners shared von Braun's aspirations for a Mars mission as the primary target of our space program.
But in the spring of 1961 John Kennedy needed a relatively quick
and dramatic space accomplishment, so he sent NASA racing to
the moon instead."[1]

Matsunaga reminds us that Robert Goddard, whose work in
rocketry laid the foundation for the American space program, while
sitting in a cherry tree in Worcester, Massachusetts, in 1899, had

a vision of "the planet Mars, red and gleaming in the darkness of space." Goddard imagined a vehicle that would take him to Mars and "spent the rest of his life working to turn his vision into reality." At the same time, Konstantin Tsiolkovsky, in Russia, was developing a fourteen-point master plan for the settlement of space; his ultimate goal was also Mars. And the motto of his successor, Frederick Tsander, was "On to Mars."[2]

At the congressional hearings on the National Space Commission's report, one of those testifying said that he had no doubt that the scenario laid out by the commission would be accomplished: there would be spaceports, moon bases, and outposts on Mars. The only question would be what language would be spoken there — Russian, English, or something else?[3]

With that vision as a foundation, I will consider some of the critical human questions that arise.

Systems Cycles Revisited

The systems cycle of equilibrium, change, and transformation was at work throughout the life of the old space program, which reached out with new exploratory efforts, followed up with times of stability during which small changes and adjustments occurred, and built up again until another time of exploratory transformation took place. In the foundation era of the new civilizations, these patterns will continue to manifest themselves as exploration, enterprise, and settlement.

Social evolution is likely to accelerate as the space frontier opens. Pioneering the space frontier is itself a metamessage, holding out images of openness and possibility, but human society in its present form cannot take on the task effectively. Each interested nation-state will have to reorganize itself to participate fully and learn new ways to compete and cooperate in the effort. The more committed to space exploration a society becomes, the more it will transform.

As the message of the Overview Effect diffuses, leading thinkers may begin to see the emerging outlines of the human space program and the great purpose and start to shape the policies of their nations to accommodate those insights, thus accelerating the process. The key to how the future unfolds will be the extent to which participants understand the vision and purpose that is being revealed in this evolving human system. Three milestones must be achieved to maximize the available opportunities.

Developing a New Model of Replication

Colonization is a typical example of replication in a human social system. It occurs when an "originating system" reproduces a version of itself and projects the replication into a new physical space isolated from the originating system as an effort to realize its own vision and purpose. For example, during the great periods of exploration on Earth, national prestige and economic gain were cited as key reasons for initiating the cycle of exploration, enterprise, and settlement. In the modern era, material benefits to the sponsoring nation are still a critical issue. When the National Commission on Space presented its report to Congress in July 1986, senators and congressmen praised the commission's vision, but expressed concern over the costs and benefits of the plan.[4]

Unfortunately, the evolution of human social systems is usually seen from a perspective too narrow to comprehend what eventually occurs. Spain's view of the New World, England's hopes for its colonies, and even the National Commission's vision of the space frontier are projections outward from the perspective of the subsystem (nation-state) of a whole system (humanity), which is in turn a subsystem of several larger whole systems.

By definition, the perceived vision and purpose of a subsystem is less universal than that of the whole system of which it is a part. In the case of space exploration, the building of overview systems throughout the universe may be the purpose, but a national space program will not be based on that reasoning unless there is perceived payoff to the originating system. For this reason, the consciousness of the leaders of those systems must be raised before a higher purpose can be seen as a justification for exploration. Colonization is an example of how past originating systems failed to achieve their stated goals in replicating. The problem has not been with the act of replication, but in the goals themselves, which are usually stated in terms of political power or economic gain.

From the point of view of the whole human system, replication is an opportunity for personal, organizational, and social transformation. On any frontier, individuals who choose to be colonists or pioneers can create a new life in a new society. Innovative organizational structures, such as the joint stock company of the seventeenth century, must be created to bring about the replication process. It is also an excellent opportunity to experiment with new forms of government, as the American example clearly demonstrates.

From the perspective of the next system level, that of planet Earth, replication has historically served a universal purpose. Spreading the human presence throughout the biosphere was a necessary step toward the larger vision of humanity disseminating conscious self-awareness throughout the solar system and beyond. In that sense, replication is an extremely successful evolutionary strategy, even though it may not achieve the results foreseen by the originators.

The American Revolution became a matter of importance to all people, bringing forth a new kind of political system and triggering a sympathetic revolutionary response in France and other countries. The British, having hoped to extend their power and influence by establishing a strong presence in the New World, found themselves fighting a losing war against life, liberty, and the pursuit of happiness in North America, then struggling to contain liberty, equality, and fraternity on the Continent. The pattern of loss after gain was repeated in many British colonies, but once the British realized their limitations and allowed the empire to be transformed into a commonwealth, they developed worldwide influence and importance because of their value system and heritage, rather than by force of arms. Overall, it has been a positive development that democracies and republics have been created in both the old and new worlds, and even the British benefited in the end.

The problem is that imperialism and colonialism, as opposed to exploration, assume that colonization is a means of extending the reach and power of the originating system at the expense of the colonists and the indigenous peoples. By definition, it implies a psychology of control and exploitation, a maintenance of the status quo. When this happens, the original system loses the strongest benefit of exploration, social evolution. In space exploration, the question is what steps to take once the investigation period begins to make a transition into enterprise and settlement. The colonial model is only one of many possible approaches, and the time has come to consider other ways of answering the question.

For example, from an American point of view, the statehood model is the least radical and has the virtue of having been the frontier model in the past. If it could be followed, American citizens might develop new settlements in space as territories of the United States, eventually applying for statehood. The statehood model fills a number of conceptual gaps in *Pioneering the Space Frontier* as an American scenario for settling space, but this approach may well be illegal under existing space law, which does not allow any nation to claim territory in outer space.[5]

The Antarctica model is unique in that many nations maintain scientific expeditions there, but none holds territory, and there are no military forces on the continent. It is a zone of relative cooperation and peace on a planet of competition and war. Antarctica offers other tantalizing analogies with space. It is a hostile, remote environment similar to Mars in many ways, including temperature and climate. Like the space environment, its primary immediate payoff is scientific research, and it can support relatively few people.

The Antarctica model works well in the exploratory stages, but may not be viable in the periods of enterprise and settlement. Its cycle has stabilized at exploration, an approach that might not work if there were current plans to create wealth-producing enterprises or foster large-scale human settlement there. However, it may be that in the short term the Antarctica model can be used in space, with the understanding that it might have to give way to something different in future years.

The international organization model takes a different tack by assuming that nation-states will continue to be the dominant political form during the early years and that they will project their current modes of thinking and acting into the new space of the solar system. But nations do not just compete with one another for dominance. They also cooperate on major economic and social issues, when mutual self-interest dictates their doing so. As activities in space increase, so will the need for an institution to play a mediating role, offering the opportunity for both national space programs and a more comprehensive human program to evolve.

The fourth model is human parenting. While it is well understood and practiced within family units, the idea of applying the concept to political systems is radical. In this approach, the replicated systems in space would be viewed the way people think of their children. When the human parenting process works properly, the parents bring their children into the world as an act of commitment, then share the burdens and pleasures of bringing them to maturity, realizing that the children will finally leave home and establish their autonomous existence.

While there is great personal satisfaction to the parents for having raised their children, no material benefits flow from their being able to control and exploit the children. On the contrary, from the viewpoint of pure material self-interest, it isn't rational to have children. The costs and responsibilities don't fit into a simple cost-benefit matrix.

Suppose that people on Earth thought of themselves as parents of the new civilizations. In creating these new societies in space, independence and autonomy could be built into the design from the beginning. Would the pride of parenthood be enough to justify the adventure?

The parenting model is also consistent with the value system of those who are apt to pioneer the space frontier. While many space-related efforts are government sponsored, there is a growing private interest in pioneering the space frontier. A settlement of the type envisioned by the Space Studies Institute, which assumes that extraterrestrial materials can be utilized to develop habitats for up to ten thousand people in free space, will presumably want to develop its own governing system.

These settlements resemble those of the Puritans in early New England, who began their colonies in loyalty to the Crown but determined to build a "city of God" in the New World. It was not surprising that their descendants became the most radical proponents of independence when England tried to restrict their development in the 1770s.

It is not so important that a specific model be selected now. We should, however, realize the need to think creatively, and perhaps radically, about issues that will be central in the evolution of these new societies. The thought that we give the matter today may determine whether the future is peaceful or filled with conflict.

Shifting Identification

The nation-states of Earth represent a recently evolved social system and exist because they have been able to create and maintain an identity that rests ultimately on the force of arms — the state's ability to defend itself and maintain its territorial integrity. The state also exists by agreement — the willingness of its citizens and those of other nations to respect its identity. The creation of nation-states is a product of social evolution's continuing search for new and more effective political forms. In the past, the process has produced tribal systems, city-states, empires, and theocracies, but the secular nation-state has proved to be the optimal form for this epoch.

However, political entities are no more immortal than human beings. They act in their perceived self-interest to extend their existence and avoid dissolution and death. Moreover, there are two ways that states can die: physical death, when another nation overruns and dismembers the state or it is destroyed by internal insurrection, and identity death, when the state gives up its sovereignty by merging into a higher order system.

It is understandable that war and insurrection cause political leaders great concern. However, identity death can be just as frightening, because the end result is the same. Fear of identity death, a primary obstacle to planetary unity, will be a key issue in the evolution of Terra and Solarius.

The founders of the United States had to grapple with the identity issue in creating a Constitution for the country. The states, having just won their independence from Great Britain, jealously guarded their sovereignty, and only because the Constitution allowed them to retain some of that sovereignty did they enter into the agreement. When the United Nations was formed, fear of identity death was so great that the founding states provided the organization with almost no powers over their individual sovereignty.

Countervailing forces are constantly at work in the nation-state; the maintenance of subsystem identity with the larger whole system is a process that is constantly threatened. When replication occurs, these pressures intensify. While the originating system justifies replication in terms of its self-interest, those who carry out the mission rapidly develop different interests based on their experiences in the new environment.

Even with brief human experience in space, the elements of potential conflict have appeared, especially in longer-duration missions. Mission Control, on Earth, often wants the astronauts to keep to a rigid, predetermined schedule that will produce many concrete accomplishments. However, the environmental conditions in space, coupled with astronaut needs, may hamper the easy maintenance of the schedule, which sometimes leads to problems between those on Earth and those in space.

Now imagine the lunar outpost envisioned by the National Space Commission beginning its operations in the year 2005. Assume a population there of as many as 100 people, all Americans or citizens of allied countries. It is possible that the Soviets would have established a similar operation not far from the American base. By the year 2010, there might be as many as 200 people at the American base and 150 at the Russian, including children born on the moon.

The Americans and Russians who first go to the moon would probably remain loyal to their nations. After several years, however, the United States and Soviet Union would cease to be the reality in which they daily live and breathe. These countries would become abstractions appearing and disappearing on Earth's surface as the planet rotates on its axis 240,000 miles away. In a crisis, these "Lunarians" would be more likely to rely on themselves or call on their neighbors than to request help from Earth, a minimum of three days away by spaceship. Being independent becomes an evolutionary virtue, while obedience to a distant authority has doubtful benefits.

The first people to go to Mars will have a similar, magnified experience, for it takes several months, rather than three days, to get there. And, as Gene Cernan points out, when you are outside the space/time coordinates of Earth, you ask yourself the question "Where really am I in space and time?"[6]

Future "Lunarians," "Martians," and dwellers in space habitats are likely to question their ties to Earth and the political subsystems they no longer see. It took some 150 years to complete the process when Great Britain established its colonies in North America, but in this more sophisticated and rapidly changing time, the issue may develop much more quickly.

When their sense of identity shifts, the space dwellers will strive to create a new one more in harmony with local conditions. At that point, the first major political crisis will occur in the evolution of the new civilizations. For this reason, the models discussed earlier are important, because the originating and replicating systems will act out of their models of reality in confronting the matter. An originating system acting out of a colonial model will react harshly, while an originating system acting out of a parenting model would be more likely to react with understanding.

A Declaration of Independence from Earth will probably come from one of the new space settlements within the next fifty years. Terra, the planetary civilization organized around Earth, can evolve either as a part of the solar civilization or as the "other" that allows Solarius to experience its "self" through conflict. Present actions can have major impact on the unfolding of those future events.

Exponential Growth

Most scenarios of future population growth on the space frontier are conservative because it is difficult to see beyond the realities of today, when we have yet to establish a permanent presence in space. However, the right conditions will lead to explosive growth and a complete change in circumstances. Growth in any system occurs at different rates, depending on the interplay between its barriers and inducements. Populations can grow arithmetically, with incremental additions on a periodic basis, or exponentially, doubling and tripling rapidly. The growth rate in human social systems depends on the "carrying capacity" of a society, which in turn depends on many variables, some of which, like food production, are quantitative and some of which, such as how human life is valued and the impact of that viewpoint on social policy, are qualitative.

The positive feedback loop of the birth rate increases population, while the negative feedback loop of the death rate decreases it. Artificial intervention in a social system's operation during crises may temporarily disturb the working of these loops, but over time the carrying capacity is the dominant force. The Earth's population has been growing rapidly since the Industrial Revolution, and the attendant problems, including desertification, acid rain, destruction of the Amazon rain forest, pollution, and the Greenhouse effect, have been well documented.

The situation resembles that of a baby in the womb. Having used all the resources its mother can provide, the baby grows too large to remain in its protected environment. It must be born into the larger world, painful though that experience may be. For the good of the mother and the baby, the child must be ejected or die.

One response to these global issues emerged in the 1970s as the "limits to growth" movement. Advocates of this position argued for a society that consciously restrains its expansion in order to preserve the planet. This is valuable thinking for future Terrans, but it reminds one of a doctor who is an expert on wombs but knows nothing of birth. He might analyze pregnancy as a disease and conclude that stopping the embryo's development is the solution to the problem. A doctor with broader training would understand, of course, that delivery is the real answer.

Can the space frontier support humanity's growing exponentially? The needs on the frontier will be the same as on Earth, in terms of supporting the complex technological civilization that has become the hallmark of human activity: ample resources and relatively inexpensive energy. Studies conducted by the Space Studies Institute in Princeton have shown that the resources necessary to begin building a space-based civilization are present on the moon and the asteroids in substantial quantities. Energy is freely available from the sun, without the interference of a planetary atmosphere. New developments in closed ecological systems, or biospheres, suggest that "miniplanets" can be created where food can be grown and self-sustaining activities initiated anywhere in free space.[7]

Using extraterrestrial materials for building space habitats and planetary bases obviates bringing costly materials from the Earth, thereby opening up dramatic new possibilities for the growth process to take off. The primary barriers to rapid growth on the space frontier are in the domain of physical technologies, especially the high cost of getting into Earth orbit. Even with the option of using materials in space, the current cost of about $2,000 to deliver a pound of payload to Earth orbit is too expensive to envision massive commercial or population development in the near future.

The shuttle is based on rocket system technology that requires an enormous ground crew to launch and return it safely. These factors account for a substantial percentage of the $250 million cost for every launch. Three technologies will change that equation: the aerospace plane and/or heavy life launch vehicles, permanent space stations, and orbital transfer vehicles.

The technologies needed for low-cost access to the space frontier are not exotic. Great Britain as well as the United States is working on the aerospace plane, and other countries are probably doing so too. The Soviet Union is close to having a permanent space station in orbit, and the United States is committed to building one in the 1990s. Orbital transfer vehicles are also on the drawing boards.

Low-cost access will not lure people to the space frontier if there isn't an attractive force to draw them. On the planetary surface, migration is a simple matter: people move from areas of low opportunity to areas of high opportunity, and a few innovators are always willing to be the pioneers when a new frontier opens up. Humans and frontiers attract one another, but if conditions are too hostile, as in Greenland and Antarctica, populations do not grow exponentially.

Space is a deceptive environment because large sectors of Earth's population who do not fit the image of pioneer would benefit *immediately* from living in a low-gravity locality. Those who are physically handicapped, in particular, would probably love to live in space. People who cannot walk may have an advantage in an environment where legs are relatively useless. The elderly would be more comfortable in a situation where the powerful skeletal and muscular systems favored in a high-gravity environment are not necessary. Those with weak hearts would find space attractive because the heart can pump with less vigor when it is not working against gravity's resistance.

Finally, it is still believed that space manufacturing of crystals, medicines, and other materials can be economically successful. If even one area of space endeavor proves to be more profitable than performing the same task on Earth, it will have significant impact. Like oil rigs in the oceans and the deserts or on the North Slope of Alaska, workers will tolerate harsh conditions to make high wages, and employers will pay for an effort that promises a good return.

Space is close. Removal of the high-cost barrier can stimulate a flood of migration to the space frontier, dramatically affecting life not only there, but on Earth as well.

The Quest

Space tourism and space manufacturing are worthy enterprises, and they should continue. However, the most fundamental issue facing humanity is its survival and evolution as a species, and the exploration of space is directly related to that issue. Human social systems that share a supraordinate or overarching goal can achieve alignment. The United States and Soviet Union are antagonists, but they were once allies, made so by the goal of defeating fascism, which posed a greater threat to their survival than did their own natural competition. Today, these two nations and the planet as a whole face a greater enemy than fascism in the institution of war itself. The United States, the Soviet Union, and all other nation-states share a self-interest in preventing nuclear war and finding a way to create meaningful arms control.

Discovering and fulfilling human purpose through the human space program is a step beyond avoiding extinction, a positive vision that can be understood by everyone on Earth. Some may grasp the idea of the great purpose, while others understand the concept of building the new civilizations. Many will be interested primarily in building a better life for themselves and their children.

There is evidence that the Overview Effect turns political thinkers toward this more universal vision. For example, it is at work in Congressman Bill Nelson when he suggests a summit meeting in space. It is also at work in Senator Jake Garn, who says that because we are all traveling together, there ought to be more equality of opportunity around the earth.

It is still at work in Senator John Glenn, who, in announcing his candidacy for reelection as senator from Ohio, said,

> Twenty-four years ago this week, I had the privilege of seeing the planet as few human beings have been privileged to see it, spinning silently and beautifully against the vastness of space.
>
> And as I looked down upon our world from space, I saw a land that was truly a *United* States. I saw a country undivided by color or class — and a nation joined together in its common humanity.
>
> And even though reality has intruded on that vision many times in the years since my return, I still hope for the day when finally — and at long last — we learn to live as brothers and sisters on this fragile craft we call Earth.[8]

On an international level, the possibilities can be seen in the work of the Association of Space Explorers at its first congress, and the words of cosmonaut Aleksei Leonov: "Astronauts and cosmonauts are the handful of people who have had the good fortune to see the Earth from afar and to realize how tiny and fragile it is. We hope that all the peoples of the Earth can understand this."[9]

Moving in a new direction will require creative choices by human beings. Buckminster Fuller once posed humankind's fundamental decision as that of creating a utopia or oblivion for all. Recently many inventive suggestions have held out the hope of such a possibility. For example, Dr. Kosta Tsipis, an expert on arms control, speaking at a forum sponsored by the United Nations Association of Greater Boston, suggested that although the energies being directed toward military efforts in space could perhaps not be stopped, they could be redirected. He urged that the military, rather than being kept out of space, be given a supraordinate goal, such as an international mission to Mars, to challenge their skills and divert their attention outward rather than toward an "enemy."[10]

Nuclear weapons and ballistic missiles flow from the same stream of scientific understanding, and on Earth they became practical at about the same time. Assuming that the same level of evolution always produces weapons of mass extinction and the tools for escaping the bondage of planetary surfaces, it may be that many other cultures have faced this choice at the same period in their history.[11] It goes without saying that a culture mature enough to abandon its nuclear warheads will find a positive use for its ballistic missiles as launch vehicles for a massive new space exploration program.

The years leading up to the millennium and just beyond will be extremely dangerous and challenging ones, but the possibilities have never been greater.

The Balance of Unity and Diversity

Establishing the new planetary civilization would bring the unity that has been a dream of humanity for centuries, but that newfound oneness may well give way to a phase of intense diversity in outer space. It seems likely that new social systems created in the inner solar system will go through a period of intensely self-reliant experimentation. Just as their members will cease to identify with Earthbound nation-states, they may stop identifying with Earth itself. Like those in the liberated colonies in North America, they will jealously guard their incipient independence.

Moreover, the new diversity in the solar environment is only a prelude to yet another transformation at the galactic level sometime in the future. The ultimate scenario results from choices; it is not an inevitability. This analysis also suggests some important potential alliances. People interested in planetary peace on Earth and those interested in living on Mars should, for example, see their common interest and begin to act on it.

If humanity makes it out into the solar system, we can predict this much, at least: someday an astronaut, finding herself on the edge of the solar system, will look back and realize how unified and fragile it is, a small haven in a vast galaxy, and she will see how all of us, Terrans, Solarians, and others, must learn to live together in peace.

18

The Psychology
of the New Civilizations

I have heard other space travelers express a perception that I have
had: the feeling of euphoria beginning and continuing several days
after launch. I think it springs from the mind's realization that the
reality without gravity is in effect a new dimension of freedom. It is
a feeling that new possibilities *must* be present where physical orientation and visual perception are under control but always variable.

— Payload specialist Charles D. Walker

Civilizations and Awareness

The self-awareness of a civilization embodies its entire attitude
toward life, including its view of itself and other cultures. The
physical setting of a society is critical to the evolution of social and
individual psychologies. Americans think as they do partly because
their country was founded on the shores of a vast continent that
needed to be developed. Politely waiting for it to happen would
have been an evolutionary mistake of major proportions. Great
Britain, on the other hand, is a densely populated island nation,
settled and civilized. Rugged individualism is not an especially
useful cultural trait to the society at this time.

As the new civilizations develop in relationship to one another,
many cultural differences will evolve as well. In each society, traits
that support the vision and purpose of the civilization will be encouraged and supported; traits that contradict them will be filtered
out.

Preplanetary Psychology

Psychology is shaped by physicality. Human beings cannot think, feel, know, or understand without brains and bodies, which must themselves be located in a physical place. Psychology deals with how people see themselves against the backdrop of larger whole systems, especially the natural system that gives birth to the society in which they live.

All psychological disciplines to date are geocentric because they have evolved on the Earth. In addition, all psychologies developed before the 1960s were preplanetary because they could not include a vision of the whole system — Earth — of which the individual is a part. The vision of the whole system now being disseminated worldwide throughout the social system has to have an effect on psychology.

A person must have a sense of self separate from others, but the option exists of contrasting the self against a very small other, such as the family, or a very large other, such as the planet Earth. Western psychology, following the lead of the physical sciences, has tended toward an isolated examination of the human being, culminating with an effort to reduce explanation of all human activities as a complex series of responses to stimuli. However, as humanity learns to identify itself in relationship to increasingly larger whole systems, there will be a necessary reversal in the reductionist trend that may well be the most important outcome of space exploration and development.

Terra: The Psychology of Homeostasis

Terran psychology will be similar to preplanetary psychology in that it will remain Earth-oriented. However, it will be different in that it will also relate human beings to the larger whole system of the planet. The disseminated Overview Effect is the foundation of Terran awareness, providing the fundamental symbol of the new planetary civilization, of which humanity is an integral, but not a dominant part. Homeostasis, or equilibrium, is the watchword of Terran psychology, because that is the fundamental goal toward which the whole system must aspire in order to survive.

Lovelock provides a good description of Terran values in Gaian perspective. Elaborating on his view that humanity might be "tamed" and become a part of the "commonwealth of all creatures which constitutes Gaia," he says, "it might seem to be a surrender, but I suspect that the rewards, in an increased sense of well-being and fulfillment, in knowing ourselves to be a dynamic part of a far greater entity, would be worth the loss of tribal freedom."[1]

During the periods of exploration radiating from England and Europe in previous centuries, millions of people passed up opportunities to migrate, staying home to enrich the civilizations that fostered the exploratory ventures. Similarly, not all human beings will leave the planet, even when the opportunity becomes available. Remaining on Earth can be a major contribution to the development of Solarian and Galaxian civilizations. Terrans need not be isolated from developments in the solar system and the galaxy. Indeed, with the evolution of the planetary technosystem to increasingly higher levels, they will be in continuing contact with those processes.

Terrans will also have access to outer space and the benefits it offers in terms of material and psychological development. The great difference between Terrans and Solarians will be that the former continue to consider Earth their home and primary point of reference, while the latter do not. Nor would Terrans be passing up exploration altogether. However, it seems probable that their exploration will be more of an internal inquiry, deepening our knowledge of planetary overview systems on Earth in ways that can be applied to other systems such as Mars. They would also become experts in utilizing the resources of space to bring its benefits to all the people of Earth.

Terrans could become experts in planetary management, balancing the different domains of a human social system on a planetary scale and learning how to live as equals with organic nonhuman and intelligent nonorganic species (the technosystem). As the message of the Overview Effect is fully absorbed, Terrans may also become experts in seeking and creating peace, a skill that will undoubtedly be in demand in other sectors of the galaxy over time.

Solarius: The Psychology of Change

Solarian psychology will emerge from Terran psychology, just as Terran psychology is now emerging from preplanetary consciousness. All those who have seen Earth from a distance have left the planet with a firm intention of returning to its surface. To one who is planning to return, seeing the Earth as a whole system calls to mind the essential unity and fragility of the planet and of human life. What will it mean to one who is focused on building a space-based civilization?

To the embryo, the mother's womb is the whole world, the totality of the environment; to the child, the mother becomes another being, for whom one is responsible, just as she was once the responsible person. A major step in the development and maturation of the individual is an increasing sense of responsibility, the ultimate cutting of the umbilical cord and becoming a mature adult. On a cosmic time scale, the human species is a recent arrival, and the metaphor used most often to describe it is infant. However, embryo may be far more appropriate.

So far, even the astronauts have not had the opportunity to experience the full growth cycle. They have had an experience of birth, but unlike human babies, they have had to return to the womb, or as Gene Cernan calls it, "the crib." Leaving the womb has an impact on astronauts, but the true understanding of Rusty Schweickart's Cosmic Birth Phenomenon will come only when the first humans depart for space with every intention of remaining there.

There will be an intense maturing process for those who make that choice, similar to the experience of children leaving home for the first time. Mother Earth will remain "mother," but those making a personal Declaration for Space will need the independent spirit of their forebears, who abandoned the mother country for unknown lands and unpredictable circumstances.

Growing up also brings the dawning recognition of new possibilities. Being limited to the planetary surface means accepting fundamental restrictions. These are not only the limitations of gravity and a finite volume of available space, but increasingly those of the social norms and values of humankind. Few places on Earth are not subject to the laws of some human social system, whether or not one wants to be subject to them.

Looking inward to the Earth, the founders of the solar civilization view the past. Looking out, they see the future. The overview turned in the other direction becomes a "preview." Solarian psychology will incorporate space dwellers' new relationship to the solar system as a physical setting. The Earth will be an object, not an environment. The space settlement, moon, or Mars and the solar system will be the overall environment.

There will be many options for experiencing that environment, including EVAs. Ordinary people living in space settlements will not only be able to see the Earth as a whole system, but can also take spacewalks and share astronaut Jerry Carr's feeling for the infiniteness of the universe. They will see many stars that you can't see from the ground. They will share his impression of a disorienting matrix.

For many, the experience of openness and infiniteness will produce conflicting feelings. Geocentric thinking limits our frustration, because it focuses one's attention on the Earth, which is finite. Heliocentric thinking, focusing outward to the solar system and beyond, opens the mind to all possibilities.

The relationship between freedom and constraint is an important equation in all of human existence. For space dwellers, that equation will exist in a new context. The universe will beckon to them with an opportunity for freedom beyond anything known on a planetary surface. However, the ability to enjoy it will be highly constrained by available technologies, lifespans, and other factors.

Solarians are likely to be a restless people, not content merely to settle into Low Earth Orbit, but eager to continue the exploration of the solar system and beyond. Some are destined to become nomads, building and boarding "generational starships" that take entire societies to the stars on journeys of hundreds of thousands of years. Life extension will become a field of intense interest.[2]

The assertive expansion characterizing the exploration of physical space puts pressure for equivalent growth on the mental and spiritual domains of a human system. For the early permanent systems in space, which will also be isolated from the main body of the species, we can expect significant development in the spiritual and mental domains, and perhaps even radical new ideas of God.

How one perceives time is also influential in the development of the sense of self. Even on Earth, time is not the same at any given moment for everyone on the planet. People living permanently in space will be outside the framework of time as humans have known it. As Solarius evolves, the sense of time as relative to position in space will intensify as different cultures are created there.

One of the first tasks in establishing the solar civilization will be to determine a standard for measuring time. All space missions to date have used Earth time scales, even as newer language has crept in. As people begin to live at greater distances from Earth, this approach may prove unworkable, especially as they settle on distant planetary surfaces.

People living in Low Earth Orbit are likely to continue using Earth standard time, adding the orbit or revolution as a separate measurement. Those on the moon base will be quite distant from the Earth-based time frames and may want to use one created by their own planetary reference point. Settlers on Mars will feel the strongest urge to establish their own time system. They will be so far from Earth that the home planet will appear only as a light in the sky, just as Mars appears to us. Thus does the conceptual unity inherent in the view of the Earth from orbit dissipate as humans spread outward into the solar system.

Just as time will be a relative concept in Solarius, so will the experience of weight, as early space travelers have already found. The "gravity option" is likely to be a matter of intense concern to the early settlers of the solar system. It will be possible to choose anything from one G to zero G and possibly to shift from one to the other, in the way that people can choose to winter in some climates and summer in others.

We already know from brief forays into space that weightlessness has an extraordinary impact on human physiology. When the body is subjected to environments unlike the one G in which it originated, it adapts. Despite all the spaceflights, we do not know what would happen if it were allowed to adapt fully. Since thought and emotions are also physically based, we must assume that those aspects of human existence will change over time as well.

Because every astronaut or cosmonaut has left the planet with the intention of returning to Earth, countermeasures have always been employed. These have ranged from specified exercise regimens to adding nutrients to the space travelers' diets and other inhibitors. Even with countermeasures, it is unclear what will happen to people living in space over a long period of time, as on the first mission to Mars. We know that the initial reaction of most space travelers to zero G is one of delight, or as Charles Walker reported, euphoria. Shuttle astronaut Don Lind said that weightlessness is "just sheer delight."

Many of our mental concepts derive from a one-G environment, and these will be altered in a zero-G situation. There is no "up" or "down" in zero G, no "higher" or "lower." But there has been too little experience of larger groups in space to determine how that physical change will affect status hierarchies such as exist on Earth.

Interpersonal communication on Earth is affected by a sense of personal space and the distance of people from one another. In a weightless environment, the communication options expand. Two people could float together side by side like dolphins or flit back and forth like dancers while discussing their work.

The most dramatic impact on human consciousness has to be that, in this environment, one can fly, a dream of human beings that has been manifested in airplanes and spaceships, and now in the human body.

Walker continued,

> The old limits fade, to reveal new, different ones — it is not enough to be hundreds of miles above the Earth in free-fall. You want to be outside the confines of the cabin, outside the confines of the pressure suit. Perhaps you even, without consciously realizing it, feel closer to being outside your body. For each person, it *is* different, but it must *also* be the same.[3]

Thus, Solarian culture is likely to focus on possibilities, on an expansive effort to embrace the infinite and eternal, and on learning to live in a relativistic universe. As a human social system, the mental and spiritual domains of Solarian culture are likely to experience dramatic transformations during the foundation era. Indeed, they must if Solarians are to maintain their psychological and sociological stability under circumstances unique in human history.

The gravity option will eventually pose the most significant set of possibilities for Solarian civilization. In particular, there is the potential evolution of a new species, not only culturally but biologically different from Terrans. "Speciation" is such an important topic that it will be covered in a separate chapter.

Galaxia: The Psychology of Transformation

Meeting with beings from other star systems will be a transformational moment for humanity and other Earth-originating species, because it will shift the self/other relationship to a wholly different plane of reality. As difficult as is the task to perceive the Terran and Solarian epochs of human evolution, it is simplified by an assumption of "no contact" with species from other star systems.

If there is no other advanced life anywhere in the galaxy, the Galaxian phase will be a grand extension of the Solarian phase, with further evolution being triggered by the challenge and reality of moving into wholly new environments. If there is intelligent life elsewhere, the optional scenarios multiply radically, raising such questions as: Are they at an evolutionary level equivalent to human civilization or beyond it? Are they friendly toward human life or hostile? Are they alone or are they themselves part of a much larger galactic civilization?

There may be a rapid telescoping of events and overlapping of relationships. Given a growing interest in the Search for Extraterrestrial Intelligence (SETI) experiments, contact with extraterrestrials could come any day, even before we have established a substantial presence off-planet. Should contact occur, every aspect of human existence and all our ideas of social evolution would be completely transformed overnight. As the chapter on contact will show, however, there is good reason to believe that open, official contact will not occur for some time.

The Psychologies Today

The initial manifestations of these three approaches to life can already be seen among the human population. The growing number of people interested in ecological concerns, world peace, and limits to growth represent the Terran psychology. The typical pro-space advocate, pushing for migration outward into the solar system, is an embryonic Solarian. Those involved in SETI are typical of a galactic orientation.

19

Terra and the New Social Contract

You recognize that the Russians, the Nicaraguans, the Canadians, the
Filipinos — it doesn't matter where they're from — all they want to
do is raise their kids and educate them, just as we do.

— Senator Jake Garn

The emergence and evolution of the new civilizations is not inevitable. They are possibilities, and knowing that they exist alerts
us to what can be done to help them evolve. Bringing these new
societies into reality will take more than rhetoric and good inten-
tions. It will require new thinking of a high caliber, which, fortunately, has already begun. For example, in a quote remarkably
similar to my description of an overview system's becoming self-
aware, the science section in the National Commission on Space
report begins, "Through consecutive evolutionary steps extending
over billions of years the Universe is now able to contemplate
itself."[1]

The commission goes on to describe the possible contribution
of science in the future:

We propose that the United States, through a vigorous program of
space science, undertake a unified and comprehensive effort to understand the origin and evolution of the cosmos by integrating the
findings of many diverse disciplines. This can lead to great discov-
eries while increasing our ability to forecast future phenomena,
including most importantly those that affect or are affected by human
activities.[2]

The need to bring the multiple branches of science together in the service of human evolution was felt before human beings began to go into space. However, space exploration and its results, including the experience of the Earth as a whole system, have rekindled the spirit of unification once again.

The "grand synthesis" advocated by the commission offers the opportunity to understand in detail the human purpose that overview systems theory reveals only as a possibility. Achieving the synthesis would, in turn, have a profound impact on society. According to the commission, the synthesis is within reach.

> There is no evidence that the processes which govern the evolution from elementary particles to galaxies to stars to heavy elements to planets to life to intelligence differ significantly elsewhere in the Universe. By integrating the insights obtained from virtually every branch of science, from particle physics to anthropology, humanity may hope one day to approach a comprehensive understanding of our place in the cosmos.[3]

The recommendations of the commission, which include a global study of planet Earth similar to the recommendations of the Earth System Science Committee, provide a specific plan leading to establishment of the sciences required to achieve the synthesis within a reasonable time frame. Developing this synthesis is an important project for the human space program because it points to the next step that must be taken for Terran civilization to emerge. This is the development of a new planetary social contract as the basis of planetary unity within a new constitutional order.

The synthesis must therefore include social sciences and a new understanding of human social systems. This would mark a return to an earlier tradition characteristic of the era of exploration in the fifteenth through seventeenth centuries, when physical science, known as natural philosophy, was considered an important tool of social transformation.[4]

The grand synthesis would explain the evolution of the universe and humanity's place within it, but also provide practical guidelines for the development of social and political systems on Earth and in space. The physical sciences are the basis for physical technologies, which are in turn the primary variables in social transformation. However, social science, to its detriment, usually does not recognize this relationship.

Systems theory may be one vehicle to heal the breach between the two branches of science, bringing them back together in a single comprehensive theory. Alternatively, it may be necessary to create an entirely new discipline even more comprehensive than the systems approach.

Social scientists should take a leading role in the evolving human space program, in contrast to their place in today's space program, in which they have had less influence than physical scientists and engineers. This imbalance has helped to create a public perception that the space program is a technological feat with minor impact on the lives of ordinary people. As research on the Overview Effect has shown, nothing could be further from the truth, and space exploration is a topic worthy of intense scrutiny by political scientists, historians, economists, and sociologists. In addition, there is much to be added by students of the humanities, who are best able to perceive the role of the human spirit in the space exploration effort.

If humanity is to pass its "final exam," as Buckminster Fuller phrased it, social scientists need to return to the traditions of such of their forebears as Hobbes, Locke, Rousseau, and Mill, who supplied the foundations of the political and social thinking for Jefferson, Franklin, and Adams. These original political scientists saw their work as being both theoretical and practical, with immediate relevance to the evolution of society and the advancement of humanity.[5]

The Grand Synthesis as a Form of Exploration

Exploration is a holistic activity, and exploratory efforts in one domain of a human system coincide with exploration in others. Improvements in the instruments of navigation in the fifteenth and sixteenth centuries, for example, were required before the great exploratory voyages could occur. In the twentieth century, going to the moon required the better and smaller computers that took the astronauts there, but also triggered a complementary economic and social transformation leading to the emergence of today's technosystem.

Exploration and pioneering are attitudes that are not limited to journeys in physical space. Exploratory enterprises encompass many dimensions of human life, especially the sciences, and the centuries of physical exploration are also times of breakthrough in human thought. The pattern held true during the founding of the United States and of other important political systems, and it will hold true as we plan to create Terra and Solarius.

As an activity, exploration is more an art than a science, and it must be funded and carried out as such. It is simply not possible to predict in advance the material benefits of experimentation and exploration. In fact, most of the positive results come from "mistakes."

Exploration, the sine qua non of an emerging human space program, should not be limited to exploration of outer space. That exploration ought, rather, to be seen as symbolic of a new age of exploration and enlightenment to rival similar periods in the past, such as the Renaissance.

Future historians will give a few paragraphs to the Saturn rockets that took us to the moon, the shuttle that conquered Low Earth Orbit, and the aerospace plane, but they are likely to spend much more time looking at the underlying principles on which their own civilization was founded. They will know that physical technologies are the vessels for the exploration that takes place in human societies, but are not the essence of the transformations that they engender.

The physical technologies of the sailing ships that brought people from Europe and England to the New World are of interest to only a few. By contrast, the mental and spiritual technologies developed to organize social and political life in that New World are the governing framework in the lives of millions.

While most Americans know that Christopher Columbus came to the Americas with three ships, few are aware that he made several return trips after 1492. Similarly, few people know that there were five moon landings after Apollo 11. Gene Cernan commented, "The technology of [Lindbergh's] voyage was soon forgotten and is taken for granted today. What people do remember and admire is the spirit of a guy like Lindbergh . . . Most people wouldn't do what he did *even* today."[6]

Cernan is right: over the long term, human beings relate to values, ideas, and feelings much more effectively than to technological achievements.

A New Golden Age

Earlier eras of exploration have carried with them a hint of the spirit of the mythological golden ages. In certain fields, such as science, they have been times of extraordinary growth and development. This was particularly true as the physical and social sciences together drove social evolution forward.

These were the times when Hobbes, Locke, Rousseau, and Mill wrote about fundamental political issues such as the social contract, the legitimacy of government, and the origin of social law in natural law. The blooming of the social sciences at that time did not occur in a vacuum. The success of the physical sciences in explaining the workings of nature and methods for mastering it excited not only colleagues in other fields, but also attracted those in political power to support their efforts.

Those who were interested in society found the scientific method a fascinating model. Since those days, social scientists have continued to be influenced by the methods of the physical sciences and have hoped to make the social sciences just as powerful in explaining and predicting. The opening of the New World made the issue of how to create successful societies a question of life-and-death importance. The nature of the social contract, the legitimacy of governments, and the possibilities of self-government had to be settled in reality, rather than on paper.

If exponential growth takes place in the solar system, the same situation will prevail again, and we will begin to search for new political forms, as did our ancestors. As the discussion of replication demonstrated, the challenge is that there is no political form appropriate to the task at hand.

In the seventeenth century, there was a similar dilemma because the nation-state had yet to come into being as the dominant political form. Thomas Hobbes argued in *Leviathan* for the creation of the sovereign state because he said that without it, people lived in a state of nature equivalent to a state of war, in which the lives and properties of even the strongest were ultimately unsafe. Even the strongest could be overwhelmed by a gang of other men or defeated through cunning or stealth. Hobbes said that by giving up some rights to a civil authority, citizens would ultimately secure much greater rights in terms of security.[7]

The nation-state has become the predominant political form on Earth, but now nations live in a state of nature. As people living in that way are equal in their ability to harm one another, so are nation-states equal in that none is ultimately safe from nuclear weapons, subversion, or conventional warfare.

As some members of our species begin to leave the planet, we are in the position of the social scientists of an earlier time. Looking back at the Earth from orbit, we can see the natural unity of the planet, but our political systems do not yet reflect it. Instead, we live in a state of nature, where equality is guaranteed by arms rather than agreed-upon rights and responsibilities. Looking outward to the solar system, we see clearly that if new political forms are not created for that environment, the state of nature will be extended to it.

The Social Impact of the Grand Synthesis

The achievement of the grand synthesis would shift human consciousness to a new understanding of how social systems relate to the natural systems out of which they are born. From this new understanding of "natural philosophy," human beings could more closely examine our societies and how to structure them to maximize our ability to fulfill universal purpose.

A new "social contract," or agreement between citizens and their governments, could emerge. It would take into account the work that has been done by social thinkers of humanity's Earthbound past, adding to that understanding all that we know about the evolution of a planetary and space-based civilization. The new contract must find the appropriate balance between unity and diversity and between competition and cooperation at a planetary level. Once it is found and articulated, the foundation for Terran civilization will have been laid.

The most powerful unifying trends at the planetary level, such as the Overview Effect, lead directly to the idea of the great purpose and grand synthesis. They are even now being disseminated and institutionalized, consistently reinforcing the unity of the planet and of the species as the core ideas for the proposed contract.

The planetization of the technosystem, and its increasingly powerful influence on human life, is also a factor supporting a trend toward planetary unity. Nuclear weapons actually provide a form of negative unity, posing a continuing threat of extinction not only to those who possess them, but to all life on Earth.

While there are many positive and negative trends toward planetary unity, the forces working to split the human conmmunity cannot be overlooked. Rather, the emerging science of planetary management must learn how to channel these energies if Terran civilization, as I have envisioned it, is to develop.

Nation-state competition for dominance will continue as long as the international system remains a state of nature in which that competition is more natural than cooperation to achieve humanity's higher purposes. Without a more comprehensive conceptual framework, fundamental cleavages between social systems organized around democracy and free-market systems and those organized around authoritarianism and controlled economic systems will also continue. From orbit, it is not possible to see capitalists and communists, democrats and dictators. However, a real-life struggle is occurring on Earth, and it is not altogether clear how these fundamentally different regimes can coexist.

The issue is at the human technologies interface of these competing societies, where their fundamental value systems are developed. It is here that the planetary social contract must be added that does not destroy the existing value systems, but encompasses them in a new system leading toward a different world view. The new system must also deal with the predisposition of competing nation-states and national movements to use terror and subversion against other states to gain their ends.

Competition between nation-states can be an expression of healthy diversity in a context of planetary unity. However, today's competition includes efforts to subvert one another's societies, so that the international state of nature is extended to the domestic arena.

The planetary social contract must also confront the economic disparity between the have and have-not nations, which contributes to the phenomena of terror and subversion. In spite of the progress that has been made in the industrialized countries, most of humanity remains poor, hungry, and politically oppressed. As long as this is so, it will be difficult to have peace, unity, or cooperation among nations or people.

One negative response to the direction of global society is the rise of religious fundamentalism on a global level, with its tendency to demonize those who do not share its belief systems. Some fundamentalists see the increasing planetization of society as a tool of Western decadence. Any planetary social contract, to be successful, must take into account the diversity of religious beliefs on Earth and the strong convictions of some believers.

If a true planetary civilization is to emerge, it must also cope with the persistence of such serious regional crises as the Arab-Israeli conflict. It is no accident that many astronauts cite the Middle East, seen from orbit, as the area that gave them the greatest feelings of sadness and the strongest wish for planetary unity. Many conflicts arise because some people, like the Palestinians, have yet to pass through the nation-state phase, and they may have to be accommodated one way or another before it will be possible to move on to a planetary culture.

Space Exploration and Planetary Unity

Earlier chapters have shown how the expansion into space and the messages sent back from the universe support the evolution of a more peaceful and ecologically responsible species. Other aspects of space exploration reinforce these trends toward unity and cooperation as well. For example, the cost of large-scale space projects encourages cooperative efforts and a natural movement toward what I have called the human space program. Because such projects are very expensive, running into the billions of dollars, joint efforts make good economic sense.

There is also increasing pressure from people and organizations around the planet to consciously use space for experiments in peaceful interaction. Congressman Bill Nelson's advocacy of a summit conference in space, Carl Sagan's support of a joint U.S.-Soviet mission to Mars, and the activities of the Association of Space Explorers are just a few examples of people and organizations lobbying for the use of space as a laboratory for peace.

The universe is so enormous and awesome that it becomes a unifying force in itself as more people become experientially aware of it. In addition, it provides opportunities for humans to interact in wholly new and different ways. The space environment will cause certain behavior patterns to mutate because they will become increasingly less viable. Special factors in the environment may promote a form of thinking that will take humanity far beyond the current understandings of unity and disunity, war and peace, competition and cooperation.

In the short term, however, some trends of fragmentation are likely to maintain themselves, at least during the initial stages of the exploratory era. For example, there is the military view of space as the next high ground from which to dominate others militarily. The Overview Effect can be experienced from airplanes as well as from spaceships, and the first flyers must have had some of the same feelings as today's astronauts. Nevertheless, the air was turned to military as well as civilian purposes and the airplane was used as a weapon of war only eleven years after the Wright brothers' flight.

The projection of military values into space threatens the peaceful evolution of a planetary and solar civilization. Nation-states will seek to extend their dominance wherever possible, including outer space. It is possible that the countries of Earth initially will carry their rivalries into space as they did in earlier explorations of their planet. But they are unlikely to be maintained for long, because far more significant matters, for instance, a potential split between

Terra and Solarius over political control, economics, and philosophies of life, will have to be confronted.

Designing a new structure to meet the challenge requires a breakthrough of significant proportions, and it must be done with the same intellect and understanding that created the political order in the New World. As in that earlier era, the new social contract must return to first principles and argue them from a position of logic and clarity. If this effort is successful, the trends toward a healthy human unity will be reinforced, while those supporting disunity and conflict will be rechanneled.

The nine principles of the Rationale in *Pioneering the Space Frontier* are most relevant to a space-based civilization and should be integrated with the new plan. The first principles proposed here should encompass what is required for developing a planetary overview system, which is in turn the foundation of a solar overview system.

The original theorists argued from the laws of nature to first principles of the social contract that would bind individuals into societal relationships and remove them from the state of nature. To achieve the grand synthesis, its authors must provide a similar foundation for the proposed planetary social contract, and supporting the achievement of that synthesis should be a high priority of the human space program.

20

Solarius and Speciation

I talk about moon colonies and large space stations. Then I spring the idea of children being born in a weightless environment and the possibility of a split in the human species because of the difference in the way bodies will develop as a result of weightlessness.

– Skylab astronaut Gerald P. Carr

As a space-based civilization takes hold, a new evolutionary variable, speciation, must be considered. It holds out the possibility that the human adventure of space exploration may lead directly to partnership with a human species related to, but different from, Homo sapiens. Biologically, speciation is the evolution of a small group from a large population in such a way that the two can no longer mate and produce fertile offspring. The process of speciation normally takes thousands to millions of years. Long before that, however, there is likely to be a kind of cultural speciation.

Space exploration is a catalyst for social evolution, but it may also be critical to biological evolution. People living in a relatively stable evolutionary epoch can easily overlook nature's propensity to create and destroy, wiping out entire lines of development and laying the groundwork for new species. Extinction is a much more common phenomenon than might be imagined. The dinosaurs are a well-known example of a dominant species that survived for millions of years and then died out for unknown reasons. Extinction is sometimes an unnecessary tragedy, but it is often a natural mechanism that allows evolution to continue. Had dinosaurs not disappeared, mammals might not have developed, and life on Earth would be quite different. Speciation and extinction are two sides of the evolutionary coin, with extinction opening up ecological niches for new species to fill or existing ones to expand. The human race is not static. Rather, it appears to have emerged from numerous evolutionary efforts to produce the next level of intelligence beyond that of the great apes. There is every reason to believe that evolution will continue its experimental efforts and that further speciation will take place if the appropriate enabling conditions appear.

Homo sapiens is the product of human interaction with the terrestrial environment, and as we initiate a symbiotic relationship with a new level in the environmental hierarchy, the likelihood of further evolution and a new round of speciation is inevitably present. In systems terms, evolution favors gradual change. A species possesses a gene pool, which mutates in response to environmental variation. Favorable mutations are adopted and unfavorable ones discarded. The gene pool changes, but the species remains the same. Moreover, the overwhelming majority of all mutations — 99.99 percent or greater — are unfavorable.

Speciation represents a shift from change to transformation. Over time, the number of changes generated by the mutations in a small subset of the population becomes so significant that a qualitatively diffferent gene pool emerges and a new species is born. Two factors are important in the occurrence of speciation: groups of organisms become isolated from the main body of the species and have to cope with unprecedented environmental pressures, and the isolated groups have to be small so that the mutations are conserved in the larger population.[1] Of course, both are characteristic of outer space explorers.

Eric Jones and Ben Finney, two of the leading thinkers in this area, suggest that much of human evolution has occurred because of exploratory expeditions to various parts of the planet where small groups became isolated, thereby triggering the necessary transformations.[2]

In their view, this process has been the engine of biological evolution in the past, but we are at an equilibrium point on Earth because it is not possible for small social groups to find the geographical and psychological isolation necessary for speciation to occur. To the question "Why explore outer space?" they respond that it is the right environment to support not only evolutionary change but transformational speciation.[3]

A complementary, but slightly different focus is provided by Peter H. Diamandis, another leader of the space exploration community. A graduate student at MIT and medical student at Harvard Medical School, he founded Students for the Exploration and Development of Space (SEDS) and the Space Generation Foundation. Whereas Jones and Finney emphasize isolation of the small groups through distance from other groups, Diamandis emphasizes isolation imposed by the environment, especially zero G. According to Diamandis, the probability of speciation in space is high; the question is how long it might take to occur.

Like Finney and Jones, Diamandis notes that small groups tend to evolve faster because mutations have a better chance of survival in them. Since many of the initial human settlements in space will be small, this will contribute to the probability of speciation among their population. Increased evolutionary pressures also accelerate evolution toward speciation, and those in space will be unlike anything we have known because the environment is so radically different.

Diamandis is cautious to point out that his theory is based on two unproven conjectures — that humans can live out their lives in zero G without serious medical problems and that normal fetal development and childbirth can take place in weightlessness. Based on these hypotheses, he advances three main propositions to support his thesis that speciation is likely to occur in space:

1. Some people will spend their lives in a zero-gravity environment by accident or by choice.
2. Zero-G dwellers will eventually stop mating with a population that remains in normal earth gravity.
3. The stress-free environment of zero G will provide a less stringent selective force on mutations, allowing for the persistence of genes that normally could be considered maladaptive.

Some people may choose to remain in zero G because they actively prefer it, enjoying the kind of freedom that the astronauts discuss or simply because they like new experiences. Zero G will be an attractive environment for old people, the physically hand-icapped, and those with medical problems. Once access to space becomes economical, we can imagine many people who have dif-ficulty living on Earth migrating to space and demanding a zero-G environment. Alternatively, on a long mission such as a trip to Mars, countermeasures against the body's efforts to adapt to zero G may fail, and a person (or group) who finds it impossible to readapt to one G will be forced to remain in zero G.

The child-raising issue may create further isolation of people oriented toward zero G. The difficulties of current custody battles and visitation rights are trivial compared to the problems of a child who must move back and forth between different gravitational environments. That might eventually prove to be unhealthy and impossible, because a child who spends its first year in zero G will probably never develop the physical attributes necessary for walk-ing.

In the event that zero-G environments are established as per-manent habitats, people may eventually choose one dominant en-vironment to save themselves the discomfort of adapting from one to the other. Over time, zero-G dwellers are likely to be-come segregated from one-G people, and even if members of the two groups are attracted to one another, the child-raising problem might give them pause. People who live in zero G will also look different as they lose muscle mass and calcium from their bones, further diminishing the attraction that one group will feel for the other.

Finally, as people with physical illnesses and handicaps are at-tracted to a zero-G environment, selective pressures that eliminate genes causing characteristics such as weak hearts or malformed limbs will no longer apply, thereby increasing those genes in the pool and moving it even further away from the current norm.

Beyond these considerations, of course, is our having no idea what will occur when two people who have lived in zero G for even a brief period conceive a child. We know that lack of gravity has a tremendous effect on an adult human body in a short period of time. What would happen to a vulnerable embryo when no countermeasures are taken? It seems logical that if muscle mass diminishes, calcium disappears from the bones, and the cardiovascular system becomes less robust in an adult body, the same will happen to an embryo. The result may be children who look more like dolphins or whales than humans. What will happen when these children, conceived and born in zero G, grow up in zero G and conceive children who in turn are born and mature in the same environment?

Reason suggests the emergence of a radically different kind of being, one highly adapted to living in the conditions of space and poorly adapted to planetary surfaces. Such a person would be unable to return to Earth, or any planet, easily, because survival in a gravity-based environment would be difficult.

Even if full biological speciation does not take place for thousands of years, a form of cultural speciation will probably take place far sooner. Human beings have shown themselves to be sensitive to such differences as skin color and language, and people living permanently in space are going to begin looking and acting differently long before biological speciation occurs.

Natural speciation is usually a slow process. In the case of higher-order life forms, it is measured in hundreds or thousands of generations, not in years. The emergence of Homo *spaciens* as a separate *cultural* being is likely to occur within the next century. The date for the emergence of Homo spaciens as a separate biological entity is unknown, but it ought to be the subject of intense study by space scientists. Such a species might find life on any planetary surface difficult and be able to exist only in the weightless environment of a spacecraft or space settlement. People who choose to live in a low-G environment may also speciate, but in a different direction from those in zero G.

If Homo spaciens and Homo sapiens can work together, the emergence of *spaciens* will resolve the problem of how human beings, who cannot endure a period of weightlessness too long without becoming trapped by it, can explore regions beyond the orbit of Mars. Just as the nonorganic species of Technos promises to be a partner in the long-term human adventure, so may this new organic species be a great help in the realization of human purpose.

Dramatic as this line of thought may appear to be, Jones and Finney might argue that it is much too tame. They state,

This advance will not be limited to the birth of one new species. Space is not a single environment, but a residual category for everything outside the Earth's atmosphere. There are innumerable environments out there, and perhaps more niches to be developed for the exploitation of those environments. By spreading into space we will embark on an adaptive radiation of hominidae that will spread intelligent life as far as technology or limits placed by any competing life forms will allow. This radiation of evolving, intelligent life through space will be the galactic successor to the other great episodes of adaptive radiation in the evolution of life — that which followed the wandering of a few fish onto land, or the opportunistic multiplication of mammalian genera and species to fill the vacuum left by the disappearance of the dinosaurs.[4]

Finally, it should be mentioned that humanity may consciously choose to modify itself in order to explore space, actively bringing on the speciation process. Considering our advances in biotechnology as well as space technology, the ultimate form of speciation may become a reality: an organism able to live in free space without a pressure suit or any artificial environment, just as a fish lives in water.

It may be that the more radical alterations of the human organism are impossible. However, it is quite possible that genetic engineering would, at minimum, be used to optimize adaptation to environments like a space habitat or Mars. If that proves to be successful, the state of the art will probably be pushed as far as it reasonably can go.

Whenever and however speciation takes place, it will contribute to humanity's efforts to make space, and all its possible environments, a permanent home. In addition, it will help humans learn to interact with a different but highly intelligent species, which promises to be the next challenge in climbing the evolutionary ladder to a galactic civilization.

21

Galaxia and First Contact

I have always believed that there were other human beings on other
planets. Not in our solar system, obviously, but I personally believe
that God created our Earth and the universe and that we are not the
only children of God in the universe.

— Senator Jake Garn

Ben Finney suggests that two strategies are generally propounded
for exploring the galaxy: SETI, the search for extraterrestrial intelligence, and IM, interstellar migration.[1] In terms of galactic
exploration, communication technology is ahead of transportation
technology, because gravity is not a limiting factor. While not a
conscious part of SETI, all the radio and television signals ever
broadcast are streaming out into the galaxy. In a more directed
effort, a sophisticated venture to detect signals from other star
systems operates as part of Harvard University's Project Meta.

Current propulsion capabilities put a strong limitation on our
ambitions for physical exploration beyond the solar system. Even
when the limits of gravity have been economically overcome, the
inability to travel faster than the speed of light will remain a barrier
to galactic exploration. As Michael Collins said, "We have learned
how to leave, but not how to go anywhere."[2]

For some time into the future, barring major breakthroughs,
humanity will be confined to the inner solar system. The development of Terra and the establishment of Solarius will occupy most
of the species' time and energy. Within the space frontier that will
define Solarius for the next half century, only Mars holds out any
expectation of discovering life of any kind. Beyond the orbit of

Mars, some of the moons of the outer planets have the right elements to potentially create life, though it would probably be in an early stage of evolution.

Is there intelligent life as we know it in the solar system outside the biosphere of Earth? It is possible. It is also possible that intelligent life can evolve from compounds other than those with which we are familiar. There could, for example, be large, highly intelligent gas balloon creatures floating through the atmosphere of Jupiter.

The question really is, What does it take to create life on a planet? It may be that it requires not only all the resources of the planet itself, but all the capabilities of an entire solar system as well. The placement of the Earth in relation to the sun, its size, and the delicate mixture of elements on the Earth are all essential to creating the kind of intelligent, conscious life with which we are familiar.

Just as a planet like Earth needs life to maintain its balance, so may a solar system have to bring forth life to fulfill its evolutionary destiny. It is also possible that a solar system evolves life on one planet, such as Earth, from which the rest of the system is "seeded" by the "mother" planet.

It is simply not known whether there is intelligent life elsewhere in the solar system. It is clear that thinking about life beyond Earth has been a concern of humanity throughout its history. Our current interest, while utilizing sophisticated technology, is ancient in its origins, pointing to the past as well as the future.

Sky Gods and Goddesses

Seen as a broad cultural pattern, the search for extraterrestrial intelligence has been an ongoing central project for millennia. History is replete with stories of sky gods interacting with humans. The Greek gods, for example, may have been the products of imagination, hallucinations à la Julian Jaynes, or even extraterrestrials, as some have suggested.[3]

At this distance from the events of those times, we cannot know the absolute truth. However, these gods did live in the sky, where they had an overview of everything that happened on Earth, and they flew to the planet when they wanted to be involved in such Earthly activities as the Trojan War. They were technologically more advanced than human beings and they were immortal, but otherwise they were not far beyond humans on the evolutionary ladder. They had family quarrels and personal jealousies, and they were capable of behaving callously toward one another and their human friends and enemies.

There is a more recent mythology of sky gods and goddesses, of course. For many, the search for extraterrestrial intelligence has ended and the quarrry has been found right here on Earth. UFO sightings have continued almost unabated since 1947, and many people claim not only to have seen spaceships in the sky, but also to have been contacted or abducted by aliens. It is risky to mention the UFO phenomenon in a book about space exploration, because it is a controversial and highly emotional issue. Whatever unidentified flying objects are, they have not yet become a common part of our consensus reality, and it is almost necessary to write an entire book about them or ignore them altogether.

It may be useful to ignore the question of what UFOs are and to see them as a phenomenon that says something significant about the current consciousness of the human social system. The unrelenting deluge of books, films, and articles about ETs illustrates humanity's continuing interest in the subject of extraterrestrial intelligence, which may manifest itself in socially acceptable activities like Project Meta or socially questionable ones like claims of having been directly approached by UFO pilots. The interest is similar, but its expression is different.

The evolution of the human vision of the extraterrestrials, from the "invaders from Mars" in 1938 to the more beneficent images of *Close Encounters of the Third Kind*, *E.T.*, and *Starman*, punctuated by a swing back again in *Aliens*, betrays an uncertainty as to whether we should embrace or fear whatever is "out there." One thing is certain: if a civilization from another star system reveals itself to us publicly, that will be a transformational moment in human history, unlike anything that has gone before. Whether it happens through a communication process or physical contact may not be as important as the event itself.

There is reason to believe that the open appearance of representatives of an alien overview system will not take place until Solarian civilization is mature. That development in turn is not expected until after an overview of the solar system has been accomplished and Homo spaciens has emerged. At that point, humanity and its progeny will be prepared to enter or begin creating Galaxia. This is the most speculative of all my predictions, and it could be contradicted in the near future by developments on a number of fronts.

Probabilities

Information has been cited as the principal catalyst for social evolution, especially in the form of metaideas. Information from outer space has further been defined as an extremely rich source of metaideas and metaexperiences. If this is so, the possibility of a legitimate, recognized communication from a nonterrestrial civilization holds great significance for human society.

Many questions are raised by this line of thought, including:

1. Has intelligent life similar to Homo sapiens evolved elsewhere in the galaxy?
2. If so, does it have the capability for interstellar travel or communication?
3. If there are other planetary or solar civilizations, are they isolated from one another, or are they linked together in a galactic overview system?
4. If they are part of a galactic system, would they contact us randomly or wait until a specific moment in our history to do so?
5. If they are not linked together, will one of our opportunities be to help build the galactic overview system?

Many of the issues surrounding first contact are matters of probability, starting with the number of stars that might be sources of life. There are one trillion stars in the Milky Way galaxy. If only one percent of those stars have planets, and one percent of those planets have life, and one percent of the life-bearing planets support intelligent life, and one percent of those have evolved societies equal to or more advanced than our own, there would be *ten thousand* planetary or solar civilizations in this galaxy.

Carl Sagan and Soviet scientist I. S. Shklovskii, using more sophisticated calculations, arrived at the conclusion that there are between fifty thousand and one million civilizations in the galaxy substantially in advance of our own. They also calculated that the average distance between these civilizations is a few hundred to a thousand light years and that the average age of a communicating civilization is ten thousand years or more.[4] It therefore seems safe to assume that between ten thousand and one million overview systems are operating in our galaxy and that some percentage of them have linked up, so that a galactic civilization is either in existence or evolving.

The outcome of first contact is unknown, because it would depend on the level humanity has reached when it occurs. The difference in contact during a preplanetary period and in fifty years, when we have a space-based civilization, would be significant.

It is clear that on Earth, whenever more advanced civilizations have communicated with less advanced cultures, the latter have suffered intensely. Our own culture understands this problem, at least in theory. For example, in the "Star Trek" television series, the crews of the Federation Star Fleet operate under a "prime directive" that prohibits any interference in the evolution of another culture. The National Commission on Space also recognized the issue by including a principle in its Rationale that commits us to "respect the integrity of planetary bodies and alien life forms."[5]

If a galactic civilization exists, it may have experienced the problems of bringing unprepared cultures into the larger domain of galactic interactions and may well choose to wait until humanity and its coevolving species are more mature. If contact comes sooner rather than later, it would put the entire space exploration venture in a new light. At the moment, it is seen primarily as a human enterprise working with the resources of Earth and of free space to bootstrap humanity outward into the solar system and beyond.

However, contact with an advanced spacefaring civilization will transform the exploration equation as well as human society. Such a civilization could telescope dramatically the time needed to achieve the next steps in human evolution and could make interstellar migration technologically possible. The launch and propulsion limitations would be lifted, and the transition to living and working in space would be rapid. In addition, a galactic civilization would probably have resolved such threats to intelligent life as nuclear weapons and would be able to help humanity through that difficult challenge. But its citizens might choose not to help, even for such a salutary purpose. It may be necessary for a culture to resolve that dilemma on its own, and being helped by others may distort the evolutionary process. A final possibility is that assistance would take place, but it would not be open or would go unrecognized because of its form.

However it occurs, contact is not the end, but the beginning of the Galaxia story. Just as the development of planetary and solar overviews are necessary for taking the next step in physical and mental space beyond these levels, so will it be necessary to achieve a galactic overview before taking the final journey into the universe of clusters and superclusters of galaxies. If humanity has something unique to offer the planet and solar system in supporting their evolution, the same is probably true of the galaxy and the universe.

It is theoretically possible that humanity is alone or that the universe is bursting with life and intelligence. Open contact may take a few years or millennia or never occur. The issue is not when or how contact will be made, but how to be ready for it, and that returns us to the task of becoming more responsible in our relationship to the universe of which we are a part.

22

Creating the Future

I have been involved with the young students in Up with People who are communicating to others via music. I was sharing with them some of what I thought and felt while standing on the moon, and they wrote a song called "Moonrider" about what it was like for one man standing alone on another planet a quarter million miles away in space, looking back home. . . . One phrase in there expresses it well for me: "Isn't it the way we perceive things that will make them what they will be?"

— Gemini and Apollo astronaut Eugene A. Cernan

I was invited to talk about space exploration at my son's day-care center, where the children ranged in age from four to six years old. In the year 2000, they will be in their early twenties, and some of them may become the new Martians or Lunarians. They will be the real pioneers of the space frontier, the creators of Solarius.

I talked with them about space shuttles, space settlements, and living in space. Then I asked, "How many of you would like to live in space?" Several hands shot up, but a little boy named Masaki looked at me with a puzzled expression on his face and said, "But Mr. White, we *are* in space." Masaki intuitively understood something I've been trying to get through to people for some time now, and it's a very important point. Humanity is in space, living on a large natural spaceship — Spaceship Earth, Buckminster Fuller called it. Taking into account the Earth's motion around the sun and the sun's motion around the galactic center, the path of the planet is a spiral, rather than just an ellipse. Even as the Earth revolves around the sun, it never passes through exactly the same quadrant of space.

We are not "going around in circles" but passing through cycles that are quite similar to one another, yet always with a slight modification. Because our environment is never exactly the same, the evolutionary process does not repeat itself. The shape of the Earth's path is found throughout nature and has long been a powerful symbol of evolution, growth, and transformation. It is the shape of the DNA molecule, which holds the secret of life, and the shape of many galaxies. Our natural spaceship traverses a path that builds in the processes of equilibrium, change, and transformation as an inherent part of life.

The spaceflight experience is really the ability to get into scout ships, leave the "mother ship," and take a good look at her and the rest of the universe. Being in orbit allows the astronaut or cosmonaut to adjust his or her thinking to a reality that has *always been there*, but has only recently been experienced.

Gene Cernan's description of returning to Earth as returning to the crib is reminiscent of Plato's famous discourse, *The Republic*. Speaking through the philosopher Socrates, Plato offers an allegory about people who are imprisoned in a cave and forced to look at a wall rather than out into the light of the sun. A fire in the background casts shadows on the wall, and people walk behind the prisoners carrying vessels, statues, and figures of animals. To the prisoners the shadows on the wall are reality, which they do their best to understand and describe accurately to one another. Because their vision is limited, however, they see only an illusion.

Socrates then imagines a person who is taken out of the cave and shown the world beyond it. It is painful and difficult for him at first, but as his eyes adjust to the light, he starts to see reality instead of shadows. He ultimately reaches the point where he can see the sun and understand it as the source of all life and goodness in the world. Socrates says that when this enlightened man returns to the cave and attempts to explain the broader reality to his fellow human beings, he will have problems, especially as his eyes are adjusting to the darkness. He will appear to have inferior, rather than superior, knowledge for having gone up into the light.

Just as our own mental universe is restricted by our understanding of the physical universe, so would be the mental universe of those people in the cave. They would be in the habit, Socrates says, "of conferring honors among themselves on those who were quickest to observe the passing shadows and to remark which of them went before, and which were together; and who therefore were best able to draw conclusions as to the future."[1]

A man who has returned from the upper world would find it difficult to analyze the shadows, partly because he has seen the light and partly because he has not yet adjusted to the darkness.

> And [if] he had to compete in measuring the shadows with the prisoners who had never moved out of the den, while his sight was still weak . . . would he not be ridiculous? Men would say of him that up he went and down he came without his eyes; and that it was better not to think of ascending; and if anyone tried to loose another and lead him up into the light, let them only catch the offender and they would put him to death.[2]

For the prisoners in the cave, the wider environment had always been there. Turning around and going up into the light did not *create* that wider environment, but it allowed them to perceive it more fully. Initially they were chained and could not leave to see the new reality. However, once one of their number had made the trek, it became their choice to continue staring into the darkness. "It didn't help *him* very much," they would say.

The people in the cave are like the imaginary detractors of the explorer fish, and they are frighteningly like us today. We fail to realize that we are in space, that we have the means to experience it on a vast scale, and that doing so will free us from the illusory reality in which we daily indulge. Instead, we spend our time trying to fit outer space into our current paradigm and criticizing our astronauts for failing to explain the light in terms that the darkness can understand. Unfortunately, this is the perfect prescription for our continued solitary confinement from the rest of the universe.

Going into space is not the point. Realizing that we are in space and beginning to deal with the broader implications is the point. We are in space and we cannot be anywhere else, ever. The question is whether our expanded awareness will have a positive impact on social evolution. Seen from this point of view, the issue is whether we are ready to mature as a species, look beyond our narrow parochial concerns, and become true citizens of the universe.

Realizing that we are in space is mind-expanding, but we hate to admit it because it brings us back up against the issues of awareness and choice today, not in the future. The new civilizations, like the Kingdom of God, are within us.

Ultimately, going into space is not about a technological achievement, but about the human spirit and our contribution to universal purpose. Space, as used in the new space movement, is a metaphor for expansiveness, opportunity, and freedom. More than a place or even an experience, it is a state of mind. It is a physical, mental, and spiritual dimension in which humanity can move beyond the current equilibrium point, begin to change, and eventually transform itself into something so extraordinary that we cannot even imagine it.

Space exploration, in all its forms, should become humanity's modern central project, and the human space program the central project for all five billion of us. The goal should be to get us out of the cave, freeing us to see reality rather than the illusions that persist for a species chained to a planetary surface. The choice of becoming citizens of the universe can be rejected, but humanity can no longer plead ignorance of what is truly possible.

Joseph Campbell, one of the planet's leading mythology scholars, said,

> The mystical theme of the space age is this: The world as we know it, is coming to an end. The world as the center of the universe, the world divided by the heavens, the world bound by horizons in which love is reserved for members of the in-group . . . Apocalypse does not point to a fiery Armageddon, but to the fact that our ignorance and complacency are coming to an end . . .
>
> It's fashionable now to demand some economic payoff from space, some reward to prove it was all worthwhile. Those who say this resemble the apelike creatures in "2001." They are fighting for food among themselves, while one separates himself from them and moves to the slab, motivated by awe. That is the point they are missing. He is the one who evolves into a human being; he is the one who understands the future.[3]

And he was the first Terranaut.

23

The New Civilizations and You

You begin to see that new values, norms, and laws will apply in space.
— Skylab astronaut Gerald P. Carr

If the Earth is a natural spaceship, then everyone on it is either a passenger or a crew member. R. Buckminster Fuller was one of the first people to realize that the Earth is not only a spaceship, but that it needs a crew. He was certainly one of the first pilots on the ship. Today, we also need mission specialists, payload specialists, citizen participants, and more. Those who qualify are the human space program's Terranauts.

The role you play is not as important as the awareness that you are "aboard ship" and can spend the entire journey asleep in a lounge chair or wake up and participate in a voyage. Becoming a Terranaut does not require you to change jobs, move to a new city, join the astronaut corps, or live on Mars. It does require becoming conscious of yourself and your place in the universe.

To become a conscious passenger on Spaceship Earth, simply put your own life and work in the context of the evolving new civilizations. Ask yourself, daily, "How does my life support the positive evolution of the human future?" Whenever possible, think of yourself as being on a spaceship moving through the universe at a high rate of speed rather then a stable platform around which the universe revolves.

Becoming a crew member requires more than simple awareness. It means a commitment to helping create the future, working with possibilities as well as probabilities. To be a crew member, you have to develop your own vision and purpose and align it with universal purpose. As this occurs, you will find yourself turning your attention to a vocation or avocation that directly supports the progress of this spaceship and this species on its journey through the universe. You will become a Terranaut.

Becoming a Terranaut

The first step in becoming a Terranaut is to determine which of the three civilizations can best use your talents. Do you see yourself helping to lay the groundwork for Terra, Solarius, or Galaxia, bearing in mind that they are all additive and mutually interactive?

The second step is to learn about what is possible. People all over the planet are already actively engaged in supporting the development of the new civilizations. Researching what individuals and groups are doing to increase planetary awareness or supporting a strong space program provides information on ways to take action.

The third step is to *listen* to the messages coming to you from the universe. Be receptive to what appears in terms of a purpose and a task. Becoming aligned with universal purpose cannot be figured out; that level of awareness means being open and following the heart. Chance meetings, unpredicted events, support from unexpected quarters can all be terribly important.

I wanted to be an astronaut, but NASA's requirements have always included a scientific or engineering background, which I didn't have. However, I continued to be open to possibilities to become involved in the space movement. An otherwise uneventful flight to the West Coast triggered the experience that led to my Overview Effect research. Later I joined the Space Studies Institute and was asked to speak there for the first time in 1983, during a meeting of people working on a "vision statement" for space.

I presented my initial findings on the overview in 1985, and people began to support that effort. Step by step, my work as a Terranaut has become that of a communicator of the overview message, and it has evolved from avocation to vocation. The publication of this book supports the continued dissemination of the message.

This work is part of my contribution to the evolution of the new civilizations. In addition to the Overview Project, I have also begun to shape all my activities within the context of a New Civilization Project aimed at communicating its message to others. My story is important not because I am special, but as a model of the possibilities available to anyone who wants to be a Terranaut. There are many jobs to do, and a career path exists, but it is not obvious to everyone. You have to develop it for yourself.

I have described a vision of a possible future. Terra can be developed as a peaceful, prosperous, ecologically balanced planetary overview system, ideally suited not only for human life, but also as the kindly mother of spacefaring children who leave to found Solarius. Solarius can become an adventurous, open, free, and successful solar overview system, full of diversity and excitement, helping humanity reach the maturity necessary to make contact with the emerging galactic civilization.

Galaxia can be an evolving civilization of the stars, propelling us to our ultimate destination as citizens of the universe. *Can* is the language of possibility, and there is nothing inevitable about this positive future history of humanity. We can be encouraged, based upon the evidence of the change in consciousness catalyzed by space exploration, to believe that the larger environment is supporting these positive directions in evolution.

It also appears that humanity, as an essential component in the creation of overview systems, has something useful to offer the universe as a whole. However, while the environment does support certain trends, it also appears to be quite sanguine about dead ends, failures, and extinctions. Species come and go, but life and the universe continue.

The Human Space Program

The embryonic human space program exists in all the national space programs, the private pro-space societies and activities around the world, and the actions of individuals working alone for a positive future. However, there is no unifying vision to balance this diversity, and the human space program is not yet a conscious human system.

In order to give power to the emergent reality, then, let us now declare the establishment of the program and provide it with a long-range plan from which it will be possible for aspiring Terranauts to choose their vocations and contributions.

The following are the fundamental elements of the program:

Purpose: to support humanity's understanding and achievement of its purpose as an active partner in universal evolution, creating overview systems that increase conscious awareness throughout the universe.

Vision: a universal civilization, a golden age, humanity taking its rightful place as citizens of the universe.

Long-term goals: establishing planetary, solar, and galactic civilizations as steps to a universal civilization.

Immediate objectives: creating conditions for planetary peace and humanity's migration to the solar system and the stars.

Participants: all human beings and other sentient species.

Spatial parameters: the universe.

Temporal parameters: the present through the next millennium, 1987–3000.

If humanity is to achieve this vision, a formidable number of tasks, enough to engage the talents and energies of the entire planet, must be accomplished. A partial list of the critical initiatives to be taken includes:

1. *Analyze in more detail how exploration effects mental and spiritual evolution.* We know that there is an inner space/outer space interface, but we do not know enough about its operation. Additional research into exploration and its impact on mental and spiritual outlook is needed.

2. *Conduct further research on the great purpose.* Is there evidence for a human purpose or is it only a metaphor? In particular, this program should look into how overview systems might relate to entropy.

3. *Support development of the grand synthesis.* Help scientists to bring forth the grand synthesis hypotheses of *Pioneering the Space Frontier.*

4. *Develop the planetary social contract.* Conduct research into social contract theory. Determine how it can be adapted to our current situation and develop a new theory.

5. *Develop a Terran constitution.* Create a constitutional framework based on understanding the social contract and human purpose and including all nations and ideologies in the context of that purpose.

6. *Inventory the technosystem and its capabilities.* Conduct research to determine the level of awareness currently imparted by artificial intelligence techniques and the extent to which the planetary nervous system is in place.

7. *Inventory ways in which space has a direct impact on social needs.* Conduct research into the ways space exploration and development can help to alleviate hunger, increase world energy supplies, prevent war, and improve the quality of life.

8. *Support the Overview Project.* Assist in disseminating its message planetwide.

9. *Explore the moral equivalent to war thesis.* Further develop the idea of channeling aggressive drives away from war and toward peaceful development of space.

10. *Help to develop the idea of a summit conference in space.* Determine a realistic scenario. When would be a reasonable time for it? Who should attend? What infrastructure must be in place for it to occur?

11. *Support the creation of the International Space University.* Contribute to the evolution of a space university, now under development by the Space Generation foundation, where the fundamental vision and purpose of space exploration can be taught, learned about, and developed further.

12. *Investigate the solar system as a whole.* What role does each of its subsystems play? How can we achieve an overview of the solar system?

13. *Conduct research to understand the role that Mars has played in human evolution.* The impact of Mars on human life in general and space exploration in particular is remarkable. More needs to be known to understand its future impact.

14. *Expand research on speciation.* Cultural evolution will be rapid in nonterrestrial environments. Biological speciation is a high probability, but the time frame is uncertain. Additional research should be conducted to determine how speciation will occur.

15. *Investigate the probable impact of contact with a galactic civilization.* Contact without preparation could be devastating, but thoughtful contact can be of great benefit to both species. Active efforts to prepare for communication may hasten the day when it occurs.

16. *Begin a campaign to inform humanity that we are in space.* Increase awareness in general, especially of the preparations for contact with Galaxia.

17. *Support adoption of the National Space Commission's report by NASA.* Adopting the report would give NASA the vision it needs to be effective and generate public support.

18. *Help to develop ideas for international space missions, especially to Mars.* Support those who are marshaling the channeling of aggressive drives into space and have begun to rally around the cause of an international exploratory mission to Mars.

19. *Inventory the human space program.* Collect information on national space programs, space interest groups, university courses, private enterprise efforts, SETI projects, and individual efforts contributing to the positive evolution of humanity in space.

20. *Develop new replication models for space communities.* In conjunction with the development of a Terran constitution, much more work must be done in this area to avoid conflict between the new civilizations.

Anyone who wants to be a Terranaut can support these projects or create his or her own. There are many other specific steps one can take to participate in the founding of the new civilizations, including joining a space interest group such as the Space Studies Institute, National Space Society, Students for the Exploration and Development of Space, and Planetary Society.

It is also useful to read *Pioneering the Space Frontier* and other publications that provide a broad view of the human future in space. Everyone interested in being a Terranaut should see *The Dream Is Alive* at the National Air and Space Museum in Washington or another site where it is being shown.

However, the most important step is to choose to take personal responsibility for the human future. As more people do so, they can help assure that the possibilities they care about will become probabilities.

Role of the Terranaut

The human space program has existed in the collective unconscious of humanity since the dawn of awareness. Over time, it has become more apparent. It represents a great hope for the future of humanity because it is aligned with universal purpose.

The Terranaut is a new agent of change on the scene. Like the human space program, the Terranaut has always been there, unrecognized and without a label. Now he and she can emerge and play a formative role in human evolution.

Do the new civilizations have anything to do with you?

The answer depends on you.

24

The Universal Civilization

Some of us think we understand how the universe is put together. But we have a lot to learn, and we are limited by current propulsion systems and life expectancies. Our capabilities will appear prehistoric to those who have a "Star Trek"–like system and can actually go to the stars. Our solar system is beautiful, but there is so much more out there!

— Skylab astronaut Edward G. Gibson

As we stand at the bottom of a deep gravity well and look out from the surface of the Earth, pioneering a space frontier stretching from Earth orbit to the plains of Mars may seem like a task far beyond our strength. The universe is so vast that we recall the ancient sailor's prayer, "Protect me, O Lord, for the ocean is so great and my boat is so small." But pioneering that space frontier, as great a step forward as it would be, is only a beginning. Even Mars, so far away from Earth, is in our neighborhood and nowhere near the limits of the solar system.

The idea of leaving the solar system is only in the realm of our imagination and cannot be easily achieved with existing technology. Nevertheless, our imaginations have always outpaced our ability to bring ideas into physical being. Today's fantasy becomes tomorrow's reality by pulling us forward into a challenging and exciting future.

Every century gives birth to individuals who hold the vision for all humanity, and the Buckminster Fullers were preceded by the Leonardo da Vincis. Leonardo, a man with a fertile and inventive imagination, desperately wanted to see humans fly, and he neglected his career as a painter of incomparable masterpieces to work on flying machines.

Few listened to him because he wasn't "practical." In the fifteenth century, the ruling powers were interested in building better fortifications and siege engines. To them, dreaming of flying was self-indulgent, but Leonardo knew that it could be done. His designs for flying machines would have worked if the technology to implement his ideas had existed. He was ahead of his time, and his descendants have realized many of his dreams.

For some of today's visionaries, Solarius is the next step, a central project to occupy many years of effort. For others, Solarius is already much too tame, and they dream of doing the impossible, going to the stars and beyond. Someday those visionaries will be proved right. Assuming that humanity makes it into the solar system, we will find a way to reach out and participate in the galactic civilization. Someone may invent a new form of propulsion. Einstein's theories may be proved wrong, allowing us to travel faster than the speed of light. An antigravity device may be invented.

However, it should be clear by now that the journey *is* the destination, the point of it all, humanity's way of serving a higher purpose. In the past, there were central projects, but now there is one universal project, which is to evolve and work in harmony with the largest whole system of all, the universe. Beyond Galaxia lies yet another step, the civilization of civilizations, stretching across the entire physical universe.

What kind of species will humanity be at that point? What will Homo universalis be like? Even the capacity to generate metaphors fails at this level, so we admit that we cannot know. However, we can be certain that they will be our children, and they will love us for being their parents, for having the courage to create the conditions for them to exist, and for exploring, for that is the human thing to do.

Let's be ahead of our time.

THE EXPERIENCES OF THE ASTRONAUTS AND COSMONAUTS

Author's Note

Part III describes the experiences of space travelers without the filter provided by the commentary and analyses in Parts I and II. It consists of reconstructions of my interviews, supplemented by selected writings, with sixteen people who have been in space.

The limits in my sample of space travelers point to research needed in the future because the interviews are primarily with American men. My request to talk with some of the women astronauts is still pending at NASA, but it was not possible to arrange an interview by press time. Since I also did not find writings by women that met the needs of this book, it seemed better to do the job right in a future work. Still, I must say that I regret the absence of this perspective.

Similarly, astronauts and cosmonauts from other countries are represented by Marc Garneau of Canada, Sultan Bin Salman al-Saud of Saudi Arabia, and diary excerpts of some of the Soviet cosmonauts. Again, the demands of presenting the international element appropriately are such that they are best left for another work.

Many of the interviews were longer than what is reproduced here, and they are not word-for-word renditions of the discussions. I have made every effort, however, to work with the astronauts to render accurately the essential points and convey the meaning of what they said. In any instance where that is not the case, the responsibility is, of course, solely mine.

Overall, *The Overview Effect* should be seen as a beginning — certainly not the end — of the process of understanding the human experience in space.

Yuri Alexeyevich Gagarin

Vostok 1

Yuri Gagarin was the first human to enter space, completing one orbit of the Earth on April 12, 1961. A Soviet Air Force pilot, Gagarin was twenty-seven when he made his flight, and spent an hour and forty-eight minutes in space. Gagarin continued his career as a cosmonaut until 1968, when he was killed in an airplane crash.
Gagarin's description is from Survival in Space.

Trembling with excitement I watched a world so new and unknown to me, trying to see and remember everything. Astonishingly bright cold stars could be seen through the windows. They were still far away — oh, so far away — but in orbit they seemed closer than the Earth. But the point was not the distance (my distance from the Earth was but a drop in the ocean compared to the light-years separating us from the stars) but the principle. Man had overcome the force of Earth's gravity and gone out into space.

Alan B. Shepard, Jr.

Freedom 7, Apollo 14

Alan Shepard, the first American to go into space, made a fifteen-minute suborbital flight on May 5, 1961. He later commanded the Apollo 14 mission to the moon in January 1971. Though his first flight was short, his total time in space is just over nine days. Shepard described his Mercury mission in We Seven, *from which his words were excerpted.*

It was now time to go to the periscope. I had been well briefed on what to expect, and one of the last things I had done . . . before suiting up was to study . . . some special maps which showed me the view I would get. I had some idea of the huge variety of color and land masses and cloud cover which I would see from 100 miles up. But no one could be briefed well enough to be completely prepared for the astonishing view that I got. My exclamation back to Deke [Donald K. Slayton] about the "beautiful sight" was completely spontaneous. It was breathtaking.

John H. Glenn, Jr.
Friendship 7

Major John Glenn, a Marine Corps pilot, the fifth person to enter space, was the first American to orbit the Earth. His flight on Mercury's Friendship 7, on February 20, 1962, lasted just under five hours. Glenn is now a U.S. senator from Ohio.
  Glenn's reactions are from We Seven.

Now, for the first time, I could look out the window and see back along the flight path. I could not help exclaiming over the radio about what I saw. "Oh," I said, "that view is tremendous!" It really was. I could see for hundreds of miles in every direction — the sun on white clouds, patches of blue water beneath, and great chunks of Florida and the southeastern U.S.

While I was reporting in by radio to the Canary Island tracking station, I had my first glimpse of the coast of Africa. The Atlas Mountains were clearly visible through the window. Inland, I could see huge dust storms from brush fires raging along the edge of the desert.

One of the things that surprised me most about the flight was the percentage of the earth which was covered by clouds. They were nearly solid over Central Africa and extended out over most of the Indian Ocean and clear across the Pacific. I could not establish the exact altitude of the various layers, but I could easily determine where one layer ended and another layer began by the shadows . . .

I found weightlessness to be extremely pleasant. I must say it is convenient for a space pilot . . . The fact that this strange phenomenon seemed so natural at the time indicates how rapidly men can adapt to a new environment. I am sure that I could have gone for a much longer period in a weightless condition without being bothered by it at all. Being suspended in a state of zero G is much more comfortable than lying down under the pressure of one G on the ground, for you are not subject to any pressure points. You feel absolutely free . . .

I witnessed my first sunset over the Indian Ocean, and it was a beautiful display of vivid colors. The sun is perfectly round and it gives off an intense, clear light which is more bluish-white than yellow, and which reminded me in color and intensity of the huge arc lights we used at the Cape . . . Then, just as the sun starts to sink into the bright horizon, it seems to flatten out a little.

As the sun gets lower and lower, a black shadow moves across the earth until the entire surface that you can see is dark except for the bright band of light along the horizon. At the beginning, the band is almost white in color. But as the sun sinks deeper the bottom layer of light turns to bright orange. The next layers are red, then purple, then light blue, then darker blue, and finally the blackness of space. They are all brilliant colors, more brilliant than in a rainbow, and the band extends out about 60 degrees on either side of the sun. It is a fabulous display.

Malcolm Scott Carpenter

Aurora 7

In May 1962, Scott Carpenter flew the Mercury mission that followed John Glenn's flight. He was the sixth person to go into space, where he spent just under five hours.

Carpenter's words are from We Seven.

The first thing that impressed me when I got into orbit was the absolute silence. One reason for this . . . was that the noisy booster had just separated and fallen away, leaving me suddenly on my own. But it was also a result . . . of the sensation of floating that I experienced as soon as I became weightless. All of a sudden, I could feel no pressure of my body against the couch. And the pressure suit, which is very constricting and uncomfortable on the ground, became entirely comfortable.

The pressures were all equal; even a change in position made no difference. It was part of the routine to report this moment to the ground as soon as it came. It was such an exhilarating feeling, however, that my report was a spontaneous and joyful exclamation: "I am weightless!" Now the supreme experience of my life had begun . . .

In the early part of the first orbit I concentrated mainly on the control system and did not really look around. When I finally did, the sight was overwhelming. There were cloud formations that any painter could be proud of — little rosettes or clustered circles of fair-weather cumulus down below. I could also see the sea down below and the black sky above me.

I could look off for perhaps a thousand miles in any direction, and everywhere I looked the window and the periscope were constantly filled with beauty. I found it difficult to tear my eyes away and go on to something else. Everything is new and so awe-inspiring that it is difficult to concentrate for very long on any one thing. Later on, when I knew that I was returning to some wonderful sight that I had seen before, I could hardly wait to get there.

I crossed the United States in early morning light. The ground seemed closer than I thought it would, and though it was 100 miles down and I was going 5 miles per second, it seemed to pass underneath me at about the same speed as in a jet at 40,000 feet — perhaps just a little faster. Where it was not covered by clouds, I could see the ground remarkably well . . . rivers and lakes — even a train on a track. And as I passed over farm country in the southwest I could tell where the south 40 was cultivated and the north 40 was lying fallow. At every new sight, my elation was renewed, and I kept waiting again for the next one.

The last hour before retro-fire passed quickly, just as all the rest of time had. Flying through space, I felt a curious compression of time, as if the speed at which I traveled had some effect on the length of moments I spent there and packed them too tightly on top of one another.

After the flight I sat for a long time just thinking about what I'd been through. I couldn't believe it had all happened. It had been a tremendous experience, and though I could never really *share* it with anyone, I looked forward to telling others as much about it as I could . . .

I felt that space was so fascinating and that a flight through it was so thrilling and so overwhelming that I only wished I could get up the next morning and go through the whole thing all over again. I wanted to be weightless again, and see the sunsets and sunrises, and watch the stars drop through the luminous layer, and learn to master that machine a little better so I could stay up longer. There's no doubt about it, space is a fabulous frontier, and we are going to solve some of its mysteries and bring back many of its riches in our lifetime.

Russell L. Schweickart
Apollo 9

Russell L. ("Rusty") Schweickart flew on Apollo 9, a ten-day orbital mission on March 3, 1969, between Apollo 8's dramatic journey to the moon and the first moon landing by Apollo 11 in July 1969. Since his flight, Schweickart has been involved in a number of endeavors, including the founding of the Association of Space Explorers.

Much of his experience, described and included in Parts I and II, is not repeated here. The following is based on notes I made during my telephone interview with Schweickart on October 29, 1985.

WHITE: Has your experience had a continuing impact on your life?

SCHWEICKART: Yes. It changed my life. It isn't something that came and then went back.

WHITE: I had quite a transformational experience in writing about your experience. Have you found that other people change when they hear about it?

SCHWEICKART: Yes, they do. In some cases, nothing is transmitted at all. It depends on the individual and the setting. Often, it is so profound and immediate that it scares me. When you are dealing with powerful medicine, it may be better to get it in small doses. People occasionally are so overwhelmed that they become inarticulate about what they get, and you feel responsible for what has happened to this other human being. It happens in ways that are very moving.

WHITE: Can you talk a little bit about the Association of Space Explorers and the impact you hope it might have?

SCHWEICKART: I'm happy to. We're a small group of people, about forty from sixteen countries around the planet. But each of us has seen the Earth as a single place with our own eyes. If we, as individuals, can go beyond our differences to act on our commonality, then the association might have a strong impact on how people view the space environment. To the extent that we can transmit what you call the "overview," that we are one life and live on one planet, it can have a very strong effect. It's not clear the extent to which we can get it across. It's much too early to tell. I hope it will, but that is a lot different from an expectation.

WHITE: Could all this ultimately have an impact on how nations will behave?

SCHWEICKART: That's a good question; I don't have an answer. My interest is in elevating the vision of the community of people on the surface to the importance of this [space] environment, and the way it's going to affect the future of humanity. We have the opportunity to wipe out life on this planet, and we can also see it as a whole. The technology available allows both.

For example, I viewed my mother quite differently when I was in the womb than I did after birth. Afterward, I was able to take more responsibility for her. There is a great deal of difference depending on the perspective one has. It's what I call the Cosmic Birth Phenomenon.

To some extent, the choice is going to be made in our lifetime. It is largely influenced by the perception or context in which it is made. If it's "They are the enemy and they are over there," one acts consistently with that perception. If you see it at a higher level, that we are all locked together in a planetary context and are coevolving, that also shapes certain actions.

Michael Collins

Gemini 10, Apollo 11

Michael Collins was in the second group of astronauts to serve after the original Mercury Seven. He flew on the Gemini mission of July 1966 and on the first moon landing mission, Apollo 11, in July 1969. As command module pilot for the latter flight, Collins orbited the moon while Neil Armstrong and Edwin E. "Buzz" Aldrin Jr. landed at Tranquillity Base and became the first humans in recorded history to walk on the moon. He spent a total of just over eleven hours in space.

Collins is author of Carrying the Fire, *an excellent description of his experiences as an astronaut. The first section that follows is from his book. The balance is from my telephone interview with him on January 17, 1986.*

I really believe that if the political leaders of the world could see their planet from a distance of . . . 100,000 miles, their outlook would be fundamentally changed. That all-important border would be invisible, that noisy argument suddenly silenced. The tiny globe would continue to turn, serenely ignoring its subdivisions, presenting a united facade that would cry out for unified treatment . . .

I think the view from 100,000 miles could be invaluable in getting people together to work out joint solutions, by causing them to realize that the planet we share unites us in a way far more basic and far more important than differences in skin color or religion or economic system. The pity of it is that so far the view from 100,000 miles has been the exclusive property of a handful of test pilots, rather than the world leaders who need this new perspective, or the poets who might communicate it to them.

WHITE: Did you find a major difference between your Gemini and Apollo missions?

COLLINS: There is definitely a different feeling. At one hundred miles up, you are just skimming the surface, and you don't get a feeling for the Earth as a whole. It's a pity that we have stopped going a greater distance from Earth, as with the moon missions.

By that, I mean 100,000 miles *minimum*. When you are in orbit, it's like a roller-coaster ride. On the way to the moon, that feeling of motion stops. It is definitely two very different elements.

Also, seeing the moon up close is really startling. When you are sixty miles away, you realize we are really lucky to be living on Earth. You sort of have to see the "second planet" [the moon] to appreciate the first [the Earth].

WHITE: You wrote a bit in *Carrying the Fire* about how your journey had changed you. Have there been any changes in your viewpoint since you wrote the book in the 1970s?

COLLINS: Well, everybody's story is different. In the last five or six years, I have been getting more involved in the military aspects of space. I am getting more and more irritated with the Russians. They have a sanctimonious attitude and there is a real difference between what they do and what they say. They are developing high-powered lasers and an ASAT [antisatellite] system. Their words and deeds are far apart, and that irritates me. They are doing it, but they have been very successful in denying it. The Third World countries are feeling that we are the ones who are militarizing space, not the Russians.

This is counter to the wonderful idea of a tiny globe we share as brothers. I am not as convinced that it will happen any time soon. I think it will take a precipitating event to bring us together as nations. Perhaps an attack by "little green men" or Khadafy blowing up a part of the Earth.

I am less optimistic about getting humankind together than I was ten years ago. Still, I think if you could send enough people up, that would have a salutary effect.

WHITE: I mentioned to Joe Allen that I had a vision of a summit conference on the space station, and he thought it was a pretty good idea.

COLLINS: I would like to see political leaders go. I'm not naive in terms of what it would accomplish. But it would be a good idea. The Soviets are acting out of fear of SDI because they are afraid of Reagan. It's a paradox. If you want cooperation from the Russians, perhaps Rusty [Schweickart]'s approach is not the best one. You don't meet with them, you aren't nice to them. I started out with Rusty on the Association of Space Explorers, but I dropped out. I asked the Russians about ASAT, and they either lied or really didn't know about it. Having said all that, I'll back up and say that talk is a good thing. There should be discussions between the two countries, doctors to doctors, astronauts to cosmonauts, and so forth.

WHITE: Do you think that space exploration is contributing to world unity in any way now?

COLLINS: Yes, space has been helpful and stabilizing in the area of spy satellites. They cannot move a truck, van, or missile without our knowing about it, and vice versa. Also, communications satellites have revolutionized our way of communicating with each other.

WHITE: In a way, you are saying that space exploration is helping to accomplish more world unity, but not necessarily world peace. They may not be the same.

COLLINS: Yes, I hadn't thought of that before. Another sense of it is this: we made a trip around the world after Apollo 11. People came up to us and said, "We did it!" Not "You Americans did it." They felt that "we humans" had done it. It was a short-lived attitude, but something like a lunar landing can have that kind of effect.

WHITE: Did you feel some of that when you were participating in the lunar landing? I know President Nixon in his phone call to you mentioned that your landing had unified all of mankind.

COLLINS: No, I felt, What is this man talking about? I felt that he was making a political statement to the United States and the world. I thought, When I get back, I will ponder this. At the time, I was too concerned with avoiding the trees to think about the forest.

WHITE: You mean that doing your job well was your main concern?

COLLINS: Yes. I have said that the best crew for the Apollo mission would be a philosopher, a priest, and a poet. Unfortunately, they would kill themselves trying to fly the spacecraft. Unfortunately, then, you are left with test pilots. We are the ones who give you the best chance of coming back in one piece. You may find someone who can master both aspects, but I haven't seen it.

WHITE: Do you have any thoughts on how space exploration will affect future human evolution?

COLLINS: I don't know any more about it than the sci-fi writers, but if you go off to the edge of the universe and look back at our corner, you will see a lot of stars. Some of those systems are surrounded by planets. They must be. If we make the most pessimistic assumptions, we are looking at ten to the fifteenth power planets that are suitable for life. They are chugging along, those with inhabitants who haven't learned how to leave, and those with inhabitants who have.

We have figured out how to leave, but not how to go anywhere. There are impediments in our way. Einstein said it would take a long time to get anywhere in the universe. But human beings will have the curiosity to want to go farther away and see what's out there. We will discover "delectable" planets and want to go there. Also, SETI [the search for extraterrestrial life] may bring humans together in a way different from spaceflight.

Eugene A. Cernan
Gemini 9, Apollo 10, and Apollo 17

Among astronauts with more than one of the available spaceflight experiences, Eugene A. Cernan, former U.S. Navy captain, stands out for the variety of experiences he can recount. Cernan flew on Gemini 9 in 1966. He was aboard Apollo 10 in May 1969, descending to within nine miles of the lunar surface. He was the last man to walk on the moon when he was in the crew of Apollo 17 in December 1972. He holds the record for most EVA time of any space traveler, twenty-four hours and twelve minutes. His total time spent in space is twenty-three days. He also set the record for lunar EVA, with Harrison Schmitt, of just over twenty-two hours.

The following is a reconstruction of my telephone conversation with Cernan on December 3, 1985.

WHITE: I'm interested in several questions. The first is whether it makes a difference psychologically to see the universe from a different point of view. Second, especially in your case, is whether different types of spaceflight have a different kind of impact.

CERNAN: Being a quarter million miles out in space has to give you a different perspective. Anyone who denies it has missed something. Being in Earth orbit versus going out beyond must be separated. Philosophically, we really have had two different space programs.

When you are in Earth orbit, looking down, you see lakes, rivers, and peninsulas such as Florida or Baja California. You quickly fly over the changes in topography like the snow-covered mountains or deserts or tropical belts — all very visible. You pass through a sunrise and sunset every ninety minutes.

Without question, when you are in Earth orbit, you get a new perspective, but you don't have time to get philosophical about it. One minute you are over the United States, the next minute, you are over another area of the world. You are invigorated over where you are, but physically you are still part of the Earth — a system you can understand and relate to. When you leave Earth orbit, all those coastlines and rivers you see in orbit become oceans and continents. You can see from pole to pole and ocean to ocean without even turning your head. You can see across the entirety of a continent. Something different is happening.

You literally see North and South America go around the corner as the Earth turns on an axis you can't see and then miraculously Australia, then Asia, then all of America comes up to replace them. You see a multicolored three-dimensional picture of Earth. You begin to see how little we understand of time. You ask yourself the question "Where really am I in space and time?"

You can watch the sun set across North America and then see it rising again over Australia. You look back "home" and say to yourself, "That's humanity, love, feeling, and thought." You don't see the barriers of color and religion and politics that divide this world. You wonder, if you could get everyone in the world up there, wouldn't they have a different feeling — a new perspective?

You can't return home without feeling that difference. But you do come back to reality very quickly. You try to share and relate your feelings to others, but you can't take a billion people back with you. It's almost as if you have come back from the future. You wonder, if only everyone could relate to the beauty and the purposefulness of it, the reality of the infinity of time and space, how our star moves through time and space with such logic and purpose. It wouldn't bring a utopia to this planet for people to understand it all, but it might make a difference.

In Earth orbit, there are things to see and feel on a more minute and micro scale. You don't tend to appreciate what it all means because the trips are so close to home. When I was on the moon somewhere out there in the universe, I had to stop and ask myself, "Do you really know where you are in space and time and history?"

I was watching time go by on Earth, but time as we understand it did not really affect us on the moon. A moon day is fourteen Earth days: in the three days we lived there, it rose ever so slightly. Time, as we relate it to day and night, effectively stood still there. Time on Earth did not; thirteen days of people's lives passed, and we watched it happen, but Earth time did not really affect us.

And again, you only see the boundaries of nature from there, boundaries God created, not those that are manmade. We could see the Antarctic continent as the summer ice cap broke away, could "view" the turmoil in the Middle East, knowing what was going on, knowing of the tension that existed there but yet could not point to any single event.

WHITE: It's like Plato's story of the people living in a cave and seeing reflections of reality all their lives. Then one man goes out and sees the sun and comes back to the cave, but no one can understand what he is talking about. One of the things this research has shown me is that the problem is not that the astronauts aren't articulate about their experiences, but that we have no context for hearing what you are saying.

CERNAN: Yes. I laugh about it a bit. I wrote a letter to Jim Beggs [former NASA administrator] because of something he said to justify why we were sending a journalist on the shuttle. He said something to the effect that they hoped a journalist would be able to communicate the experience after a quarter century of astronauts in space being unable to do so. I personally took grave issue with him because I know what it takes to allow people to identify — to relate through me the answers to How does it feel? What did you think? Were you scared? I happen to be in support of journalists in space, but for other reasons.

I can talk about it for a long time. It is one of the deepest, most emotional experiences I have ever had. I have been involved with the young students in Up with People who are communicating to others via music. I was sharing with them some of what I thought and felt while standing on the moon, and they wrote a song called "Moonrider" about what it was like for one man standing alone on another planet a quarter million miles away in space, looking back home. It's a moving song with a strong message and equally strong impact. One phrase expresses it well for me: "Isn't it the way we perceive things that will make them what they will be?"

At the pleasure of the president, we traveled around that same world after our Apollo 17 flight in order to share our experiences with others. The native folks in West Africa, for example, seemingly out of touch, were enthralled and wanted to know what it looked like, what it felt like when you looked back. They somehow wanted to be there through us.

People can relate to feelings, but not very well to technology. And through us, they vicariously experienced what they might have seen or been moved to believe. The space program by its very nature has at least philosophically brought the world closer. It is truly one of the greatest endeavors in the history of mankind.

But, like Lindbergh, the technology of his voyage was soon forgotten and is taken for granted today. What people do remember and admire is the spirit of a guy like Lindbergh who had the guts to do what he did. Most people wouldn't do what he did *even* today. It's the human spirit of those who dared challenge the future. Perhaps we were ahead of our time when we went to the moon — but then, somebody has to be.

WHITE: Several people in Houston mentioned that it was really only the space program that kept the American spirit intact during the sixties and early seventies, almost as if we reached beyond ourselves to make up for some of the suffering we were enduring as a nation.

CERNAN: The space program was the only thing that allowed us to keep our heads high. When Neil walked on the moon, you could have been an American anywhere in the world, and you would have been a hero. Perhaps this was true even in the prisons of North Vietnam.

It's special. When I worked on the Apollo-Soyuz mission, Alan Bean and I were the only people involved who had actually been on the moon. The Russian people couldn't subdue their enthusiasm: "There's a man who has walked on another world."

WHITE: It's a universal feeling.

CERNAN: We won't go back to the moon or on to Mars perhaps for another generation, not until something new challenges us. President Kennedy challenged us, he challenged our spirit, our commitment as a nation. He said we should do it, "not because it was easy, but because it was hard" — and we did it.

Until there is a new motivation, we won't return, but it will happen. Traveling 240,000 miles out in space will always be unique, but it will happen again. Going into space has almost become relatively routine, at least an acceptable risk, but you must remember that going beyond near space, detaching yourself from the planet's "routine" and voyaging out into the universe, will always be philosophically different.

WHITE: There is a difference between exploring and developing, I suppose. [Apollo 7 astronaut] Walt Cunningham told me that the shuttle astronauts are not really exploring space, they are sampling it.

CERNAN: Well, I believe they are exploring, but equally important, they are beginning to exploit space in a positive and appropriate sense. Economics is one of the stimuli now. Walt is right; they are not really exploring in the true sense. We would have to go back to the moon or Mars to really be exploring again.

WHITE: Did you leave the space program because it was no longer an exploratory activity?

CERNAN: The shuttle is still a space adventure. I would have stayed to fly the shuttle, not simply to see more sunrises and sunsets in Earth orbit, because I am a pilot. I'd have had to wait five to six years to fly the shuttle, and I thought, I have to be the luckiest guy in the world already; what else can I do?

If there were a Mars or lunar mission getting ready to go, that would be different. I don't believe I would have wanted to spend ninety days in Skylab the second time around. Now the first time they went up, that was exploration.

WHITE: Is it true that you are working with companies involved in space development?

CERNAN: Yes, with companies that are involved in the development of space in one way or another. But I must say, it is sometimes hard to find a challenge that compares . . .

Alan L. Bean
Apollo 12, Skylab 3

Alan Bean was lunar module pilot on Apollo 12, November 14, 1969. He later commanded the Skylab 3 mission. His total time of just under seventy days in space included almost ten hours of EVA. Since leaving the astronaut corps, Bean has taken an unusual path for former astronauts by becoming a professional artist. All his scenes are related to space exploration and development.

I interviewed Bean on July 28, 1986.

WHITE: Could you compare the Skylab experience to the Apollo experience?

BEAN: The thing that I noticed most about the difference was that it's easy to maintain interest and enthusiasm when the tasks are always new, you're going somewhere, new visual stimuli day after day, or hour after hour, and that's what the lunar mission is. It's a trip for ten days or so, and everything is new along the way, except maybe for a couple of days on the way back, when you are just gliding.

With Skylab that wasn't true. The first few days were different and the last few days were different, but through the middle things stayed the same day after day. So I felt it was a more challenging situation for the individual to keep up his production and his sense of humor and all those other things that go along with being able to perform day after day.

WHITE: Just the experience of being in space is not itself novel enough to overcome the boredom.

BEAN: It's novel enough for a little while, but then, if you look out the window, what else is new? It's still an incredible, stimulating experience, but not stimulating in a different way. Of course, on the days you go EVA, that's a lot of stimulus and fun and enjoyable and you wish you could do it more. But usually, day to day, you're not doing EVA. You're waking up and you're operating experiments and things like that, and you might as well be on Earth for all that you're aware. You are in zero gravity, and you know it, but it's not an important aspect in your day-to-day tasks.

WHITE: How about the view of the Earth? Several lunar astronauts have commented that there is a very powerful difference in seeing it from the greater distance than from seeing it up close. Did you find that, too?

BEAN: Yes. It's more unreal, your sense of separation from the Earth is greater, and you feel the danger more. So there is a great psychological difference. There is a difference between knowing you are just going to go around and around and around the Earth and knowing you're headed outward from it, and it's going to be a long time before you come back. Apollo 13 found out how difficult that could be. Once you headed away from Earth and had a problem, you couldn't just turn around and come home. You had to go all the way around the moon and come back, hoping your supplies would last long enough, which they barely did on that mission.

WHITE: How about landing on the moon? Some astronauts have talked about a very sharp contrast between Earth and moon, between a living planet that can support life and a dead planet that cannot. Was that important to your experience?

BEAN: Well, it really wasn't, at the moment of landing. I've been to places in the United States where there might as well have been nobody else, because the only people there were you and one or two friends. I noticed the contrast when I landed on Earth and looked out the window and was aware that the waves were moving and the clouds were moving and the ship was coming toward us, and then it was more of a realization that for the last ten days I hadn't seen any of those things. It wasn't that I had missed them so much when I was gone; it was more that when I got back and saw what was here, I recognized immediately that I had been deprived of them for the previous ten days.

WHITE: You had an EVA for Skylab, and walking on the moon is another kind of EVA. Did you find that strikingly different from being in the spaceship?

BEAN: I think it's more science fiction to do an EVA outside the spaceship as on Skylab because it's not like anything you've ever done before. If you went outside an airliner and somehow could crawl along the wings, and it kept moving along, that would be similar to Skylab. Walking on the moon is similar to experiences in which you've walked in dirt, under bright lights, or in the dark, in areas that have been kind of strange. However, because of the distance from Earth and the fact that it really was the moon, I've pondered and thought much more, many times more, about my lunar walks than I have about my Skylab EVA.

WHITE: I asked Jerry Carr whether he thought a lot about being in space, or was it something that was in the back of his mind. He said something would stimulate thoughts and then it would come up. Is that your experience, or is it something that you tend to ponder quite a bit, integrating it into your current life?

BEAN: Since I'm an artist painting my experiences and those of others on the moon, perhaps I think about it more than other people, because I'm doing it a number of hours per day. But I find that I think about it the most at times like this, when I'm being interviewed. I give speeches a couple of times a month, and I think about it a lot then: getting ready for the speech, trying to remember what would be interesting to the audience.

WHITE: We're in an extraordinary situation in that so few people have had the experience of space travel. When you think about walking on the moon, you realize that only twelve people have ever done it. It puts a burden on the astronauts when all of us want to know what it was like.

BEAN: I think people want more from the experience than is perhaps there. I have to admit that if I ran into somebody who had climbed the Matterhorn, I would probably say, "What is it like?" The answer might reasonably be, "It was just like climbing all the other difficult mountains I've ever climbed."

WHITE: Do you think it's possible that the media are creating a mythological description of the space experience? You have said that people want more of it than is there —

BEAN: I said people want more than *might* be there. I don't know, maybe it is there. I think that's quite possible about the media. As an astronaut, you think of all these experiences in a different way when you're doing them than people are interested in hearing about when you get back. Your mind is set one way as you do the job — you're thinking about getting a particular experiment done, staying on time, and watching things. It's a situation in which you're doing a lot of different things, requiring thought and skill and trying to do them right. These thoughts dominate the mind.

With each experiment, for example, you have to know how to get it out of its box or how to get the foil off and then how to set it down and how to align it so that it has the right direction. All these things that nobody gives a damn about, but that's what you're really thinking about when you're on the moon or in space.

When you come back, people want you to talk about it in a completely different way. It's nice to get the attention, but these philosophical thoughts aren't what you refined during the training period. You begin to think about them only when people ask you. You were really refining other skills.

It's like my paintings. I start off with masonite, it's brown, and a bunch of tubes that all look the same except they have different colored labels on them, and a bunch of brushes, and that's about it. Yet, pretty soon, when I use these materials the painting starts to be an astronaut. Day to day, I put on paint and try to get the shadows right, making the action look interesting and paying attention to other technical considerations. At the end, people want to talk about the story told and the hidden meaning of the painting. I've created something beautiful, but my moment-to-moment work was not creating something beautiful, it was making each of those little details right.

WHITE: What led to your decision to leave the space program and take up painting?

BEAN: I've been painting for twenty-five years as a hobby. I began when I was a test pilot, at night school, taking water color, drawing, and so on. Over the years, I studied with a number of different teachers, and I was an average to slightly better-than-average amateur painter, but never imagined I would even think of it as a profession.

At one point, my lawyer's wife, Pat Brill, asked me, "What are you going to do when you leave the space program?" I said, "I think I'll probably go to work for an aircraft company or something like that," then added, "What do you think I ought to do?" She said, immediately, "I think you ought to be an artist." At the time, this seemed to be a crazy idea, and I said, "You're nuts."

But the more I thought about it, the more I realized that I had a unique opportunity to preserve something important. If I didn't portray the birth of our space program artistically, nobody else would, because none of the other astronauts were interested in doing so. The more I thought about painting my experiences in Apollo and worked at it, the more I liked the idea, and realized that this was what I ought to do for the future. I left the space program earlier than I would have left it if I were going to go into any other profession, because I was concerned about having enough years left in my life to create a body of work that would be representative. I believe if I hadn't decided to paint the beginnings of our space explorations, I would have stayed and flown the shuttle maybe two or three times, then thought about leaving.

Apollo was a great adventure and a great accomplishment of man, the first visit to another world. I realized the people all down the line would be curious about it and that I could perform a function similar to Thomas Moran's or Frederic Remington's. I used to look at their paintings and I was always glad that they had done them. I would think, Well, I'm glad he did this, because now we know what cowboys really looked like. They don't look like John Wayne, they look just the way Remington painted them.

Real astronauts don't look the way they do in the movies, either, and they certainly won't one hundred years from now, when they have a movie about Apollo. I feel that I'm filling a human need and that people generations from now will say, "I'm glad that guy Bean quit flying spaceships and created these paintings."

WHITE: I would like you to comment on your work with the Association of Space Explorers.

BEAN: It's hard to tell what effect an organization like that can have, because it's a small group and we're also dealing with the Soviet Union and realize the restrictions put on cosmonauts. I'm well aware from my visits to the Soviet Union that even if the cosmonauts feel a certain way, they're not able to be interviewed and tell that. The cosmonauts are going to tell the party line if they're smart, and they are smart.

But I feel that the cosmonauts are personally very sincere about world peace and cooperation. Working with the Soviets has both negative and positive sides. The positive side is, it's something I personally can do, and it's better to try to do something than just say, "Don't try because it might not work." If you do nothing, then nothing will happen, so it's more a case of seeing the Association of Space Explorers as an avenue, to try something positive, though I'm not sure what effect it will have. I believe it's better than just giving up and not trying somehow to establish friendlier relations with the Soviet Union. Maybe someday these cosmonauts will rise higher in their country, and the feeling for our motives can somehow have a positive influence. Maybe they won't; at least it's a try.

WHITE: Do you think your common experiences of being in space and seeing the Earth from a distance make a difference when you get together?

BEAN: When we get together, it's mostly as individuals. There's not a lot of difference in individuals, once they realize they're not trying to take advantage of you and you're not trying to take advantage of them. You can see that the Soviets, individually, don't want nuclear war; they're worried about their children growing up, without radiation and other bad things. You can see that the words they use are very natural for them, in the way they talk sincerely. At the same time, you know that if their government calls on them to do certain things, they will do them, just as we will do what our government orders us to do.

WHITE: What do you think has been the most important effect of the space program on society?

BEAN: I think one of the reasons that the Challenger accident bothers people so badly is that the space program bought for Americans a feeling of competence and being number one, that they could do anything they put their minds to. When the Challenger blew up, that whole idea of our perfection became unsettled in people's minds because they don't want to feel that they are not still number one. But at the same time, one of the foundations for their belief that America was the best was the great success of our space program.

I think that the feeling that we can do things is the most important effect. It's a measure of the best that our society does, when we're doing it right, and there are so many things that we do that you just can't feel too good about. But the space program has been one that we did that was difficult and worked out, and it makes us feel good. We don't feel quite as good right now.

WHITE: If there is one thing you would like readers of this book to know about space, what would it be?

BEAN: I guess I would have to say that humankind is going out into space whether any individual or any country likes it or not. If we glance back through history, we find that humans have always seemed to go anyplace they can once they're able to.

And if Congress cuts or doubles the budget, no matter. It will have a minuscule effect. Just as whether Columbus got here in 1492 or 1496 or 1502 made a big difference to him, but it doesn't make any difference to us at all. That's how I feel about space exploration. It's on the way and we don't have to worry about it.

Some people are worried about the effect of the Challenger accident. I worry about it for the people who are involved, but for the long term, it'll be like the ships that Magellan started around the world with. I think only one of them got back home from the voyage, but we've forgotten about that. We only remember that he still got around the world.

So we're headed out into space, which is wonderful, and I guess we ought to prepare for and think about its effect, as you're doing in your book, because it is going to keep happening.

Edgar D. Mitchell
Apollo 14

Edgar Mitchell was selected for NASA's Group 5 in 1966 and in February 1971 participated in the third moon landing as the lunar module pilot on Apollo 14. His total time in space was nine days, during which he had a number of deep personal experiences. Since resigning from NASA, he has founded the Institute of Noetic Sciences to further the study of human consciousness and has written a book on SDI.

The following is the reconstruction of my interview with Dr. Mitchell in Palm Beach, Florida, November 18, 1986.

WHITE: Everything I've done in the interviews for this book has confirmed that the initial idea was right, but it was far too simple. The variety of experience is a lot greater than I expected.

MITCHELL: I would challenge that. The variety in the *interpre-*

tation of the experience is a lot greater than you expected. The experience is the same. I have developed a whole philosophy around the notion that the first-person experiential event is valid for every human, whatever it is. The problem is, how do they interpret it and how do they express it?

That comes through the belief system, which is the key to how you see and interpret all these events. If your belief system accepts that information as different, you get an expanded belief system. If you happen to be closed off and are happy with the former belief system, you reject the information and nothing happens. Or if it happens to be too challenging or threatening, then it'll be consciously rejected, thrown out. But otherwise, it can be absorbed and expanded into the belief system, and you have a different view.

That, to me, is the difference in what happened to us in space. Some of us accepted the experience; some of us were open and eagerly looking for its meaning. Some of us already had pat answers as to what it all meant, and therefore any new information that came in didn't change the perception at all.

WHITE: I've divided the spaceflight experience into two types; some people had a confirmation experience, which *confirmed* what they knew — that the Earth is a whole, it is very fragile, and things like that. Other people, and I tend to put you in the category, have had more of a conversion experience, a shift from the way they thought about things to a really new way. You've talked, for example, about being a test pilot, scientific and rational, and shifting to a more intuitive way.

MITCHELL: But it's the same phenomenon. I've always been oriented toward philosophy, toward the fundamental cosmological and theological questions. But that wasn't my day-to-day way of operating, which was test pilot–engineer. So what happened was that the experience simply exploded me to the other end of the spectrum. I was ready for it because I'm a curious, questioning sort of guy.

I didn't hold any preconceived notions in my belief system as to what this meant. I knew what I was going to see. But the *meaning* changed. And that's the role of the value system, the belief system, in the organization of the information from this different point of view into a different structure.

I spent sixteen years doing that. It was a very powerful experience for some of us, because we were open to whatever it meant, without prejudging what it was going to be. That may be the reason some of the people you talked to seemed confirmed. They were people on later missions. We had been putting out that information, and they had been getting ready, so they were prepared for what they saw. But they probably absorbed more information if they were receptive and saying, "Let's look at this."

To me, the difference between getting and not getting an "aha" experience out of it is whether it shifts your structure a bit. Do you get a sense of freedom, of expansiveness because you've just experienced something that is different from your previous experiences and beliefs?

We see the "mountaintop experience" all the time, with poetry, with great works of art, and so on. You see something that touches you and elevates you to a different sense of being because you've got a new piece of information coming into the organism. To me, that's what it is. I think the only thing that would make me different from the way some of the other fellows express it is that I may have been more open, more ready, because I was looking for something. I was saying, "This is going to be great; let's find out what it means." I was looking for meaning, not just observational data. I was open to that, and man, I got all the information I ever needed in order to find a new meaning. But it's taken me sixteen years to organize that information and do something I'm very satisfied with.

I can talk so lucidly about this process because I had a similar experience on an airplane coming home from San Francisco. Everything that had been confused as a result of the spaceflight experience suddenly got collected as a result of my contemplation for sixteen years.

WHITE: Were you just sitting on the airplane, or were you looking out the window?

MITCHELL: Well, I had a little stimulus. I'd been working on some philosophical concepts, and all of a sudden, "Pow!" they suddenly clicked into place. There was a flood of information in the space experience that caused me to reexamine my belief system and say, "Does it still fit the way I thought it did?" and the answer was no. So I had to restructure my belief, but there were some missing pieces. Recently it all fit. I feel a joyous, wonderful experience, a feeling that I can explain it now. I'm happy. My belief system is fully integrated again. Before, I couldn't quite get all the loose ends tucked in. Now, I think I have.

WHITE: What you're saying is that the spaceflight experience doesn't just begin when you get into the ship and end when you land. You've spent many years interpreting what took a few days.

MITCHELL: The sort of approach you're talking about — and I hope my next book adds to that — is going to portray the psychology and the shifting viewpoint of the spaceflight experience as far more powerful and important than it has ever been described in the past. It is precisely this shift in viewpoint and what it implies for the capability of the human being and for our view of the universe that makes it so powerful. Until the last twenty years, all philosophers, thinkers, scientists, and poets have been Earthbound. They had an Earthbound point of view. Spaceflight is one of the more powerful experiences that humans can have, and the technological event of breaking the bonds of Earth is far more important than the technology that went into it, because of this perspective.

It's going to be left to historians to find out if it really makes a significant difference, but I characterize spaceflight as the metaphor for the technology of the twentieth century, during which science and technology have exploded. The unfortunate thing is that our morals and value systems are still rooted in the thirteenth or fourteenth century. Spaceflight, getting outside of Earth and seeing it from a different perspective, having this sort of explosive awareness that some of us had, this abiding concern and passion for the well-being of Earth — a more universal point of view, to use your words — will have a direct impact on philosophy and value systems.

Only now are we starting to develop a structured philosophy and saying this is important to the very structure of philosophy. Out of philosophy has to come not only the physical but the metaphysical side. Out of the metaphysical side must come the value system by which we guide twentieth-century technology. We don't have that yet, and we've got to have it soon. It's like a rudderless ship in the ocean.

That's why I see what you call the overview, what I call the

explosion into a more universal awareness, an explosion of the belief
system, as a very important psychological event, with impacts not
only in psychology, but in philosophy and moral systems. Psychology can examine it, but what's coming out of it is a new meta-
physic.

WHITE: Have you gone back into Earthbound philosophy as a
groundwork to see how it fits?

MITCHELL: That's what I've been doing ever since my flight.
I've studied virtually every philosophy and theology, and I've gone
to the Eastern traditions to study their theology and their philosophy. Descartes, Locke, and Spinoza were on the right track, trying
to show that the universe is mind *and* matter, not mind *or* matter.
I think that the integration is at hand. We have to have a philosophy
that does what Descartes and Spinoza could not do, to show that
there is not an impenetrable membrane between consciousness
and matter. Indeed, it's what I call a dyad.

They have to be together; they have to arise together. It's like
the poles of a magnet: you can't have a north pole or a south pole
isolated; you have to have a north *and* a south pole. It's a dyadic
concept, and I'm approaching it from that point of view. I'm also
working with phenomenological philosophy of the twentieth century, and the viewpoint that brings about.

My recent experience resulted from my recognition that the
dyadic approach suddenly makes everything fit, that you can do
away with most of the paradox of ancient cosmology. It turns out
to be meaningless or simply a point of view from which a paradox
will arise. If you go to another point of view, another paradox will
arise. But if you see that it's simply a point of view, the paradox
vanishes.

WHITE: The *Omni* article about the righteous stuff said that as
you were coming back from the moon, you were looking at the
Earth, and you realized that spirit and matter were not separate.

MITCHELL: I can articulate it better now. I have a structure
within which to describe it. What happened was that I knew that
the materialist point of view that everything is the result of matter
was not a correct philosophy. It assumed away consciousness, and
you couldn't do that. What happened to me was truly a consciousness experience. So the question was, Are the idealists right? Can

you construct an internally consistent philosophy in which matter is the projection of mind?

Of course, we've all been doing that. We've got theisms all over the world that do that. So the only other thing you can do is go to Descartes's view. But it was never developed, never pulled together. We had to wait until the concepts came around, and that's in this century. In this century, I think we can pull mind and matter together into a consistent philosophy that makes sense. And that's what I'm trying to do.

WHITE: Does your approach have a definition of consciousness?

MITCHELL: Yes. Everything depends on the precision of the definition. That's been one of the problems of prior philosophies. They mixed up their definitions with their thought processes. So we've got connotations of words that screw things up. They tried to experience and describe at the same time, and you can't do that. You have to experience, do away with your presuppositions of what the meaning of the experience is, and then interpret your experience. If you can learn from the empiricism of science, particularly the science of this century, the method is very powerful. As a philosophy, science is terrible; as a method, it's superb. Learning to use that scientific method on one's own observations and consciousness is a vital part of the process. You don't try to interpret and explain while you are experiencing. You miss data that way.

WHITE: Would it be fair to say that while you were in space, it was the experience part and since then it's been interpretation?

MITCHELL: Yes.

WHITE: It makes sense to do that. We would expect it with scientific experiments, but never with our own experiences.

MITCHELL: That is precisely what this philosophical approach suggests you do, and it is why the subjective experience has not been accepted as valid in the past. The experience and the interpretation get all mixed up. The interpretations are quite often terrible, but the experience is valid. You have to train yourself to be an observer and interpreter of your own subjective experience, just as you have to train yourself to be an experimenter and interpreter of a physical experience. It's just a different kind of training.

WHITE: But you didn't know this before you went on the moon mission, did you?

MITCHELL: No. I had the knowledge typical of a Ph.D. from MIT and a test pilot, and all of this has had to sort itself out. What I did was done accidentally, not even knowing I was doing it, just sitting there saying, "Gee whiz, wow," to the experience, not trying to make anything new of it.

WHITE: I've been arguing that experiences normally don't have a transformational effect because we can fit them into our existing model. When we go into space, we try to do that, but unlike most Earthbound experiences, it doesn't let us. It forces us to do what you're saying we ought to do more often —

MITCHELL: I will contradict you only on that one point. It doesn't *force* you to. If you don't want to accept any experience, you are totally in control of your belief system, totally in control of your experience. So the forcing part is really only an allowing part, allowing your belief system to be open enough so that you accept the information of the experience, and say, "That's interesting, isn't it?"

WHITE: In terms of information of the experience, it seems that going to the moon is more powerful than going into Low Earth Orbit.

MITCHELL: Let's say it's different — a different set of information. You say "more powerful." I use a slightly different word: it gets you closer to a more universal experience because of the distance and wider view. You identify more with the universe as it is instead of the Earth as it is.

In dyadic terms, there's the individual/universal dyad. On the spectrum of consciousness, points of view can be anywhere along that. Most of us are clustered down toward the individual point of view. The moon experience catapulted us toward the other end.

WHITE: It seems, too, that that mirrors typical views of the spiritual process. The spiritual growth process tends to be one of identification with wider whole systems.

MITCHELL: Yes. I'll use the word *spiritual* anecdotally. When I come to defining things precisely for philosophy, I don't use that word. I will show its connection to consciousness. That is the word I use because that is the word that expresses our ability to be aware: we say we are conscious.

Just as the energy field is the fundamental stuff of which matter is made, the consciousness field is that fundamental stuff of which awareness is made. Just as the physicists have their quantum field, I try to decribe the consciousness field, which organizes information the same way the quantum field organizes energy and matter.

Consciousness organizes information in a similar way, and thus it is dyadic with matter. All matter is conscious at some level of organization, the electron possessing little organized information, but it still has some informational content. You can see how close this gets to physics, by the way. Mind is an organized consciousness. It is a field of consciousness organized in a particular way with certain informational content.

WHITE: How do you see perspective fitting into that?

MITCHELL: The point of view, or belief system, is then just a construct of mind to organize the information of experience.

WHITE: So when you change where you are experiencing from —

MITCHELL: The information content changes, and therefore the whole belief that has to be integrated into the belief system in some way, into a consistent structure of reality. The whole field of consciousness studies suffers from that, because unlike science, it's not precise. It's got to be made as precise as science.

WHITE: And that's your goal?

MITCHELL: That's my goal.

Edward G. Gibson
Skylab 4

Ed Gibson, a solar scientist, was a member of the three-man Skylab 4 crew for the third and last mission in 1973–1974, which set an American record of eighty-four days in orbit. Using recycled Apollo technology, Skylab was the first and only American space station. While less sophisticated than the permanent station being planned for the 1990s, it did provide us with the first glimpses of what it would be like for people to live for extended periods in space.

I interviewed Gibson by telephone on August 15, 1985.

WHITE: Did being on Skylab have an impact on your view of life?

GIBSON: Yes and no. We have to be careful in talking about this, because many times it is the nature of the people involved rather than spaceflight itself that is important. You have to remember that we were in line for a mission for eight years. It's like a double doctorate degree. You feel both a euphoria at what you accomplish and a letdown at achieving it and having to search for new goals. This is typical of such experiences and not unique to space or the space program.

There are areas in which there were real changes. First, you are able to really picture the physical universe after being in space. It is not a concept anymore. You can actually see the colors and physical textures of the Earth. Now that I've seen the red wind-swept deserts of North Africa and other features of the Earth, I have a physical feel for them that is different from the experience down here, except on brief airplane flights.

Then, also, you see the sun against that black sky and realize it is just one of the stars. You have an appreciation for what we have here on Earth and for what may be possible out in the universe. It's like hearing a description of a rose garden and then actually going into a rose garden, saying, "Wow, this is a rose garden!"

WHITE: Have those feelings stayed with you since being on Skylab?

GIBSON: In a sense, yes, for all of us. You just don't put as much importance on other things. You see how diminutive your life and concerns are compared to other things in the universe. Your life and concerns are important to *you*, of course. But you can see that a lot of the things you worry about don't make much difference in an overall sense. The result is that you enjoy the life that is before you; you don't sweat so much about the next milestone. Also, you are more comfortable. It takes the heat off. Your perspective changes in terms of frustrations about not going anywhere. It allows you to have inner peace.

WHITE: Did the fact that this was such a long mission make a difference?

GIBSON: Yes. These feelings became ingrained even though we had a problem in that Ground Control tried to control our mission pretty rigidly, so we didn't have so much time to think about it.

WHITE: Was Earth-gazing the important activity that some reports make it out to be?

GIBSON: Yes. There just wasn't enough time to do it. We had a lot of plans for Earth observation. We spent a lot of time with principal investigators to determine what we could observe. There was always something coming up to see. You could see the very thin atmosphere. Interestingly, we talk about the Earth being too crowded, but often you could not tell that a continent was inhabited unless you saw a small, isolated city.

WHITE: Some reports have said that you could see the interconnectedness of it all.

GIBSON: Yes. You learn that you certainly cannot understand meteorology without understanding oceanography, and so on.

WHITE: Will these insights be deeper on the permanent space station?

GIBSON: Probably. On the space station, people will have more time to talk about it and think about it. That might make the difference.

WHITE: How about the future? How might the experiences of the astronauts change the views of the larger society?

GIBSON: Our coming back and sharing our experiences is like a drop of dye going into the ocean; it is quickly diffused. I think the pictures of Earth have made an impression, but it will be a matter of osmosis over a long period of time. The more who go, the more difference it will make, but then the more who go, the less publicity they will get. Showing motion pictures, such as the I-Max films, seems to make a difference.

WHITE: How about the impact of EVAs?

GIBSON: I had three EVAs. The comparison to other experiences of spaceflight is like the difference between being up on a tall building and looking out over the edge or hanging over the ledge with someone holding on to your ankles. It changes your perspective. That is really the great outdoors. You feel as though you are a satellite yourself. It really makes the heart go. You understand that it is you and the universe, and you really feel like an individual.

A frustration goes with it too. Some of us think we understand how the universe is put together. But we have a lot to learn, and we are limited by current propulsion systems and life expectancies. Our capabilities will appear prehistoric to those who have a "Star Trek"–like system and can actually go to the stars. I'm a bit frustrated. Our solar system is beautiful, but there is so much more out there!

Gerald P. Carr

Skylab 4

Gerald Carr was the commander of the three-man crew on Skylab 4, with Bill Pogue and Ed Gibson aboard. Since then, he has continued to work as a consultant for the planned permanent space station. He is married to an artist/psychologist, and their work together holds significant implications for the structure of future space settlements.

The following is a reconstruction of my telephone interview with Carr on February 6, 1986, the first interview for this book after the Challenger accident.

WHITE: Could you talk a little bit about your background in the space program?

CARR: I was CapCom [capsule communicator] on Apollo 8 and Apollo 12. I probably would have been on Apollo 19 if it hadn't been canceled. It was a black day for me when the Apollo program was truncated. As it turned out, I was commander of the Skylab crew, and I think I may have made more contributions on Skylab than I would have on Apollo.

WHITE: How so?

CARR: We set up housekeeping in space. In Marine Corps terms, man had established a beachhead from which he could extend his presence. We were looking at the question of what it takes to exist in space permanently. Our tasks were, first, to study zero-G effects on the body and see if there was anything there to worry about. We were to look particularly at cardiovascular deconditioning and loss in bone density. Those mechanisms suggest a limit as to how long we can stay in space.

Second, we were to look at the sun from outside the Earth's atmosphere, and third, we were to look down at the Earth from the point of view of Earth resources data. This was a consolidation of the beachhead. We went to see what it would take to live there, and we added a lot to the body of understanding. Also, we did it with a lot of off-the-shelf equipment from Apollo, except the MDA [multiple docking adapter] and airlock.

WHITE: At the Johnson Space Center, I had a chance to look at the full-scale mock-up of Skylab, and it made me sad to see that such a successful program had been abandoned. I'm reminded of what David Webb, a member of the National Space Commission, said on television, which is that we allow our technological projects to be aberrated by financial considerations. In any event, what was unique about your Skylab experience?

CARR: Aside from the gravity environment, living and working on Skylab was a lot like the mock-ups and simulators, but what was really the most remarkable thing was looking down on the Earth. When you first arrive, everything is very disorienting, but you rejoice inwardly when you finally see something you recognize. I remember looking out the window and seeing Italy. It really was shaped like a boot! It was wonderful!

In eighty-four days up there, I never got tired of Earth-gazing. I remember one particular evening when it was eleven o'clock at night in Houston. I floated up to the command module as we were coming over Japan, where it was afternoon. Japan was familiar; I had lived there for a year. I saw a volcano erupting, our eighth or tenth pass over the eruption area. Then we peaked out over the fifty-first parallel, and I saw the Aleutians. The wind was blowing gently from the south, pushing low clouds. I could see them scudding between the volcanoes like whipped cream.

From the fifty-first parallel, we came down in a southeasterly direction, over Oregon and Northern California, past the terminator and into the darkness. I could see from San Francisco Bay clear down to Baja California. The bay looks like a bean from there. I could see it and the Golden Gate Bridge and cars going across the bridge.

In Southern California, the Los Angeles basin was like a velvet bowl full of pearls. I could even see the white/green flash of lights at Lindbergh Field in San Diego. Looking down, you could really see the manifestations of people at night. During the day, there wasn't as much evidence.

WHITE: Did you come away from your experience with a different feeling about life?

CARR: Yes. More a feeling of universality, or the commonality of human beings. As Ed Gibson noted, you can't see the boundaries that man puts up, only those of nature. You have to sense that humans are down there. I came back with a real interest in people, a humanist or behaviorist attitude, you might say. I have been doing a lot of intenational traveling and speaking, and it has served to validate the feeling of universality.

My presentations are a short history on what we have done in space. Mercury, Gemini, and Apollo flights were really about transportation. Skylab was our first look at permanence. The shuttle brings us back to transportation again. Then I talk about where we are today, with transportation and commercial enterprises. The space station is to be our first permanent human presence.

I talk about moon colonies and large space stations. Then I spring the idea of children being born in a weightless environment and the possibility of a split in the human species because of the difference in the way bodies will develop as a result of weightlessness.

WHITE: What do you think will happen then?

CARR: I'm a little worried about that. Most bodily functions are unaffected by weightlessness. But I worry about the effects on an embryo. Of course, it could just turn out normal and natural.

WHITE: The changes in the body as a result of being in space are really an adaptation to weightlessness.

CARR: That's true.

WHITE: How about the space station being built? Will there be any gravity there?

CARR: No, there won't be any gravity there. You have to rotate a large-diameter structure for artificial gravity to work. The humans on the rim of a rotating space station which develops artificial gravity have to see the velocity as linear rather than curvilinear or it doesn't work because of Coriolis acceleration on the inner ear.

WHITE: The real concern about gravity and the effects of weightlessness are relevant primarily if you assume that people are coming back to Earth. If they were to stay in space, they would probably evolve to live in zero G. It's like a lot of other things relating to space, in that it is geocentric rather than a heliocentric view.

CARR: Yes, my thinking was geocentric. We never thought we wouldn't come back from Skylab.

WHITE: Do you think that seeing the Earth as a whole system

will have an impact politically? When I talked with Michael Collins, he expressed concern about the Russians.

CARR: I think it could. Space exploration could be a vehicle by which the major powers achieve the understanding to overcome their problems. The cosmonauts and astronauts get along great when we get together. We're just a bunch of fighter pilots. We have never had time to philosophize. I would be interested in learning the basis for Mike's fears.

My wife, Pat, and I have been doing some interesting things. She is a behavioral scientist, a psychologist. When we first met, she asked me, "What kind of psychological studies are being done on the astronauts?" There weren't any; that was the power of the original seven astronauts. They wouldn't tolerate rectal thermometers or psychologists!

Pat decided to weave space into a creativity course she was teaching at the University of Houston, Clear Lake. She would hypothesize a group of people selected to become the nucleus of a larger group of people on a space colony. She would say, "You are heading up a group of a thousand people scheduled to live on a space station for ten years. Your challenge is to decide what values, laws, and so forth, apply there. You may adapt what is appropriate from Earth. You may need to come up with unique values."

You begin to see that new values, norms, and laws will apply in space. On Earth, one can enjoy a great deal of freedom. On a space station, one doesn't have that freedom; individual freedom is constrained because of the more constrained environment. One cannot go off and "do his own thing." In Pat's course, there is conflict and miscommunication for the first few weeks. Then they realize that to accomplish anything, they have to really listen to each other and try to arrive at some compromise. The most common government form selected is the town meeting. It is a good adaptation. It keeps a single person or group from getting a lot of authority.

WHITE: Along those lines, what was it like when you were on Skylab?

CARR: Though the command relationships were clear, we reached tacit agreement about who played what role to get things done. We had very compatible personalities. We actually came back better friends than when we left. Pogue had the creative ideas, Gibson saw how to do them, and I was good at implementation. So we gravitated to roles fitting our personalities. None of us were experts on any one system, so we divvied up the systems, and that's how we got it done.

WHITE: From what I have been told, the EVAs are a very special experience. Did you find that so?

CARR: Yes. I was out three times for a total of about fifteen hours. Being outside gives you a sense of openness. I think my greatest thrill was standing on top of the ATM (Apollo Telescope Mount). I reared back and looked at Earth with no local frame of reference at all. It was a fine experience. I also looked at the comet Kohoutek and got a feeling for the infiniteness of the universe. There are billions of stars, many that you can't see from the ground. It's a disorienting matrix in which our common navigation stars are embedded. You see millions of new stars, and it's hard to navigate. There is a real change in their relative brightness.

WHITE: Has there been a long-term effect? Do you think about Skylab often?

CARR: It subsides and then a stimulus brings it back. You store it away, I think, but the data and experience are retrievable.

WHITE: What comments do you have on the Challenger accident?

CARR: It's reminded us that spaceflight is a serious and dangerous business. It was seeming too easy. Losing the crew has made space exploration more of a "cause." It seems more important to people now, when you realize that the gains and successes are not without loss. I haven't talked to one person who has said, "We should stop." It's too important and people realize that. Space exploration is still one of our nobler activities.

Valentin Lebedev

Soyuz 13, Soyuz T-5

Valentin Lebedev, with Anatoly Berezovoy, spent 211 days in space on the Soyuz T-5 mission, launched in May 1982. He had previously been a flight engineer on Soyuz 13, which went into space in December 1973.

Lebedev's Soyuz 13 mission took place at the same time as the Skylab 4 mission flown by Jerry Carr, Ed Gibson, and Bill Pogue. This was the first time that Americans and Russians were in space simultaneously. Then, in 1982, Lebedev's Soyuz T-5 flight coincided with two American shuttle flights, including that of Joe Allen.

The following excerpts from Lebedev's diary were reprinted in Pravda, *August 15, 1983.*

18 June. Today Tolya and I looked at an island near Cape Horn. A solid massif covered with snow against the background of the blue ocean and the trails of various kinds of cloud. Very beautiful. For the first time I saw in the water dozens of tiny white ships (icebergs). They are quite large in size, comparable to the largest ships. The end of Cape Horn is covered in white. It is winter now in these latitudes.

Each evening they transmit us the latest news. Tolya and I sit at the first post, arms folded across our chests, and as we fly calmly above the Earth we listen to Radio Moscow. We admire the azure of the Mediterranean and the Italian mountains, with Africa and the Red Sea coming into view. We study geography and admire the planet.

Above my bed there hangs a photograph of little Vitaly, and there is a package of photographs: Lyusya and myself, father and friends. Each evening I kiss the photograph of my son. He looks out at me so kindly that when things are difficult I say to him, "It's nothing, son, I'll manage. Papa will not let you down."

31 July. Well, it is all behind now. The space walk is over. It lasted two hours thirty-eight minutes.

Space is very beautiful. The dark velvet of the sky, the blue halo of the Earth, and the lakes and rivers and fields and cloud formations speeding by. All around there is perfect silence, no sense of the speed of the flight. No wind whistles in your ears, nothing weighs on you. The panorama is calm, majestic . . .

The fact is that in open space you sense the Earth's roundness much more strongly than through the station port. And everything that you see on the Earth — the lakes, the rivers, the mountains —

is perceived as on an enormous rotating globe. The silence is striking. The station is frozen in space like a block.

10 December. Everything is over; no more journeying! We are
home. We past the terminator, into night. I see the Earth in the
port, pink in the clouds lit by the low Sun, with a blue light on
the edge of the bright, sunset horizon. Beautiful.

Anatoly N. Berezovoy
Soyuz T-5

*Cosmonaut Berezovoy flew as the commander of Soyuz T-5 with
Valentin Lebedev in May 1982. While it was his only trip into
space, he is one of the most experienced travelers, with just over
211 days in space. Like Lebedev, he kept a detailed diary, portions
of which were published in* Aviatsiya I Kosmonavtika, *July 1983,
August 1983, and September 1983. Berezovoy is also a founding
member of the Association of Space Explorers.*

A few excerpts from those published accounts are included.

On Patrol. Like many of my comrades, I particularly like visual
observations. Why is this? It is difficult to answer in one word. I
saw, for example, how happy Jean-Louis Chrétien was when he
was observing his own Brittany and Paris through the port.

It must be said that the longer you stay in orbit the more you
value normal life on Earth. Any person who has been in space
values his own place on Earth in a new way. He begins to think
more, and his thoughts become broader and his spirit kinder.

Visual observations from space were for us a unique way of
communing with our own nature, which brought exactly the same
kind of joy as on Earth. From orbit we observed all the seasons of
the year; the launch was in the spring; we flew throughout the
summer and fall and the start of winter.

It was very interesting to trace the way in which our planet moved
through the procession of the seasons. At first the whiteness gave
way to the onrush of the greenness, and then gold covered the
fields and forests, and then the whiteness again; only now, its

frontier was moving in the opposite direction. But in general there was not much time to gaze on the Earth's beauty; we were required to carry out the orders of a number of organizations.

The Return. The 211 days were behind us. The time had come to bid farewell to the Salyut. It was not as joyful as we had thought. I had mixed feelings. On the one hand was the desire to go home. On the other a sense of dissatisfaction: it seemed that on such a long mission more could have been done. Yes, during those seven months the station had become home. But — it was time!

Joseph P. Allen
STS 5, STS 51-A

A scientist with a doctorate in physics, Joe Allen flew as a mission specialist on two shuttle missions — the Columbia STS 5 in 1982 and the Discovery STS 51-A in 1984. His 1982 flight was in orbit at the same time as the Soyuz mission of Lebedev and Berezovoy. Allen spent just over thirteen days in space and was involved in a dramatic satellite rescue effort on the 1984 mission. An excellent photographer, he is the author of Entering Space: An Astronaut's Odyssey. *Allen is executive vice president of Space Industries, Inc., Houston, Texas.*

This interview, the first for the book, is based on notes taken during my telephone conversation with Allen, May 14, 1985.

WHITE: How did being in space affect your outlook philosophically?

ALLEN: I have never been of a philosophical or religious, or historical, bent, for that matter. I am typical of people in the hard-core sciences, so I haven't been too interested in those kinds of philosophical questions. I have been interested in some general things like travel and new experiences. I have believed in the benefits of education. I've had faith in other humans and have striven to learn more.

In striving to learn, I have enjoyed traveling and new experiences. I wound up reacting to my space journeys as an extrapolation of those interests, as a grander journey. I always felt travel was good because it taught a person a lot about where he'd been. For example, when I went to Germany, I learned a lot about the United States by comparison.

I found that travel in space was a grand extension of the principle that taking a journey is a good thing. I didn't find it a real discontinuity from experiences leading up to it. It was not a major anomaly. It was extraordinarily different, but not anomalous. I was not overwhelmed with it. I have always felt that there was a greater reason for all of this. I was not overwhelmed with a feeling of brotherhood for my fellow humans; I always had that.

I think sociologists should be careful of getting too exact in an area in which it is not yet warranted. It is helpful to look at group psychological studies, as with people in Antarctica or on a submarine. When you are in space, you are in an environment you can't get out of, and it brings certain pressures to bear. It's different from an office or similar working environment, because you can get away from those, but there may not be much difference between a spaceship and a submarine. In some ways a spaceship is less psychologically confining. The view of Earth takes your breath away. In particular, you see subtleties and nuances in the view. The best description I have seen of it was Don DeLillo's in *Esquire* magazine a few years ago.

It is endlessly fulfilling. You never see quite the same thing as you are orbiting. There is a different ground track every time. The time of day is different; the clouds are different. The cloud patterns show different colors. The oceans are different; the dust over the deserts is different. It doesn't get repetitive.

WHITE: Do you agree with Michael Collins that if the political leaders could see the earth from 100,000 miles, it would bring a fundamental change in their perspective?

ALLEN: Collins is right. He is exactly right. A lot more like Senator Garn should go. A steady stream of world leaders should go into orbit. It would have a profound effect on their wisdom.

WHITE: I have a dream of a summit conference on the space station.

ALLEN: I hope it isn't a dream; I hope it can happen in our lifetime. I have no doubt that the picture of the universe in the mind of the man on the street is different from what it once was. It is similar to the time of Copernicus; we have a broadened view of our place in the universe, a more educated view. For several hundred years, we have had a certain image of the Earth. Now an intellectual understanding is being replaced by an intuitive, emotional understanding.

WHITE: Sometimes I think that the impact on Earth may be the main reason for the space program.

ALLEN: Yes. For example, you wouldn't have gotten a penny for EPA [Environmental Protection Agency] before those pictures from orbit. With all the arguments, pro and con, for going to the moon, no one suggested that we should do it to look at the Earth. But that may in fact be the most important reason.

That argument, long recognized by travelers as a reason for going to another country, is equally true for going into the "third dimension" of space. Another wrinkle is that travelers many hundreds of years ago were seeing things for the first time. The modern age has made quasi travelers out of everybody. The invention of cameras enabled the astronauts to make beautiful replications, to be shared with all Earthlings, of what our journeys were like.

A hint of it came into everyone's consciousness. As later astronauts have gone into space, it hasn't been such a shock because they have "been there." The difference is in the actual experience of the quiet, the weightlessness, and so on. It's like the difference between seeing a good PBS special on the Grand Canyon and being there.

Byron K. Lichtenberg
STS 9

Byron Lichtenberg flew on the ninth shuttle mission, launched on November 28, 1983. It was the first flight of the European Space Agency's Spacelab, the first spacecraft with six people aboard, and the first to carry payload specialists, of which Lichtenberg was one. Lichtenberg worked toward the opportunity of going into space for many years. He had been a fighter pilot in the U.S. Air Force and conducted research at MIT with the goal of becoming an astronaut. He participated in over seventy scientific experiments during his ten days and seven hours in Low Earth Orbit.

The following is a reconstruction of my interview with Dr. Lich-

tenberg at his company, Payload Systems, Inc., Wellesley, Massachusetts, on August 19, 1986.

LICHTENBERG: The tough part about the flight was that because it was so crowded and there was so much to do, we really started running. We set up the Spacelab three hours after launch, and five hours later we were doing experiments. I was on the first shift, so we went right through, working about ten hours after launch. It was about a fifteen- or sixteen-hour day. That set the tone for the whole flight.

I don't begrudge that at all, because how often do you get to fly in space? I really felt a sense of responsibility to the scientists as their surrogate in orbit. What I'm getting at is that it was incredibly time-packed, and consequently I didn't have a lot of time to sightsee. There was not much time to sit up there and be reflective, to look down at the Earth.

That's the one thing that I would envy people going up for longer periods of time, for example, a three-month space station tour. There, you'd put in a good eight or ten hours a day of work, but then you'd have ten or fifteen hours to yourself. So that was something I missed on the first flight. When I go up again, I think I'll take a little more time out and protect my free time a little more.

WHITE: That's been a characteristic of spaceflight: two levels of experience. One is that it's an extraordinary environment, yet because of the costs and the responsibility, people who are there don't have that much time to experience it.

LICHTENBERG: That's exactly right, and that's why I think that the idea of taking people up, be it teachers or reporters, is a good one. I'm into music and I would love to have a musician or poet go up there, because lots of times I can get these mental images in a song or through music that is really powerful.

Most of us were trained as scientists or logical thinkers, and we were much more into the technical parts of it. Maybe it's a cop-out, but you subdue other parts of yourself to narrow down and focus in on something. In training to be a technically good experiment operator or pilot, you are taught to take in all this stuff and process it and come out with A, B, C, D, E. Not to think, Wow, this is a great experience, man, this is neat; and then the plane crashes.

WHITE: Given that those limits were there, what feelings or impressions did you have?

LICHTENBERG: The first thing that everybody notices is weightlessness. The first words into my little tape recorder describe it as a totally euphoric feeling. The first experience was when I unhooked my seat belt and tried to walk, which everybody does. I put my feet on the floor, and the next thing I knew I was up on the ceiling on my back, sort of like a fly, up in the corner of the ceiling, hands hanging down, looking down at all these people, and I said, "Wait a minute, we're in negative G here, we're not in zero G." My partner, Owen Garriott, said, "No, it's just that you touched your foot to the floor." Then I just put my hand up and touched the ceiling and floated on down to the floor. That was the beginning of it. It was just amazing to go wherever you wanted. You could fly up in the corner, you could hang upside down. There was no "up" or "down" anymore.

WHITE: Did this feeling of euphoria stay with you?

LICHTENBERG (laughing): It stayed with me for about two hours, and then it was replaced by a feeling of sickness. We were really busy, trying to get experiments set up and put things together, so we were moving around a lot. Of course, our MIT experiments were designed to investigate space motion sickness and how the body and brain adapt and how sensory data is being interpreted.

I didn't expect it because I fly a lot, and during the ground tests I was generally not susceptible to motion sickness. I thought that if it were psychological, there was no problem there because I knew that I was not going to get sick. There was just no problem about this *at all*, and it was going to be great. So it was a big surprise to me when all of sudden I started feeling grim. That goes away after about three days for most people, and it's gone completely. Then it goes back to the feeling of euphoria the whole time.

I could go into Spacelab, and within a very short time grab a handrail, very much offset from my body, and say, "I want to go to the knob on that locker at the other end of the lab." I could just push on the rail and go straight for that spot, and I wouldn't miss it by more than a few inches. It was the same thing if you were trying to go from one end of the Spacelab to the other: you could push off and start tumbling, and you could look around and watch what's going on and have a perfect trajectory right down the middle of the Spacelab, head over heels, until you got to the place you wanted. Then you could come out of it just like a gymnast, with hands on the floor and feet on the ceiling, and you just stop and you're right there.

Those types of things never went away. After ten days, I was still totally in awe of that environment, to be able to move like that and have those feelings. It was neat.

WHITE: So one could imagine that a zero-G society might have a different psychology from a one-G society.

LICHTENBERG: Could be. I don't know, but you're giving yourself another dimension, and it's so different from our experiences on the ground, which are totally two-dimensional, unless you're a trampoline artist. Pilots, I think, experience this because, even though it's not your body, you have control in three dimensions. In talking to Owen Garriott, who was up for two months on Skylab, the sense I get was that that feeling didn't go away.

WHITE: Charles Walker commented that being weightless gave him a sense of possibility. I got the feeling that if it translated into a larger culture, that would be a societal feeling of possibility, of limits being lessened. Gravity is a limiting force in our lives. We just accept it; we don't think about it.

LICHTENBERG: That's right. We never had the opportunity to experience anything else until a few years ago. There are wonderful things about zero gravity and, as we have found out, a lot of things that are a pain in the neck. It would be nice, I think, to be able to go back and forth, somehow. Of course, the question becomes, How does the body adapt and readapt, and can you really do that? The other thing we can talk about is the long-term problems of being in weightlessness and what happens to your bones and cardiovascular system.

There very well could be a total rearrangement, if you had generations of organisms living up there. I think you would be surprised at how fast they would adapt to that new environment, and those adaptations could make them totally unsuitable for coming back to Earth, which is something we need to take a look at and study seriously.

WHITE: What about the view of the Earth?

LICHTENBERG: So many people ask me, "What did the Earth look like, a little ball hanging out there?" I have to tell them it wasn't a little ball. In terms of a globe, I was only about a thumbnail's width above the surface of the Earth, just 135 miles. You could see the curvature, but it was still big; it filled about half of your field of view.

I experienced several things. The first couple of days, when I was sick, I didn't even want to know where the Earth was. It was so distressing to go by a window and catch a glimpse of it somewhere where I didn't think it should be. That's rather a strange statement, but I would be thinking about something else, and suddenly, out of the corner of my eye, through a window, I would see a part of the Earth. I would say, "I just want to concentrate on what I've got here. This is down, right here, the floor, and I need to make sure that I'm upright, and that everything I think of is down. If I see the Earth up here, it really blows my mind."

It wasn't until I got over a lot of the motion sickness that I was able to go out and start looking at the Earth. We were seldom able to see it during a work shift because there weren't many windows in there, and those generally had cameras or instruments on them because they were collecting data.

My only opportunity, really, was after I got off shift. I'd grab my dinner, then float up to the cockpit and strap myself into the pilot's seat and sit there, generally chatting with John Young while I ate, because he was on the other shift, so he was working. He would be pretty much alone there, with the other guys working back in the Spacelab. It was just like the advertising scenes in the airline magazines: the dinner tray with the silver and the napkins and wine glasses, but out the window you see the moon and the Earth. Only we didn't have silver or wine.

We were strapped in with a little set of tins and foil packets and plastic cups, so it wasn't nearly as elegant as in the advertisements, but the view was just as good. Thinking about eating your dinner around the world in ninety minutes is really something. I took advantage of that time; then I would stay up and look for another half orbit and end up going to bed exhausted.

One thing that is really amazing is the different colors. Every color in the entire rainbow is there. You think about a blue-white-gray-brown planet, but it isn't at all. It's incredibly colorful. Even from 135 miles, you can see the clouds three-dimensionally. You can tell the height of the clouds. The mountains look flat, but you can recognize them by the shadows. You can see the ripples of the sand dunes in some of the deserts.

But I think the biggest thing in going around the Earth is that your perspective really changes. You look down and see land you can identify. You don't see any of the borders, you don't see any of the cultures, you don't see the different languages, and it just flows right on in.

You say, "I wonder where the border is between India and Tibet, Nepal and China, or Afghanistan and Pakistan." You just don't see those, and that's so striking because on every globe you look at, the lines are there, and it's always brought home to you. It'd be interesting to put out a globe that had no borders, no names of countries, just continents and physical features. So there's the sense of no difference, just a subtle gentle blending from one region to the next.

That's why the Association of Space Explorers really excites me, because when I read some of the things Rusty [Schweickart] wrote and then heard Jake Garn talk, for example, and heard other people who had been there, it was like, "They felt this, too, and they had that same sense," and the more we talk to people, the more we find it's pretty much universal.

I think that's one of the things that really got us all going, this universal feeling that there really isn't much distinction around the world. Once you go around in ninety minutes, you realize that that's all there is, there is no more, you've seen it all. I may not have seen every piece of it, but . . .

WHITE: That's really what I call the Overview Effect at work. It's not just that you have the experience, but you do something with it.

LICHTENBERG: That's right. I think all of us feel that way, and one of the reasons I give a lot of talks is to try to give people their money's worth. After all, it was the taxpayers who paid for it. I try to make it real for people in the best way that I can, to give them some feeling of direct connection to the program.

It would be really interesting to get the world leaders up in a spacecraft to see and experience that same thing. I think that could make some big differences. Maybe once the space program gets really reliable, instead of jetting off to Camp David or a mountainside somewhere, they could go to the space station for a week and have a conference there.

WHITE: The more you think about it, the more it makes sense, if you had a reliable vehicle and a place. In twenty years, the leaders could be former astronauts, as far as that goes.

LICHTENBERG: That's right. Let me just talk about one other thing about the Earth here. Going into space right now is like a camping trip. You set up in your mind, and say, "Well, we're going to go camping for a week, or ten days, or two weeks, or whatever." You fix that length of time in your mind and plan for it and get provisions.

People say, "Would you have wanted to stay up longer, or did you want to come home?" It was interesting, because you look down and it's very stark and it's black and white in space, and of course, the spacecraft is not the most hospitable place in the world to live. As it's coming up to eight or nine days, you say, "It'll be kind of nice to get back. I sort of miss hearing the breeze in the trees and the butterflies in the fields and the bubble of the streams and watching the flowers grow."

WHITE: If there were one key message that you wanted to disseminate about space and the space program what would it be?

LICHTENBERG: To make the program grow the way other programs have grown, it's important that you bring in a wide base of support. You need some government help, because it's just too expensive to ask any one company to go in there and do something. You can make comparisons to the railroad system. You think about the railroads and waterways and highways: it's an infrastructure that the government really supported. They subsidized it, built it, and paid for it, yet they didn't have the Army Corps of Engineers dig the ditches and the roads. Private industry did that.

People say, "What good is it? Why do you want to do these

foolish things like go into space?" It really galls me, this whole question, "If we can go to the moon, why can't we . . ." Fill in the blanks, whatever you want to do: feed the hungry, cure cancer, eliminate war, whatever. It's not like that. The space program is not a panacea; nothing is. But it gives us a whole new area that's just opening up.

All I know deep within me is that this is something that is bigger than all of us that is going to help the human race make that first giant step. To be able to be there and help it happen, or help give one little push of my finger to the whole program, is what really turns me on and gets me dedicated. We're not going to be able to predict what's out there. We're in a very early learning stage, and the only way to do it is to go out there and make mistakes. Lots of times you learn more from your mistakes than from your successes. The last thing is that the whole space program can be an area where we as a world could get together on projects, whether a manned mission to Mars or a planetary expedition. A lot of people are getting interested in a large collaborative effort.

It's amazing that when you don't know people, it's "them and us." Then, when you meet them directly and personally, it's "We know them and it's all of us." You have a contact there. You talk to them, and whether it's a Czechoslovak, Russian, Saudi, or Mexican, you talk about your kids, where you're going on vacation, or your daughter falling off her horse last week.

Those are things you can relate to because humans are humans, and there are a lot of differences around the world. But if we can emphasize the things that unite us and bring us together, I think that's extremely important. Doing that may be the hope of the space program. If it does nothing else, it would have paid for itself a thousandfold and more. That's the dream.

Ronald E. McNair

STS 41-B

Ron McNair died in the accident that destroyed the Challenger in January 1986. He had made a previous flight as a mission specialist on Challenger on February 3, 1984. McNair, who held a doctorate in physics, was also a musician. He played several appropriate songs on his saxophone while floating above the Earth.

The first passage, apparently from a letter McNair wrote, was included in the memorial service held at the Massachusetts Institute of Technology on February 12, 1986. The second is from the report of that service in the student newspaper The Tech, *February 14, 1986.*

Truly there is no more beautiful sight than to see the earth from space beyond. This planet is an exquisite oasis. Warmth emanates from the earth when you look at her from space. I could no more look at the earth and see anything bad than I could look at a smiling little girl or boy and see a bank robber. It's impossible to see anything but goodness. My wish is that we would allow this planet to be the beautiful oasis that she is, and allow ourselves to live more in the peace that she generates.

Her husband intended to complete on the January mission a message he had begun during his first shuttle flight in 1984, but which had been cut off. Cheryl McNair read her husband's message and played a tape of him on saxophone — silk-smooth runs which filled Kresge Auditorium for the first, and perhaps last, time.

McNair wrote, "Over the past 25 years, space travelers have repeatedly spoken of the astounding beauty of earth as seen from the unique perspective of space. In the next few years, NASA will be flying private citizens equipped with the talent and expertise that will enable them to better describe the space experience. In the meantime, you're stuck with people like me: scientists, pilots, engineers.

"It just so happens that I brought along my soprano saxophone . . . I wish to present to you a medley of songs . . . dedicated to every man, woman, and child in every continent on the planet. [The first song] offers a solution to the malice that exists among us. The second song addresses what we as individuals can do to make the world a better place for everyone."

The songs he played were "What the World Needs Now Is Love, Sweet Love" and "Reach Out and Touch Somebody's Hand."

Charles D. Walker
STS 41-D, STS 51-D, STS 61-B

Charles Walker, a former design specialist for McDonnell Douglas Astronautics Company in St. Louis, is now special assistant to the president of the company. One of the most active payload specialists, he has flown on the shuttle flights of August 1984, April 1985, and November 1985. He conducted electrophoresis experiments, which may lead to major breakthroughs in the development of a purification process and a proprietary drug.

I conducted two separate interviews with Walker. The first was a telephone conversation on July 2, 1985. The second took place at the space development conference sponsored by the L-5 Society in Seattle, Washington, in May 1986. He later added a written addendum.

WALKER: I see the experience of spaceflight as an extension of my previous perceptions and experiences. Fifteen years ago, I was involved in environmental activities in my community. I participated in the first Earth Day. At Purdue, I was interested in the same activities. I took civil engineering courses, but largely to learn about how human actions were affecting the environment. My interests were quite broad. I also took courses in astrophysics and oceanography.

I found the experience of seeing the world as one distinct entity an enlightening one, and realizing with my own senses the interrelatedness of the environment on the globe and the magnitude of the universe in which the globe sits. It extended my desire to have a firsthand feel for the world around us, and it sensitized me to learn as much as I could about the interconnectedness of the environment.

It created in me a lot of sensory stimulation, much more than I could absorb. You have a sight clearly in view for perhaps ninety seconds when you are moving at orbital speed. There is such an influx of visual information that you can only try to accept and interpret as much of it as possible.

I came back with a mass of stored data. I wanted to spend a lot of time thinking back on it and how it related to my experiences here on Earth. It takes a lot of time to do it. I don't think I can assimilate it all in a lifetime, but I'm going to try!

WHITE: How did you become an astronaut?

WALKER: At first, I was just one of the masses from outside, an observer in junior high school watching Shepard's suborbital flight. I had an extreme desire to make the trip. I visualized the experience. I think many of us have been there in our mind's eye.

It gives you a good feel. You say, "This is a lot like I thought it would be." There is a sense that you have seen it before, in your mind's eye, but that vision was limited in scope, two-dimensional.

WHITE: It seems that different people react differently, as in any situation.

WALKER: Yes. If you take people and send them to the Grand Canyon for the first time, different individuals will respond differently. But there will be a familiarity for them, and, at the same time, a feeling of the awesomeness of it. That can be equated to the experience of being in Earth orbit.

The scope of human experience in space will really be as different as the different people who go. We haven't yet seen a wide variety of backgrounds.

WHITE: Is it different in Earth orbit than going to the moon?

WALKER: Yes, there is a difference. It's something that hasn't been described or well defined yet, but it is obvious.

WHITE: Does space exploration play a role in human evolution?

WALKER: Yes. Over the decades and centuries, global surface exploration has been a strong undercurrent of change in Earthbound society. Changes in perspective will affect overall social structures. You can equate it to the European experience of the New World. But that was one of a number of perspectives. The African colonial experience was not the same as the North American. Also, consider that the Chinese withdrew and became isolated in response to the exploration of others. So the European analogy alone is somewhat simplistic.

Today, we have a lot of communication capabilities that did not exist then, and societies have similar perspectives, commonalities that didn't exist earlier. The space perspective is generalized more quickly around the world. But it becomes diluted and is not seen as a saving grace of mankind. It seems to take time for it to affect society on a large scale.

The localized societal impact is greater. The Soviets see spaceflight as driven by dialectical and economic principles. They see space as an integral part of their future. They are integrating into the lives of their people the idea of colonies on planets and in orbit.

We don't do that. We saw our manifest destiny in conquering the continent. The impact of spaceflight has been more limited in our culture than in some others.

WHITE: Is that because of a difference in their ability to communicate specific messages to large segments of society on a sustained basis?

WALKER: Yes. There is a difference in the systems. They can sustain their programs over long periods. In the United States, so many organizations see it as an either/or proposition, as space versus other social needs. There is a trend toward unification of different space-oriented groups now, which will help speed this country's deeper understanding of space as more than a diversion.

The space station activities are also focusing interest. That will be the direction over the next ten years. Focusing on manned objectives will hopefully bring about a surge of interest, and I hope it creates an escalation of advances. We can build on it and generate momentum. It will allow us to overcome low points and give us enough momentum to advance on exploration and utilization.

WHITE: What is the effect of multiple trips into space; do you eventually adapt to being there?

WALKER: Yes. Each person adapts with successive trips. You feel more comfortable each time, and you know what to expect psychologically as well. You adapt more readily to the environment and are less stunned by the perspectives and the sights. But each time you have mixed feelings about what you see and feel. I don't know if *that* diminishes. Your perceptions are shaped by your previous trips.

The character of it depends on each individual's internal makeup, but also on what happens between flights. When you come back, you are still digesting and integrating. There is also the interaction with the people you talk to. The predominant question is "What is it like in space?" Each time you verbalize it, that affects your thoughts and the context. When I verbalize something, it generates something new; there is a different answer each time the question is asked.

This process is different for each person, depending on the flights and their contacts between flights. I had three flights in fifteen months' time. The company allowed talks and presentations between flights, and I addressed a lot of different groups. So you prepare for flight, go into the flight, experience spaceflight, and then process it verbally.

Each time I was able to study more of the view in detail because of its familiarity. The immediate and superficial impressions that flooded me lessened. I could study them more carefully.

WHITE: Does space ever seem like home, or is it always strange?

WALKER: After some extended period, I would feel, This is home; this is the home that stays with me. I would cross over a boundary in time and think, Given a choice, this is where I would reside. But when I've gone on the shuttle, it wasn't home because in a few days I returned to Earth. It was another place and another experience; it was pleasant and exciting, but it was not really home.

It is analogous to my feelings on a jetliner. I've flown tens of thousands of miles in aircraft now, and I can sleep right through a takeoff. But it is a limiting environment and temporary. The space shuttle environment is that way. You know there is a "max stay time." There is no way you can feel it is really home. Until there is a place you can go in space, no one will feel it is that comfortable. It will even take some time for people to feel that way about the space station.

WHITE: How was it compared to expectations?

WALKER: Having gone through all of it, I find there were many gaps in my thinking way back when. You don't realize what it takes, the attitude preparation, and so on, to accept all the experiences that are part of spaceflight, such as living with seven other people for five to seven days.

Many of us, in thinking about spaceflight, are expressing our hopes, desires, and dreams for what can be. It is like the early pioneers of this continent, in the diaries that they wrote. From

what I've heard, many were not prepared, and it may be that way
now. Human nature hasn't changed in that regard; it is the same
reaction, but to a new environment.

WHITE: So you think the pioneer image is pretty accurate?

WALKER: It's not far off. We also have some immediate analogies
in the people who have gone to the South Pole, for example. It is
not quite as artificial and alien as the orbital environment, but it
is a similar situation. Early on, in the 1950s, the people who went
to Antarctica were certainly pioneers. Even today, they are pioneers taking on hardships. It will be some time before the space
station will be like that.

WHITE: Do you want to go to the space station when it is built?

WALKER: Yes. I do. I keep trying to position myself for that.

WHITE: What do you think will be the impact of the Challenger
accident?

WALKER: My guess would be that over five years or so, it will
produce a "legend in its own time" for the astronaut corps and the
public. The Challenger Seven will be like the original seven twenty
years ago. We will have a voice that will be listened to with less
reservation regarding the realities of spaceflight and the necessity
for it. Polls have showed 70 to 80 percent of the American people
supporting continuance. That will be the effect for five years or so,
but not after that.

Bureaucratically, I don't know. Gramm-Rudmann has had a real
impact, and it could push the program toward privatization. Then,
people may get frustrated again if nothing grand happens. You ask
the question, "Are NASA's funding levels okay?" but most people
don't know what the funding levels are, how small that level is. I
think people do want to support the program, but they may get
frustrated.

*The following comments, dated August 7, 1986, were added by
Walker to his copy of the original transcript.*

The new mythology of heroes is being born from the Challenger
disaster. The Soviets have their heroes, but their names are not
well known in Western society. We have our own. I hope this
post-Challenger period is not going to be a dark age for American
manned spaceflight. But my deepest fear is that too many of us

are two-dimensional and too myopic, chained as we are to the surface of this planet. And in this existence gravity restrains not only our physical bodies but our expectations and our perceptions of what is possible. An accident of human failing may, unfortunately, be enough to start that dark age. But then maybe the "legend" will soon bring the decision makers back to the light.

I have heard other space travelers express a perception that I have had: the feeling of euphoria beginning and continuing several days after launch. I think it springs from the mind's realization that the reality without gravity is in effect a new dimension of freedom. It is a feeling that new possibilities *must* be present where physical orientation and visual perception are under control but always variable.

The old limits fade, to reveal new, different ones — it is not enough to be hundreds of miles above the Earth in free-fall. You want to be outside the confines of the cabin, outside the confines of the pressure suit. Perhaps you even, without consciously realizing it, feel closer to being outside your body. For each person, it *is* different, but it must *also* be the same.

Marc Garneau
STS 41-G

Marc Garneau, one of six payload specialists selected by Canada in 1983, was the first Canadian to enter space. He flew on Challenger on October 5, 1984, and spent eight days in space conducting experiments designed by the Canadian space program.

The following is part of my interview with Garneau in Ottawa, Canada, on July 11, 1986.

WHITE: You went on 41-G in October of 1984. Can you talk about what you did?

GARNEAU: I can remember walking into the one-G trainer and saying, "Gosh, this is a very small place for seven people to live in." Psychologically, as I got to know the crew better, the area expanded for me, and by the time I was ready for the flight, I was saying, "Well, this is bags of room. No problem."

It's not really the classroom work or the hands-on training that's the biggest factor. It's the psychological adaptation, the interpersonal relationships that are probably the most important thing on short notice.

WHITE: The space experience is the period that you are actually in space, but it's also the period before you go, and the period after, isn't it?

GARNEAU: Very much so. In fact, I was probably dull company for the three months prior to the mission. I can remember my parents and my wife commenting to me afterwards that when they phoned me I just wasn't there. I was answering all the questions, but literally, from the moment I woke up in the morning until I went to bed at night, I was just thinking about the mission. It was very, very absorbing.

WHITE: What was the most important aspect of the experience itself, and how did it compare to what you thought would happen?

GARNEAU: A lot of things come to mind when you ask that question. I would describe it as a little bit of a dreamlike experience. Sometimes, in hindsight, it may take on a certain different quality, but trying to be objective about it, and thinking about how I felt at the time, it is a dreamlike experience because space is a very magical place to be.

I'm not trying to be whimsical here. Floating around in a place where you seem to be working and living almost in slow motion, yet being on top of the planet and going around it in ninety minutes, has a magical quality about it. It's a bit like Alice in Wonderland. Things do make sense up there; it hasn't got the chaos of a normal dream, but you are walking into something that is so strange compared to any other experience that you have been exposed to in your life.

It doesn't prevent you from working. I don't think I lost my head; I don't think I was distracted in any appreciable way in the sense of not being able to do my work, but I was continuously amazed at the whole thing. It didn't lose any of its magical quality while I was up there.

WHITE: On the one hand you're in this extraordinary place, while on the other hand, you have to do very disciplined tasks. Every minute is really accounted for.

GARNEAU: No doubt about it. It's a unique opportunity for a Canadian scientist to get some good space science done, and they, the scientists, want to pile on as much as they can, not realizing that things do take a little bit longer to perform up there. Each one is saying, "Well, I'll only add twenty more minutes to his day," but there are six others who are doing the same.

You end up doing a lot of work that is regulated minute by minute, and you have to carve out a little time for yourself, so you don't come back to Earth after this unique experience, and say to yourself, "I didn't have any time for myself to feel the experience."

I did what everybody else, at least on our mission, did when we had some free time — I found a spot where I could gaze at the Earth.

I've had people ask me, "Did you take a book to read with you?" It's just the most ridiculous suggestion in the world. You don't go up there to read a book. Perhaps it's because they don't realize what this view is that's available to you.

WHITE: What was the experience of looking at the Earth for you?

GARNEAU: There's a mixture of things. One is just the sheer wonder of looking down at the Earth. It is very, very beautiful. There are wars going on, there's pollution down there, but these are not visible from up above. It just looks like a very beautiful planet, particularly when you see it interface on the edge with space. There you suddenly get the feeling that, hey, this is just one small planet which is lost in the middle of space.

If you're looking straight down, you don't get that feeling, but if you can see that limb, then you see that boundary between Earth and space, and that gives you a very important feeling about the fact that we're just drifting through an immense universe.

It also makes you realize that this is a friendly place where humans can live, and there probably aren't too many of these for a long way from our own planet, so you become a little more conscious about the fact that we shouldn't be doing silly things on Earth like fighting and killing each other.

I'm sure this is a commonly related thing: you lose your feelings of national belonging. We went up on a 57-degree inclination, so we would see quite a bit of Canada. The Americans, who were used to doing 28-degree inclinations, would see a lot of the United States they don't normally see, north of Florida. And you couldn't tell when you crossed from Canada into the United States. I had spent a lot of time before that studying maps so I could take pictures of various parts of Canada to show my friends or look at geological formations of interest to Canadian geologists.

I was almost expecting to see these boundary lines, and they are not there. They're not there when you go through all of South America and through all of the Asian continent, and after a while you realize it's a very artificial thing to put boundaries between us. In that sense you become more of a global citizen and less concerned with your own petty problems, at least during the time that you are up there.

When you come back down to Earth and you get away from all the media razzmatazz, you're back to such mundane concerns as I've got to fix the washer on my tap here, and I've got to put the garbage out. But for that short time, it's part of that dream, that magical quality, raising you to a level where you feel you're an extremely privileged person. You're conscious of the fact that not too many people have had this.

WHITE: How about weightlessness? You talked about the floating and the dreamlike nature of it.

GARNEAU: Floating and weightlessness were what I really enjoyed, and I think everybody will tell you the same thing. I think the right word for it is that it is so much fun; it's no more complicated than that. I really took to that environment. I enjoy scuba diving and I've done that for a long time. I like the feeling of being suspended. I liked the floating so much that I slept that way. Most people get into sleeping bags or strap themselves in one way or another. I didn't, I just floated.

You can't hurt yourself up there, and I felt totally comfortable closing my eyes at nighttime. You obviously position yourself so that you can at least start out not moving. Eventually, you will be moved; forces will move you throughout, but I felt very comfortable with that. A lot of people feel they should tie themselves down somewhere, that it's not right to be drifting all over the place.

To me, it was no longer a factor. I really did release myself from my reference system. And I think that if I was up there ten years,

I'd still get as much of a kick out of floating as I did on those eight days.

WHITE: I have a sense that if you just stayed in a weightless environment and didn't come back to a planetary surface, you would become more fishlike. Do you have any feeling about that?

GARNEAU: Perhaps there is something we don't know about that after five years would kill everybody living in space, because nobody has been up there that long.

There's going to be a loss of calcium, but we don't really have enough information. We are extrapolating beyond the present maximum duration, which is less than a year. Making a simplistic guess, I would assume that the muscles in our legs and arms would atrophy and become skinnier. Our legs would probably just disappear eventually, because there is no use for them. You can move around very well just with your arms.

I don't think your arms would stay the same size as they are now, because you don't need much strength. You do need their dexterity and manipulating capability, and you use them to stop and start and move around, but they don't need to be as big or as strong as they are normally.

I can't see things like our eyes and ears changing much. You still need your senses up there. The sense of touch would remain. Basically, I think our members would change substantially.

I have a feeling that we will dabble with artificial gravity because we will want to see what it's like, and it's quite possible that when we have permanent space habitations there may be a tendency to revert to artificial gravity, but it's not a big factor at the moment.

WHITE: Does this sort of experience have long-term impact? What's it like being back with us Earthlings, trying to understand what it was like, trying to explain to everybody?

GARNEAU: It's not easy to explain because it's a very personal experience. It's also difficult for me to separate the experience from all the hype that followed it. When I got back down to Earth, before I knew it, I was carried off into a maze of publicity in this country, which was very exciting and a very busy time. I never had to come back down to Earth, if you know what I mean, for quite a long time after actually getting back.

Also, I would say that the experience of being in Low Earth

Orbit is substantially different from going to the moon. Going to the moon, a quarter of a million miles away from your own planet, and seeing it from that far away, has to be much different from being in Low Earth Orbit.

Setting foot on the moon must be very emotional and special. I think that for people who have been profoundly affected by their space experience, it's proportional to how far they go away and whether or not they set foot on a foreign planet.

So it has changed me as a person, but I think the publicity has changed me more than anything else, in the sense that I had to go from being a private person to one who is often asked to appear in public or speak about some particular topic and has to adjust to expectations from the public.

That adjustment is considerably more profound in terms of my personal life than my eight-day experience in space, which remains a very personal and beautiful experience, but not one that has substantially changed me. I think I would have to go for a lot longer and a lot farther before I would say that.

I would add one last thing. One part of the total experience is the sheer adventure of the launch itself. That internal adjustment, making peace with yourself and squaring off your conscience and preparing for that short experience, is an adaptation as well. You have to come to terms with yourself if you are going to go through it.

You have the choice of backing out, but when you decide that you're not going to do that, you have to tidy up your mind and sort out your priorities. This is something most of us don't have to do in the normal course of events. But here you're consciously saying, "I'm going to take the chance that something could happen. I believe it's a small chance, but I'm prepared to take that risk." That personal decision is a part of the overall experience.

WHITE: It must be an amazing feeling when the shuttle lifts off to realize that you are actually doing it at that moment, and you can't go back.

GARNEAU: Yes, it is. This dreamlike feeling begins in the morning when you wake up, which is still some four or five hours prior to actual takeoff. This time, you are going up to that launch pad and up in the elevator, and you know you're not going to come down.

You're going up there to get on board, and this is no longer a practice.

The two hours before the mission are probably the hardest of the whole thing, because you haven't got a heck of a lot to do, just sitting there. If you are the pilot and the commander, you're a little busier, but even they are not that busy until the last twenty minutes when they start flicking switches and doing a lot more talking.

It's something like playing football, waiting for the first contact on the line. After that, you relax a little bit, but you're saying, "Let's get on with this game." It's that sort of feeling.

But it's an overwhelming sensation, and your ears, your eyes, your whole body is attuned to everything that's going to happen, particularly if you're where I was, which is down in the middeck, where you don't have the additional visual element that the people at the windows have.

Then the whole shuttle comes to life, and it's moving and it's going, and you say to yourself, "Oh, good, I don't feel any lateral accelerations that I wasn't expecting. We're going to the right place." You suddenly become the most sensitive sensor in the world.

WHITE: I'm interested in how we are going to evolve as a society in space and how it's going to affect life on Earth. What thoughts do you have about what is going to happen as we spend more time in space?

GARNEAU: I think my vision is probably a fairly common one, but I feel very strongly about it. Certainly, we are drawn to space. That is irrefutable in my mind, and we're going to continue going up there. We may have slowdowns and buildups, depending on budgets and the political scene, but we're not going to turn our backs on space. That would be unthinkable for me. I think it's going to be like Columbus's setting off five hundred years ago and starting the trend of people going out to explore the world beyond the European and Asian shores. He initiated this flurry of "Let's explore the rest of our world," and even to this century new places were being discovered.

I believe that we are going to become comfortable with our space environment. We are going to go back to the moon and set up a base there eventually and use it as a staging place. There will be people living up there on a long-term basis. We will have a space station that will blossom into several space stations — co-orbiting platforms and polar platforms. Within my lifetime we will send human beings to Mars.

But beyond that, I would say that within the next fifty to a hundred years, we are going to have people being born and living in space, if not for their whole lives initially, at least for a substantial amount of time. Probably in a couple of centuries people will live their entire lives on places like the moon or on large space stations that are orbiting our planet.

We will explore our entire solar system in the next four or five hundred years, but we won't be able to go beyond that point. To do that, we have to take a magic step to propulsion systems that allow us to approach the speed of light. I believe it's possible, but it'll be a long time. When we do get that capability, we're going to visit our neighboring solar systems. Eventually we will reach other intelligent life.

I believe there is intelligent life out there, but it could very easily be a million years before it contacts us. Somehow we get impatient if it doesn't happen within our lifetime. It may be watching us now; it may not. We may be the first to contact. I think the contact will eventually happen, but we're not going to be in a position to do that for a long time.

I think it will be very exciting. I think that within my lifetime, someone will be born in space, and that will be a thrilling moment for that child and that child's parents.

WHITE: Do you have a feeling for how the political and social relationships might evolve?

GARNEAU: I don't think we'll ever become "one" on Earth, in the sense of all becoming friends, until somebody contacts us from out there. I think we need that strong a force to bring us together. Otherwise, I think regional interests will prevail. It's within our human nature and it's too strong to break down. Although we all espouse brotherhood and friendship, it's unrealistic to expect all of us suddenly to be brought together by our common desire to do something in space for the common good.

There will be lots of cooperation, and we will maintain civilized relationships, but I think we will still see countries preserving their autonomy. Only when we reach the point where we are contacted from outside will we suddenly pull together and realize that it's more important that we be together.

WHITE: Is there any one thing you would like people to know about space and space exploration?

GARNEAU: What comes to mind is that it's inevitable. It's not something that we're going to sit down and discuss whether or not we should. It's something that's going to happen, and nothing is going to stop it.

There are people who would like to turn away from that, who cannot reconcile the fact that we have a lot of problems here on Earth with the fact that we should be trying to go out and spend a lot of money doing this other thing. Really, the two can be reconciled quite easily, depending on how you look at it. The bottom line in my opinion is that no matter what we do with our government money, it's still going to happen. Nothing can prevent it; it's too strong a human instinct.

Jeffrey A. Hoffman

STS 51-D

Jeff Hoffman, an astronomer, made his first spaceflight as a mission specialist on STS 51-D, which was launched on April 12, 1985. During that mission, he made an unplanned spacewalk in an attempted rescue of a malfunctioning satellite.

I heard Hoffman speak at the Smithsonian Center for Astrophysics, Harvard University, in October 1985 and interviewed him at the Johnson Space Center in Houston in November 1985. Excerpts from Dr. Hoffman's talk at Harvard, integrating answers to a few audience questions, are followed by material from our discussion.

We had fifty hours' underwater training for spacewalking. When I first went out on my spacewalk, I was overwhelmed for a few seconds, but then it is remarkable how the training takes over. For an hour, I was out there "watching the world go by." It was overwhelming, the high point of the trip.

One of the hardest parts of working there was trying not to spend too much time looking back at the Earth. You have a "gondola" mode of observation, looking out of the top of the shuttle. You have a sense of the three-dimensional nature of the clouds. I spent a lot of time taking cloud pictures. You also get a lot of views of global weather patterns. We spent a lot of time before the flight going over a list of pictures to take. We had a few sessions studying ecological problems. You see things happening all over the world that are appalling.

You have a continentwide view, but you can also see individual buildings with fourteen-power binoculars from three hundred miles. We took a lot of pictures of sunrise and sunset, and I counted twenty layers of atmosphere. There is a halo around the Earth, which becomes visible about eight minutes after the sun sets.

On reentry, the rear view is dramatic. A huge standing shock wave is visible even after the sun comes out. It is a spectacular phenomenon. There is a bright white light right in the middle of it. It is like a huge totemic figure. When I showed it to mission specialist Rhea Seddon, she said, "Maybe we should bow down and pray to it."

WHITE: Since you have read some of my material, we can start by getting your reaction to it and the idea that spaceflight does have some impact on one's perspective on life.

HOFFMAN: One thing I will say in general about some of your opinions is that I don't think you have to fly in space to have that psychological impact. For instance, the idea of the Earth as a closed ecosystem, a sense of the fragility of life, of the remarkable difference between the Earth and Venus or Mars.

We appreciate it more because of what has come from the space program, but that perspective is not necessarily available only to a person in orbit looking down and seeing it. What I saw reinforced rather than created new feelings.

I think that is true of most of my experience. That may not be true of somebody who didn't spend as much time before the flight thinking and reading about the experience, but although I saw a tremendous amount of stuff that surprised me, in terms of overall philosophical impact, I didn't go through any sort of conversion experience that some people have talked about.

The direct experience of being in orbit is something you can't get just by reading about it. But I don't translate that directly into psychological or philosophical consequences. I think you draw philosophical or mental consequences from an experience like that only if you think about it a lot. A lot of people fly in space and really don't think much about it; then, when they come back, it was a fantastic experience.

I know about the phenomenon of going to Tibet and sitting on a mountainside for two years and all of a sudden achieving your inspiration or revelation or whatever. Perhaps something like that could come out of the space experience too, but [laughing] not when they keep us so busy. Most of your contemplation is done during the wee hours of the sleep period.

WHITE: I heard you talk on the radio on the topic "Why I took six years out of my life to do this." You said something like "Perhaps when we look back on it, going into space might be the most important thing we've ever done."

HOFFMAN: I feel very strongly that this is part of a long-term development of human civilization and that what we are doing now is taking the very first steps. Of course, I was raised on science fiction, so the idea of people living on other planets and traveling to the stars doesn't bother me.

WHITE: As an astronomer, you had some predisposition toward this being a natural way for people to live.

HOFFMAN: Yes. A lot of the limitations that we perceive on human life come from what we are used to. You often hear people say that travel to the stars is impossible just because they're too far away. That presupposes that you want to come back to the Earth eventually, and as far as I'm concerned that is not a justifiable assumption. It is for us now, at our stage of development of civilization, but I suspect that eventually there will be people who don't live on the Earth.

I don't think that there is any real sense of humanity as being cosmic. Humanity is very much of the Earth, and so it should be, because we really are, we depend on the Earth. But that will not necessarily always be the case.

WHITE: It is certainly a primitive beginning, but almost every month, some human beings live a fairly complete life for one week away from the Earth.

HOFFMAN: We are all waiting for the chance to do it on a longer basis on the space station. It's sad that that is still a long time in the future for us. The Russians are getting a lot of good experience. From what I've heard, space as a new frontier, society coming out of a revolutionary past and looking to the future, is very much a part of their tradition, too. I think that space research is very important to them, not just from the military point of view, but as a general philosophical basis for their whole culture.

WHITE: Yes, I think that's true. We have a physical frontier culture, and they have a social frontier culture. Building a new society is very strong with them. Going back to your experience, what would you say was the most important thing?

HOFFMAN: Leaving aside the technical aspects of the flight itself, I would have to divide it into several elements, because clearly the most important thing we did on the flight was to show the adaptability of having people up in space who could react quickly to a situation.

First, there is the direct experience of weightlessness, which is the overwhelming factor at the beginning. It's both an external and internal experience. You see how the other people move around, see the freedom that you have, and also have the internal sensation of what your body feels like, which is completely different from anything — well, not anything, because we have done parabolic flights — but once you get used to the fact that it's not over after a quick thirty seconds, it becomes a very different experience.

There's no fundamental philosophical importance, I think, to the experience, except that it is a fascinating one internally. Externally, it's quite interesting. It's the first time you have true freedom in all three dimensions — much more even than birds or airplanes, because you don't need any power to stay where you are. Of course, we can't really take full advantage of it because the shuttle is such a small environment, but looking ahead, I can see fantastic opportunities for space construction because of this freedom.

It is a completely new physical environment, and there will eventually be whole new fields of engineering and design to build structures that don't have to support their own weight, using novel materials and all sorts of things which come out of this basic three-dimensional freedom. Obviously, gravity still exists up there, but as a force, it's very different.

You certainly build up a new sense of what gravity is. We don't normally, just standing and sitting, think of it as being a constant acceleration. We think of it as something that holds us onto the Earth, but when the shuttle first lands and you step out, you feel it as an acceleration down to the ground.

WHITE: You actually realize that it is always pulling you to it?

HOFFMAN: Yes. So it certainly gave me a lot of insights on a very physical basis, an appreciation of how these basic forces, gravity and fluids, work. That's part of the fascination, watching how things behave so differently in free-fall.

That's the first part of the experience, the whole concept of weightlessness. The other part is the location, what you can see from Earth orbit that you can't see from the ground. That's a constant fascination from the beginning to the very end of the mission, because there's so much, and you can always see new things out the window.

WHITE: It's one thing to be there, to be able to see the Earth, but also it's changing all the time.

HOFFMAN: It's not just the Earth, it's the environment of space, the atmosphere, and the nearby environment of the shuttle and the stars. From the top to the bottom, it's a very different perspective.

WHITE: So you did have that sense of not just the Earth, but of the solar system.

HOFFMAN: Yes. Even as close to the Earth as we were, I still felt I was able to create in my mind a picture of the Earth in space. The sky around you is black, and you can really see the atmosphere from above, the tops of the clouds and the airglow on the horizon. It's certainly not like being on the moon, where you can see the little globe in the sky, but with a little jump of the imagination, it is possible to appreciate that.

WHITE: How about the time sense?

HOFFMAN: I quickly stopped carrying any ground clock in my mind. It became irrelevant. Obviously, if I had wanted to figure out what time it was in Houston, I could have. But there was never any need to, and I certainly lost track of that after being in orbit for only a few hours. Everything went by our orbit clock, Mission Elapsed Time, because all our activities were scheduled in its terms. For my internal planning activities, I tended to use the orbit as the basic unit of time.

When our scheduled activities were finished, I would think to myself, I have a little work to do, and then I want to get ready for bed, and then I want to look out the window. I might say, "I guess I'll look out the window to see the next sunset, or I'll spend a half orbit looking out the window." Sometimes when I was ready for bed, and we were scheduled for eight hours of sleep, I would say, "I don't need eight hours of sleep. I'll spend the next orbit looking out the window, and then I'll go to sleep," knowing, of course, that it was an hour and a half, but basically thinking in terms of an orbit.

WHITE: I've been interested in time as a subset of space and realizing that time is really measured by what Earth is doing.

HOFFMAN: Time is measured by change, not just of the Earth but of anything, at the subjective level. One year is one year, but subjectively, the more things are changing, the deeper your impression of time. I've always thought that's why a year seems much longer for kids than for grown-ups, because there is so much more change in one year in a child's life than there is for you and me. And certainly, there is much more change in one week in orbit. Of course, that is not unique to space travel. The same thing happens if I spend a week in Europe. Or on a vacation, when you do something different while you are there, every day seems so jam-packed full of new things that time somehow seems expanded, and the experience lasts a lot longer. Whereas you go from week to week around the office and because it's the same, you get to Friday and say "What have I done all week?"

WHITE: One essential factor to the whole experience seems to be that of excitement and adventure.

HOFFMAN: At the point we are now, the emphasis, the training, the preparation, is not at all on the adventure. It's on accomplishing tasks, learning how to function in space, and you carry the adventure along with you. It's not like you go to climb a mountain because the goal is to climb a mountain. We are no longer at the point where we are going into space because the goal is to go into space and just experience it. They are not sending me up and spending all that money so I can have an adventure. We spend all our training time on learning how to do useful work up there.

I think that in itself is an adventure, if you take the big picture, because we are setting the groundwork for the next years of human development and whatever humanity ends up doing in space. That is an adventure, and it's worth all the hard work.

WHITE: I've studied Zen, and the promise is of a great experience, but they never talk about the experience. They talk about the work that it takes to get there, and there is a real focus on the practice.

HOFFMAN: Well, I don't think it's for the same reasons. My understanding of Zen tells me that the reason for not talking about the experience is that you don't want to be grabbing for it. It has to come and get you, and if you grab for it, you never get it, and that's not at all true about going into space. You can think about it as much as you want to, and when you get there, you are there. It's all over. So I think it's not apt from that point of view. I think the reason we don't talk that much about it is that that's not what we are preparing for; we are preparing for the work we have to do.

Then who is to do the talking to whom? I don't have to talk with a fellow astronaut who's been up there about what the sunset looks like in space, because he's seen it. And when we talk to people coming back from other flights, we don't try to tell each other what zero gravity felt like, because we assume that we understand that. What we tend to talk about is the unique things they might have done on their flights that I might not have done. We come to share a language.

The main thing is to talk to other people about it, which is one of the reasons I agreed to have my diary made public. People don't ordinarily have much opportunity to find out what it was like, so I thought it was a nice way of sharing the experience. But by and large, it's hard to share, and it's certainly not something that's directly relevant to our training, so we don't talk with our trainers about it. I think the sharing is done more through pictures. Everybody expects us to bring back good pictures, and that is the way we communicate the experience.

WHITE: Do you feel that you are successful in sharing it?

HOFFMAN: By and large, people tell me that I share it reasonably well, and I'm willing to accept that. I enjoy it. Even before I flew, I liked to talk about the space program. I'm willing to talk about something that I'm interested in and people are willing to listen to.

WHITE: Have you had the sense that some people have really been affected as they have listened to you?

HOFFMAN: Some have said that especially listening to my diary gives them a direct sense of what actually goes on during spaceflight that they have never had before. All that most people ever hear is conversations between astronauts and Mission Control, and that is not what goes on during a mission.

Without aviation experience, most people don't realize how artificial that language is, and it's developed that way for a very real purpose, because historically radio time has been very valuable. That's changing with relay satellites, and we can put scientists on the line and talk to them without any radio discipline at all.

Even displays of emotion are frowned upon on the radio, and for good reason, because they are not necessary. The tradition of aviation and nautical radio is to keep the radio quiet unless you have something necessary to say. And anyway, because you are limited, the only thing anybody ever says is, "Wow, isn't this beautiful?" It's become a cliché. Perhaps some people can't say anything better, but a surprising number of people can; it's just that they don't. We kind of get a bad name because of it.

WHITE: I don't know that you showed a lot of emotion in the diary, but I could sense your feelings.

HOFFMAN: Well, I was certainly excited the whole time. I was on a total high.

WHITE: I want to talk about the EVA because I have the sense that for a lot of people it's the most interesting experience.

HOFFMAN: I think that all of us would like to do it, especially the people who do the EVA training for the shuttle. I think it's another step of adventure that's much more exciting. It's also a more immediate sense of the environment of space.

WHITE: I would think that out there the Earth would loom even larger in your view.

HOFFMAN: The shuttle's windows are surprisingly good compared to those of previous spacecraft, where it was like day and night between being in a space suit and looking through a small window. The shuttle actually gives you a remarkably good view.

It's still not as good as out of a space helmet, but I think it was not so much that the view itself was intrinsically so much bigger; it was just knowing that I wasn't looking through a window. I could look at my hand, and there was the vacuum of space between my eyes and my hand. That's a very strange feeling.

WHITE: Did you have any of that experience, either when you were inside or on EVA, that Rusty Schweickart talks about, of a shift of your identity, from identifying with a specific place on the Earth, to identifying more with the Earth itself?

HOFFMAN: I don't think of that sort of shift as being unique to the EVA. Maybe it was different for him because of having so little view when he was inside. But we got a very real sense of our position in relation to the Earth in the shuttle, because there are windows all around no matter which way you are pointing, and you can see a large chunk of it.

I think the most unusual experience I had was the feeling of being able to become detached from the shuttle and be an independent satellite. Philosophically, I could have that experience even inside, because in terms of the laws of physics, when I'm floating inside the shuttle's cabin, I am an independent satellite, a satellite inside a satellite. But it's different, obviously, when you are outside, and the shuttle's over there. That was exciting. I don't think there is any great philosophical importance behind it, but it was interesting to me that I could get a feeling of detachment relatively easily.

WHITE: In physical terms, you were really a planetary body. Were you tethered?

HOFFMAN: Oh, yes, all the time. But at the heart of the matter, if I was exerting a force on the shuttle, moving around, doing work, translating from one part to another, then the shuttle was this big massive object. Of course, it was I who was moving and the shuttle that was standing still, and therefore everything I was doing was in relation to the shuttle. But if I just had my hand lightly on the handrail and was floating, and there was no force on my hand between me and the shuttle, then I'm equivalent to the shuttle, there's no difference. We are both equal satellites around the Earth, and I'm under the same laws of physics as the shuttle is, and that's what made the difference. Luckily, I had enough spare time that

I could do that for a while and just get that part of the experience.

WHITE: There was a time when you were lying on your back, looking up through the shuttle windows at the clouds, and you said it was like looking at clouds when you were on the Earth, but from the other side. It sounded like a big daydreaming session, a kid lying on his back, looking up.

HOFFMAN: It was very much like that. Looking at the tops of clouds, you get all kinds of neat patterns, just as when you are looking at clouds from here. I found it very relaxing just to look at them from the top. It was also neat to go from day to night, and sometimes you would get magnificent thunderstorms.

WHITE: Did you notice any difference in your dreams?

HOFFMAN: Only one night was I aware of any dreams, and I was actually dreaming about the flight, so I would have to say yes, it was different. I was dreaming that I was back on the ground asking people how the flight was going, and they were saying, "Aren't you supposed to be up there?"

WHITE: So you dreamed you were back on Earth.

HOFFMAN: Yes, but the dreams were concerned with the flight, because I was back on Earth asking people what they thought about it.

WHITE: I've wondered if dreaming on the shuttle would be different for people, whether the weightlessness would have an effect.

HOFFMAN: I would be surprised if it did, except that it might make it easier in the future to dream about being weightless. Only rarely do I remember my dreams, and of those I have remembered since my flight, none has had anything to do with spaceflight, which is a shame because that would be the one way I could recapture the feeling of weightlessness. Once you've lost it, you've lost it; you can't bring it back. The very first night on the ground, when I lay down in bed, before going to sleep, I could sort of bring it back. It's probably not dissimilar to what a hypnotist can do when he or she makes your arm just lie there, and it truly feels weightless, but you get that feeling through your whole body.

WHITE: I have speculated a lot on the long-term impact on society of the space program. I wonder if you have any thoughts about how the experience has affected people's perceptions.

HOFFMAN: I think that the technological impacts are likely to be more important than the philosophical in the near term. I think the impact of worldwide communications has already been tremendous. There has been an almost revolutionary change in terms of twentieth-century politics and economics compared to the whole previous time. By and large, things don't happen around the world without other people knowing about them. That is probably the biggest thing the space program has done in terms of changing human consciousness, although very few people recognize it as the space program. But it is because there is such a thing as geosynchronous orbit with the satellites up there.

I certainly don't think we have gotten anywhere near the point where people think of space, with the exception of people like the L-5 Society, as being a safety valve for human populations. That may happen someday. It may be that new types of cultures and societies will form in space colonies or on Mars. Intellectuals would say it is important as a metaphor, but I think it is important in how it affected the rest of the world's idea of what America is, and the fact that Americans went to the moon.

It's also interesting how important the existence of the space program is as a motivating force for young people. Many other areas of endeavor, from my point of view, are just as exciting: exploring the bottom of the ocean, researching the human brain, all sorts of things which are just as revolutionary as space. But there is something about space travel — maybe science fiction has a lot to do with it, because there is that sense of adventure and excitement. There is no "Star Trek" equivalent under the sea, so space is a metaphor and it makes a big difference in motivating a lot of kids to work a little bit harder.

WHITE: Finally, if there were a single message you would like to offer, what would it be?

HOFFMAN: As the shuttle program becomes more and more routine, I think there's a danger that people will lose sight of how much we are still working in the unknown. It's expected now that every mission is going to go perfectly. And in fact I don't even know how the country would be prepared to take a major failure. [This was before the Challenger disaster.] But we are still working in a very unforgiving environment. Number one is just the physical survival of the crew and the ship. After all, ships still sink in the

ocean and airplanes crash to the ground. I like to think that we
spend a lot more time preparing our spaceships for every flight
than we do the average airplane. But realistically speaking, someday . . . who knows? Spaceflight is not always 100 percent safe.

That's one aspect of it, but more important is that we're going
to go up and try to do some things that don't work. I don't mean
like what happened on our flight. We tried to fix a satellite, and
it turns out to be a problem you aren't going to fix. But I don't
think people realize what a new environment we are working in.
We still have an awful lot to learn.

WHITE: So your message would be that even though it appears
routine, it's not.

HOFFMAN: Yes. We'd like to make it seem that way, because
that means that everything is going well, but we can't get com-
placent about it.

Edwin ("Jake") Garn
STS 51-D

*Republican Senator Garn of Utah was aboard flight STS 51-D,
launched on April 12, 1985, with Charles Walker and Jeff Hoffman.
Garn had been a pilot in the U.S. Navy and chairman of a committee that oversees the NASA budget in the Senate.*

*What follows is a reconstruction of my interview with the senator
in Washington, D.C., on July 23, 1986.*

WHITE: What was the experience like, especially seeing the Earth
from a distance, and have you noticed a change in your view of
the political system as you've been working here again?

GARN: First let me say that it is virtually impossible to describe
the beauty of the Earth. I don't have the vocabulary, and I have
felt very frustrated in trying to describe it. You can take people to
see *The Dream Is Alive,* but spectacular as it is, it's not the same
as being there. That's because you are not only seeing it with your
own eyes with an even broader perspective than the I-Max camera
does, where you can scan the whole horizon, experiencing the
forty-five minutes of daylight with the forty-five minutes of dark-

ness, but then you couple that with the mobility of weightlessness while you are doing this, and the feeling is absolutely euphoric.

Toward the end of our mission, after we tried to rescue the satellite, I wanted to do one complete orbit of the Earth, uninterrupted, all the way around, which I did, floating on the flight deck, listening to *Swan Lake*. It was so fantastic and so beautiful, and I felt guilty, thinking about my family, my wife and seven kids. My feeling was that I'd seen and done it all, and I didn't care whether I came back or not; it really didn't make any difference. It wasn't that I didn't want to, but if something happened, and we didn't come back, fine, so be it, just utter peace and contentment and fulfillment.

So there was that feeling and something that is not original with me — I've heard it for years from other astronauts — you certainly come to the recognition that there aren't any political boundaries out there. You don't see any asterisks or stars for state or national capitals or any political subdivisions. You see it as one world, and you recognize how insignificant the planet Earth is when you look at ten billion stars in the Milky Way and recognize that our sun is a rather minor one. You look out there millions of light-years, and it is impossible to comprehend the vastness of space.

I have always believed that there were other human beings on other planets. Not in our solar system, obviously, but I personally believe that God created our Earth and the universe and that we are not the only children of God in the universe.

I said that to one of my colleagues after I got back, and he said, "I don't believe that, Jake. I don't believe that at all. We're the only place where God has chosen to put his children."

"Oh, come on," I said. "If you could look out there at billions of stars, recognizing that there are stars and planets out there millions of light-years away — I can't even comprehend 186,000 miles per second times six or seven million years. The vastness of a ten-billion-star system that is our own galaxy: how many planets are out there that we can't see any more than we can be seen by someone?

"I would come to that conclusion if I didn't believe in God just on the basis of the law of large numbers. Even an atheist mathematician ought to be able to say that it is statistically probable that someplace out there in the vastness of those numbers there is another planet, or many, that have the same atmospheric conditions and all of that."

Either way, from a Creationist or evolutionist standpoint, there is no doubt in my mind that there are human beings out there. Not just life, but people who don't have ears like Spock and are not green and don't have different shapes, but are like you and me.

The other intense feeling is that, along with the great beauty, you also have great feelings of sadness. At least I did, because you fly over Ethiopia and you have vivid pictures in your mind of those starving little kids with their bony ribs, or Iran and Iraq and the war that is going on there, or Afghanistan or Nicaragua, and you look at the trouble spots. You fly over Africa and recognize what occurs in so many of the Third World countries around the world, and you think, How sad, because certainly we have the natural resources to take care of all of God's children. We have the capacity to grow enough food that nobody needs to go hungry, so I sat there and questioned, "Why, why does this have to be?" You recognize that the Russians, the Nicaraguans, the Canadians, the Filipinos — it doesn't matter where they're from — all they want to do is raise their kids and educate them, just as we do.

So you think, Well, the problem is government. It isn't people, it's government, and when you look at the history of mankind, there have been such a few individuals who want to impose their will on others. That is where the trouble is. Just a very few of the billions of people who have lived on Earth who want power and dominion over their fellow citizens, not for wealth or material gain particularly, but just to control. Just for power itself.

When I've said that, I've often been asked, "Well, do you believe in one-world government?" Oh, no, no, it even greatly strengthened my patriotism, because also, as I sat there in orbit and thought about the differences in governments and why we have so much freedom and opportunity and material gain here in this country, to me it was obviously the freedom of the individual.

So as you fly around you look at the controlled countries compared to the democratic ones, and there is such a vast difference. It made me feel even more strongly that as Americans who enjoy so much, we really have an obligation and responsibility to our fellow human beings to try to help them have freedom and opportunity. It didn't really change any beliefs, but it certainly strengthened a lot of beliefs that I had, and it made me feel very sad that these conditions had to exist.

In that way it is a changing and a softening in my attitudes in some ways — a lot more compassion for some people who have a lot less than we Americans do. I suppose that's true because we become so accustomed to how we live in this country. We take it so for granted and think that everybody lives that way. Even though I have traveled extensively all over the world, it wasn't the same perspective as "Here is the planet Earth." Again, this is not something that is original with me, because other astronauts have talked about Spaceship Earth. But we really are all traveling together, so there ought to be more equality of opportunity around the Earth. We are God's children; why such disparities?

WHITE: A lot of the astronauts have said that they had an intellectual understanding of Spaceship Earth, but now it is real to them. No one has said, "I have totally changed my point of view because of being there," but rather, "I *feel* something that I previously just knew."

GARN: It's hard, sitting here, being held down by gravity and walking around on the Earth, to really visualize that this Earth is rotating on its own axis and orbiting around the sun. I don't care how many times you look at the globe or the models that show us in relationship to our solar system, it isn't quite real to you. You know it intellectually.

But the first time you look out at the Earth and see that, it's a heart-stopper. You say, "My goodness," and you just want to look all the time, because it finally is clear to you that this Earth really is round and it really is traveling through space. You've seen it for yourself. And it's like the difference — I don't care how many pictures you've seen of the Grand Canyon, it's not the same as looking over the side and saying, "My goodness, it really is that deep!"

It's a spiritual feeling that you know, not just because somebody told you or because you read it in a textbook or saw models of the universe, but you have personally seen that it really is like what you learned in school.

WHITE: Looking at the future, what do you see, from having

been there, in terms of the evolution of society as we become more of a spacefaring civilization? Do you see vast changes in human behavior?

GARN: I don't see vast changes quickly, but there's no doubt in my mind that if more people fly, there has to be more understanding of what I'm talking about.

Don L. Lind

STS 51-B

Don Lind waited almost nineteen years for his first flight on the shuttle. It occurred on Challenger on April 29, 1985, when he served as a mission specialist on Spacelab 3. A Mormon and a physicist, he brings an interesting combination of spiritual and scientific training to his experience as an astronaut. His total time in space is just a few minutes over seven days.

My interview with Dr. Lind was held at the Johnson Space Center in Houston on November 12, 1985.

LIND: In the Apollo program, there were a number of things I read where people were having profound religious experiences and changes in their whole outlook on life, and most of that, I think, is pretty much humbug because, at least back in those days, I was interested enough in what I read that I polled just about everyone. I know I polled everybody who went to the moon.

Obviously, the people who had a profound religious background before they left were impressed in those terms, and those who were too busy to be religious before they left were too busy to be religious when they came back. So I don't think that sort of thing changed anybody, and I think that, to a man, is true.

After talking to a lot of people, I found there were two almost universal experiences, and almost nothing else. One was basically what you would call nostalgia, looking back at home. You can easily understand that because of the dramatic situation. It was rather more forceful than it would have been on other forms of transportation.

The other I guess you would call a feeling of brotherhood. People who had a religious background expressed it in religious terms, and people who didn't expressed it in more humanitarian terms. But the idea, and I experienced this myself, was that you looked down and you could see how incredibly thin the Earth's atmosphere is and realize that if we pollute it, we all breathe it together, and if we are so dumb as to start a thermonuclear war, we all go together; there is no lifeboat, and everybody is in it together.

You can't see the boundaries over which we fight wars, and in a very real way, the inhabitants of this Earth are stuck on a very beautiful, lovely little planet in an incredibly hostile space, and everybody is in the same boat. That feeling was very widespread and very intense, and people expressed it in different ways. But there were those two things and not much else. I have read a lot of articles about a lot of other things people are supposed to have experienced in space, but I don't think they happened.

WHITE: There is an interaction between what you are expected to or expect to see and what you see. But do you also have the sense that the media in some sense create these ideas?

LIND: Yes, I do. I think, at least in the Apollo era, some people wanted to believe that going into space would reinforce religious beliefs, and therefore they almost read that into anything the astronauts said. That offended me, because I don't think you get converted to religion by going on a trip to the moon or to Cincinnati or anyplace else. I think religion is a more profound experience than that. People wanted astronauts to say something, and if they said anything close to that, they would embellish.

WHITE: By religious, do you mean a strict religious notion, such as "God spoke to me on the moon?"

LIND: No. I've got some very strong feelings myself, so I hesitate to read into other people's experiences something they would put into totally different words. I was saying it in a much broader sense: just a very profound, moving experience that had any connotation whatsoever of deity in it. That's what I was talking about as their religious experience.

WHITE: I've picked out three insights that people have in space. Do they square with anything that you or anyone you know experienced? One is the sense of an overview of the Earth, which you called brotherhood. I think I have confirmed that a lot of people have experienced that.

LIND: Very definitely, in my experiences and those of all the people I have talked to. Absolutely.

WHITE: A second is a realization of the Earth's place in the solar system, a physical experience of what I call the Copernican Perspective. A realization that Copernicus was right, and we are a part of the solar system as a whole. A couple of people have told me that although they already knew that, they felt it very strongly.

LIND: Yes, I would concur with that.

WHITE: And the third is a sense of the Earth's place in the universe as a whole, a feeling of the vastness of the universe, how large it is and that the Earth is just a part of that. Do those three sound valid?

LIND: Yes, they do: they sound valid. I would add one other, and I'm talking basically about my own experience, but I tend to think this might be more widespread: the almost overwhelming beauty, in an aesthetic sense, of the Earth. Intellectually, I knew what to expect. I have probably looked at as many pictures from space as anybody, except for two or three specialists here at the center, so I knew exactly what I was going to see. There was no intellectual preparation I hadn't made. But there is no way you can be prepared for the emotional impact.

I had been on orbit for two days. We had a laboratory mission, and we had all sorts of experiments that people had spent ten years getting ready to fly. So we had a sense of responsibility, trying to get all those experiments started. I had been up on the flight deck at night, taking pictures of the aurora and other things. I had certainly looked down at the Earth, but I was busy, in a professional mode. It was the third day on orbit before I had a chance to take ten minutes out of the flight plan and, just as a tourist, look down at the Earth.

When I did, it was a moving enough experience that it brought tears to my eyes. It was on two different planes. One was pure aesthetic beauty. I paint, and I was estimating how many colors of blue there are just in the transition through the Earth's atmosphere from the horizon to the incredible blackness of space. I can remember twenty very intense shades of blue. Then you look down at an archipelago with hundreds of shades of green and blue-green and yellow in the shoals and the atolls. That also brought tears to my eyes.

I've seen a lot of sights in my life, but that was an incredible one. For me, it was a mixture of the spiritual element because I'm an active member of the Mormon church and have a strong testimony of the existence of God. Looking down, I thought of half a dozen Scriptures that say, "If you've seen the heavens you've seen God moving in his majesty," and "The heavens declare the glory of God."

To me this had, in the very narrow interpretation of religion, a very strong religious component to it, which added to the emotional impact of seeing the beauty of the Lord's creations below me, and it's very, very meaningful for me in a religious sense. But even without the religious sense, it would have been a very moving experience. I have heard other people comment on that, and I suspect that this may be more universal and widespread.

WHITE: Just hearing you talk about it gives me the desire to do it myself.

LIND: I highly recommend it. It's the kind of thing no film system can ever record. *The Dream Is Alive* comes closer than any mechanical reproduction process I've ever seen. Maybe they get 50 percent of the way there, but that's better than anything else. It's like going to a live concert and then hearing a fairly good recording. The live concert has something that a good recording will never get. It was the sheer beauty of the scene, that I could see the Earth out there, this huge ball just rolling, rolling.

Your sensation is always that you're right side up and stationary. Intellectually, you know you're moving and the Earth is basically stationary, but you get the other impression. You get the impression that you're floating and the Earth is rolling. That's a nice picture.

WHITE: Joe Allen mentioned that as you're looking at the Earth you never see the same scene, because it's constantly changing.

LIND: That's right. I remember one time I had just a couple of minutes and looked out when we were just passing the Iberian Peninsula. We were going essentially right up the English Channel, and Europe was cloud-free that day, which was very unusual. All the Low Countries and France were open. London was covered, but you could see the mouth of the Thames and up through Jutland and across Scandinavia, it was all clear.

I could see the town where my grandfather was born in Sweden, the Baltic States, and then Leningrad was cloud-covered, but Moscow was open. So we essentially went from Bordeaux, France, to Moscow in something like six minutes. And I thought, Look at world history. I just passed over it. The fact that you are scooting along, looking at whole different cultures within a few minutes is very impressive.

WHITE: In addition to the view, which is spatial, the change in time sense must be extraordinary.

LIND: Yes. You decouple yourself totally from day and night. I've experienced half of that. I've been to Fairbanks, where you have almost total daylight or almost total darkness, and you tend to decouple from the sun. But when you're around the whole world, you're not in one place. Five minutes later, you're going to be in a different continent. That kind of total decoupling from a local time didn't seem strange at all. I don't know whether as astronauts we do much practicing and rehearsing and simulating relative to that, but it was unlike the visual experience where I had been prepared intellectually but not prepared from the emotional side.

It was exactly what I had expected, and it had no emotional impact. It was a very interesting scientific and intellectual experience, but it didn't seem strange in any way. I was totally prepared for it.

WHITE: One other element of the experience is the weightlessness. How about that?

LIND: Oh, that's marvelous, sheer delight after the space adaptation syndrome. It's a sort of Peter Pan mobility. That was absolutely delightful.

WHITE: The whole of the spaceflight experience is greater than the sum of the parts. What is most exciting about the whole thing?

LIND: That is probably different for everybody. I'm a scientist and science is fun. It's an intellectual game, like a treasure hunt that is all right for adults to play. The intellectual excitement was there for me, and it was what I had expected, what I'd experienced before in other kinds of sciences. But then you add just the sheer high adventure; there's obviously inherent risk. There's no fear, but it's the respect for the situation, both ascent and reentry. That gives it an element of high adventure.

Then there are all the other elements you talked about, the experience of weightlessness, and the overwhelming visual beauty. And the sense of significance, either because a lot of money goes into it or in our case, hundreds of man-years of preparation for these experiments. Whole teams of people are going to spend the next four to five years analyzing the data that you take in a week.

The purposefulness of what you're doing adds an importance to it. Money notwithstanding, there's an importance to what you're doing. It's like going to the circus and your oldest child's first birthday and your first date, all the fun things wrapped into one.

WHITE: One other issue I'm interested in is the effect of all of this on society as a whole. What are your thoughts on that?

LIND: I maintain a scientific research program with Western European collaborators, who pointed it out to me better than I have experienced it for myself. Back in the sixties, Americans didn't think very much of themselves. It was the "ugly American" era, and we were burning down campuses, and Americans were lost and purposeless. I think the national pride in the space program uniquely countered that trend. Some of the Europeans showed me that their perception of Americans in that decade was strongly modulated by the space program. Without that, it was a pretty dismal decade.

I could look around and see in society a sense of national pride. The Sputnik experience had been devastating for the national psyche. All sorts of things came out of that. The new math was a response to Sputnik, as were the successes of the Mercury, Gemini, and Apollo programs and the scientific programs that went with them. The space probe trips to the planets were significant and probably therapeutic as well.

The other thing is the response to this idea that I call brotherhood, that people almost sense it. If they had never seen the pictures or heard people talk about it, they wouldn't get it, but I think they almost feel that rather than hear it on an intellectual basis.

Think about the picture of the Earth coming up over the horizon of the moon, which I call the picture of the century. Every crew that went to the moon took that same picture. It is probably as moving as anything in reorienting people's idea to the whole-world concept. I believe it was not coincidence that this generation began to think of the Earth in that way when they saw those first space pictures.

We probably would have responded to the Ethiopian famine without space pictures, because we obviously responded to the Tokyo earthquake in the twenties. But the intensity and the personal involvement wouldn't have been the same. We've removed the concept of exotic distant lands like Bali or Afghanistan or Tibet. Where I grew up, there were faraway places with strange-sounding names, but only Lowell Thomas got there. We've taken that away now, and you realize that Tibet is just around the corner.

WHITE: You waited a long time for a flight. I gather from what you've said that it was really worth it.

LIND: Oh, yes. If I had been waiting in a vacuum, not doing anything, it would certainly not have been. Nothing that is one week long could be worth nineteen years. But I was doing extremely interesting things. And I had a front-row seat for great history.

Sultan Bin Salman al-Saud
STS 51-G

Prince Sultan of Saudi Arabia flew on the shuttle Discovery launched June 17, 1985, as a payload specialist. The occasion was the launch of a satellite for ARABSAT, a telecommunication consortium of Arab League countries. Prince Sultan, a member of the royal family, a pilot, and a television broadcaster, became the first Arab astronaut.

The following excerpts are from Sultan's interview with Bob MacDonald of Christian Science Monitor Broadcasting for the "Conversations with the Christian Science Monitor" *program of September 9, 1985.*

SULTAN: I think the minute I saw the view for the first time was really one of the most memorable moments of my entire life. I just said, in Arabic, "Oh, God," or something like "God is great," when I saw the view. It's beyond description.

MAC DONALD: The experience of flying through space has really had an effect on a lot of our own astronauts here in America. They come back and their lives are changed by being up there. How has it changed your life?

SULTAN: I think it has changed my insight into life. I've got more appreciation for the world we live in. I happen to be a believer that we have the best planet, so we really don't have to go out and look for another one. I think God has given us so much to be thankful for, and we are wasting so much time trying to destroy it.

The message that I came back with is that material things that used to interest me are of less interest to me right now, and I'm more of a person who wants to go out and do things and be involved rather than isolated. My experience was such a wonderful one, and I want to share it.

Back home, we had two weeks' worth of receptions that you would not believe, especially among kids and teenagers. Our reception was beyond description. They are all excited about it, and that I think was the main goal, and I'm glad that was accomplished.

MAC DONALD: What do you think you mean to the people back home?

SULTAN: I think they look at me as a symbol of their country's accomplishments. Saudi Arabia has worked very hard for the last twenty years to go somewhere and to develop itself.

MAC DONALD: The reaction was strong, of course, in your own country. How about the other Arab countries? You were the first Muslim and the first Arab to become an astronaut. What was the reaction around the Arab League?

SULTAN: I can tell you the human reaction from individuals. I get a lot of letters — three, four, five hundred every day, which I look at myself and answer. Most of them are not from Saudi Arabia, but from other Middle Eastern countries — Morocco, Algeria, Lebanon, Syria — and everyone is excited about it. I've got invitations to visit many people's homes, all over the Arab countries.

MAC DONALD: You come from a tradition of great religious faith, and I was just wondering what it meant to you from that foundation, how did it change your understanding of God?

SULTAN: It really strengthens your convictions. To me, it's an opportunity to prove that there is no conflict being a Muslim, or any other religion, and pursuing a scientific or space mission, which is almost at the peak of technological achievements in the twentieth century.

I did go up, I did practice my faith, the rituals, very simple things, whereby you resort to God and think about him. I did think about what the Koran, our book, my religion, has told me so many times, when I was looking at the Earth, the view. It is really the most incredible thing. I was asked by a Spanish magazine to come up with one word to describe what I have seen, and I said, "The word I come up with is that there are no words to describe it; it is beyond description."

Loren W. Acton

STS 51-F

Loren Acton, an employee of Lockheed, flew on the space shuttle in July 1985 as a payload specialist. His flight, scheduled for July 12, 1985, aborted on the pad three seconds before the scheduled lift-off. Ultimately launched on July 29, the shuttle experienced a premature engine shutdown, resulting in an "abort-to-orbit," which caused it to fly in a lower orbit than planned. Since returning from his flight, Dr. Acton has been an active member of the Association of Space Explorers.

My telephone interview with Acton took place July 15, 1986.

WHITE: What was the most profound part of the experience for you?

ACTON: It was the obligation and responsibility to carry out my job in an error-free way and a feeling of enormous frustration and defeat when I made mistakes. I carried a burden of obligation which was perhaps out of proportion, so what really affected me most was the work.

We had an extremely busy mission. We worked around the clock, and there were a lot of experiments. My failure was that I let it get the best of me and was not willing to focus on the good stuff that was happening a lot of the time. I ended up the flight feeling totally defeated. My poor wife had to put up with me on the plane going back to Houston, and instead of talking about the wonders of the mission, all I could talk about was my mistakes.

The healing process began when we landed in Houston, and there was an enormous crowd of astronomers out there feeling really good about how well things had gone and that began to raise my spirits.

WHITE: What would your comment be on the experience beyond the work?

ACTON: It's a little difficult to separate. I'm a kind of a loving guy, and those sorts of feelings were amplified in connection with the whole experience. I loved my crewmates, I loved those people on the ground, and in a very emotional sort of way. For the whole week, it was difficult for me to say anything over the voice loop of a loving nature, or a word of thanks, without choking up. I could talk nuts and bolts pretty well, but when I started to thank one of the investigators or the ground controllers or the payload specialists for something, I would just choke up something fierce.

But aside from that, with respect to the broader scope of a person's feelings toward the Earth and toward the experience, frankly, I am not able to untangle those that were simply self-fulfilling prophecies. I was supposed to be amazed at the beauty and fragility and finiteness of the Earth. I went up expecting that experience, and I had it. Gordon Fullerton said on his first flight that he was amazed at how thin the atmosphere was. I looked out the window and said, "By George, the atmosphere *is* really thin." Maybe I would have done that anyway, but I was primed. I'm an astronomer, I understand that the Earth is not infinite, and I was impressed with the fact that it is very finite.

The Earth is beautiful, and I like colors, so I loved the blue of the ocean and the white of the clouds and the red of the deserts and the green of the jungles. It was what I expected to be impressed with, and I was.

Did it change me? Yes, because all at once it made these rather pedestrian realizations something that other people want to hear about. And I had enough sense to realize that this was going to be the case, that people were going to be a lot more willing to listen to what I had to say than they would have been if I hadn't gone into space. I was going to be prepared to come back and say things that were constructive from my frame of reference. I would like to save the world, I think the world is pretty neat. I think we are on a dangerous course, that we have to evolve, to change, to solve problems differently than we used to. We've got to be prepared to be less insular. I was prepared to have an experience that made it possible for me to come back and contribute to this process.

WHITE: So this was a kind of consciousness you had before.

ACTON: I think so.

WHITE: It was a confirmation of what you felt, and even more than that, you realized that it would make your saying it more meaningful to others.

ACTON: Yes. I don't think that being in space changed me significantly. I was already there, but what it did do was provide an opportunity which I feel an obligation to make use of, so I've spent a lot of postflight time honing up on the experiences I had in space so they sound really impressive, and I don't think it's dishonest, because they *were* impressive. But I wasn't dramatically changed.

WHITE: Let's move on to another aspect of your work, the Association of Space Explorers. You went to the first congress in Paris. How would you characterize that? Were the national barriers and divisions really less present?

ACTON: Well, my perception of what was happening there was that the political barriers were minimal, that folks were pretty much on an honest basis. The language barrier is really enormous. It's awfully hard to sidle up to somebody and begin a trivial conversation. We had excellent interpreters, so if you wanted to talk about something substantial, you could get Natasha or one of the other interpreters over, and it would go fine, and we did that.

But if you just wanted to develop a friendship, it was hard, even though there was no reluctance on anybody's part to talk to anybody else. That's why it's important that these meetings be long. It was five days, and at the end of five days I had made friends with at least two or three people who spoke little, if any English. Making friends resulted from working together on subcommittees, stuff that I really don't give a hoot about, but simply doing it together caused us to learn to respect each other's opinions. After we had done that, we began to share personal experiences.

Quite a few of the cosmonauts speak a smattering of English, and some of them speak pretty good English. But the opportunity for the development of misunderstanding, if you're communicating with someone who speaks your language poorly and you speak his not at all, is overwhelming.

Time and again, I would start down some track, and I would see misunderstanding beginning to develop. If you didn't have a good interpreter there to sort it out, you rapidly bogged down. But the political things were not allowed to interfere with our ability to communicate. I didn't feel anybody had a hidden agenda at that meeting, and that was very refreshing.

WHITE: I've read the press release of the first congress, and I think I understand what the association is trying to get at, but could you say some more about what the goals are, how they're evolving, and what the association ought to and could do?

ACTON: I wish I could in a lucid way. Those statements were agonized over by Schweickart and Leonov and the fellows to try to state worthy objectives that could be translated into both languages and mean the same thing. My agenda is satisfied by simply having the Association of Space Explorers exist, but we do need a program, something we can talk to people about. Of course, the objective of the use of space, access to space, development of space for the good of the Earth and the people who live on it is something I believe in.

The Apollo-Soyuz test program was an example of doing an adventurous thing that made us both look good. But in terms of where we ought to go, I wish I had the wisdom to know. I feel like someone who has inherited an enormous bank account, and I am responsible for investing that wisely and making it grow and flourish. But I don't know anything about investments, and nobody else does, either. So the risk of blowing the money is very real, and the other risk is if you don't do anything, you blow it by definition, and it goes away.

I feel inadequate to the job at hand, so we just do the next step, which is to try to broaden the participation of people who have flown on both sides. The next step is to produce a book which contains pictures of the Earth and quotes the constructive things that people who have seen the Earth have said about the Earth and the space experience.

The next step is to manage to hold another congress and come out of it wihout having gotten into politics. We must at some point begin to be seen publicly throughout the world as an organization involved in worthy things. We must develop channels of communication to influential people throughout the world that are connected with the future of humankind in space, so that we can talk about it.

WHITE: Do you have a feeling for the possibilities in terms of the competition that's going on between East and West on Earth?

ACTON: I don't think anything is going to happen because of some automatic course of history. I think it will happen because of decisions people make. Right now, a lot of forces are driving us toward the ability to achieve a global compensation for our different political, social, and cultural systems. There are very big forces that drive us apart. On the other hand, people evolve. I use the example that there are other complex social systems, if you look at anthills and beehives. Collective endeavor lets them achieve marvelous things. But if you look at anthills and beehives from the time of Nebuchadnezzar, they look just like the ones we've got now.

If you look at our particular beehive, the human animal has changed dramatically in attitude and capabilities over that same period of time. So we are capable of evolving, and thereby I find reason for hope. If you look at the Soviets now, they are not the same system that they were, by far, in the days of Stalin. The problems are big, and I don't think that space represents anything particularly unique, except that it is the one area where we are both proud of ourselves. Maybe from that point of view it gives a bridge that is easier to cross than some of the other bridges.

You're not going to make much progress with somebody that already has a bit of an inferiority complex by addressing him in areas where he is sensitive. But if you can work with him in areas where he feels pretty good about himself, you're going to have a lot better chance of establishing common ground that can let you talk about the more sensitive areas. I think space is an area where, despite the fact they didn't go to the moon, the Soviets can feel proud of themselves. And despite the fact that our Challenger blew up, we can by and large feel proud of ourselves, and that helps.

The space experience provides a starting point which is inspirational at the same time that it's experiential. It's something about which we can both write flowery words, but they are still meaningful sentiments: the beauty of the Earth, the fragility of the Earth, the world without boundaries. All these are things we can agree on and sound good about.

The adventure, exploration, is meaningful to them and to us. There is a common ground of substance and significance which can be phrased in words that don't sound political. So it represents a unique area of common interest that can catch the attention of the public.

Bill Nelson
STS 61-C

Congressman Nelson, a Democrat from Florida, represents the district in which the Kennedy Space Center is located. He is chairman of a House committee that oversees NASA. Nelson flew aboard the shuttle in January 1986, the last successful flight before the Challenger accident.

I interviewed Nelson by telephone on August 7, 1986, and in September 1986.

(August 1986) WHITE: I would like to talk about your feelings when you saw the Earth from orbit and what that led you to think about how you wanted to do things when you came back to Earth.

NELSON: The Earth is an incredible sight. It's primarily blue and white, blue from the oceans and white from the clouds, and it's suspended in this black void of space that just goes on and on. On the night side of the Earth, that inky black is punctuated with brilliant stars, and it seems that you can see forever. I frequently recalled what King David had written thousands of years ago in Psalm 19: "The heavens declare the glory of God, and the firmament showeth His handiwork."

That order, that creation was very apparent to me as I looked back on this beautiful planet that looked so fragile at the same time. I was so busy with my experiments during the work periods that the time I spent in front of the window had to be while everyone else was asleep, and I soaked in those views and just floated there for revolution after revolution.

All those views combined with a view that I saw on a pass on the night side of the earth, coming up over northern Africa — out the window appeared this ribbon of lights with a crown jewel of lights and then a fan of lights. It suddenly occurred to me that I was looking at the entire Nile River, the crown jewel being Cairo, the fan being the delta as it flows into the Mediterranean. And in about five seconds, going eastward, there was the whole eastern Mediterranean — all of Israel and Syria and Jordan and Egypt. The irony of that view struck me, that it was so neat and so contained and so packaged in my window, when in reality it was anything but that 220 miles below.

All of that led me to conclude — I can't remember whether it was while I was in space or reflecting back after I returned — that if the superpower leaders could be given the opportunity to see the Earth from the perspective from which I saw it — perhaps at a summit meeting in space in the context of the next century — they might realize that we're all in this with a common denominator. It would have a positive effect on their future decisions concerning war and peace.

It is so beautiful, and yet it looks so fragile.

WHITE: I've also been interested in the summit. I talked about it with Joe Allen and some of the other astronauts. Is it a project that you're actively pursuing, or is it more an idea that you are floating for people?

NELSON: There is no way that you're going to plan a summit today in space, but you can surface the idea and let people start thinking about it. It's a natural for me to talk about this as a follow-up to our committee and the Apollo-Soyuz astronauts' visit to Moscow for the tenth anniversary reunion of their link-up in space. We were there as the guests of the Soviet Academy of Sciences to talk about cooperation in space.

WHITE: It sounds as though the experience did have an impact on what you've done since you've been back.

NELSON: It confirmed what I already knew and what I'd been working on, which is space as the unique environment in which adversaries can come together to cooperate. You hear so much about the opposite. You hear the SDI side, about using space for war. But the fact is that eleven years ago we used it for a giant symbolic act of peace, and it can be done, though we've had very little cooperation over the course of the last five to six years.

We could have a continuation of exchanges at the working group level. The Soviets have a Mars project scheduled for 1988, and we are planning a Mars observer in 1990. We could exchange data on those before, during, and after the missions. We could plan the initial discussions of a joint unmanned Mars mission and look into the next century for the possibility of a joint manned mission. That would dramatically affect the politics of the globe.

But that was not something that just happened to me in space. My notions about space being an environment of cooperation were confirmed by this extraordinary view, looking back at this planet.

WHITE: The trip probably makes your views more powerful to others, because when you speak, there's a conviction in your voice, and one has to say "This is a man who's been there." It makes a difference, I think.

NELSON: It makes a tremendous difference, given that only 132 people, including eleven foreign nationals, have flown into space on American vehicles. It makes a difference substantively in that I can now relate what I've seen. It also makes a difference in the mind of the receiver of the information, knowing that you've been there.

WHITE: So it was really a confirmation experience that also gave some credibility and passion to what you had to say. I had the same feeling in talking to Senator Garn, who said that his beliefs were strongly reinforced. Do you and he communicate and work together?

NELSON: Yes, very much. Because of the nature of this institution, the Senate and the House don't get together that much. However, when we do, there's a whole new dimension to our relationship with this shared experience. Jake was very supportive in encouraging me to fly. So that relationship has built up, and not just since the flight.

WHITE: I presume that you would also think, as more people of all types fly, that this shift toward a new attitude toward space might develop.

NELSON: Yes, but as a practical matter, that's not going to happen for some time. When you talk about summits in space, you're looking into the next century, into much more routine spaceflight. You're not really talking about this generation of space vehicles.

(September 1986) WHITE: In our previous interview, you were talking about how you had come to see space as an arena for peaceful cooperation and suggested ways in which supporting joint missions and that sort of effort could lead to a change in political relationships on Earth.

NELSON: I can see the potential for that change. I can't say that we've actually seen any enormous and lasting change thus far. Adversaries are adversaries, and despite the good will generated by the Apollo-Soyuz mission, we went back into the war of words, a rejuvenation of the Cold War.

However, it was obvious when we were in Moscow that the Soviets were extending every courtesy, and the hidden agenda was that they wanted to resume cooperative ventures in space. We talked at every level, all the way up to the president of the Soviet Union, Gromyko.

That session with him was two and a half hours long, eyeball to eyeball. He had a big delegation on his side of the table, and the members of Congress, plus our astronauts and Dr. Tom Paine, the head of the National Commission on Space, were on our side. The important thing I suggested was that we get these working groups reestablished so this kind of exchange of information could start. I am told by NASA that some of that has been restarted.

WHITE: Is it accurate to say that there is no magic potion in space, but that by working incrementally, you can move things more toward peace and away from conflict?

NELSON: Yes. It's also ironic, since so much is made of Star Wars and the militarization of space. That, of course, was the number one topic on the Russian agenda — since we were in Moscow a month before the summit — to talk about how bad SDI is, and so forth.

It was always the secondary agenda that we would like to cooperate in ventures in space. So your characterization of that is correct. I think there's probably a realization in the Soviet Union as there is in America that to go to Mars in a manned mission would be such an expensive task that shared resources would be very helpful.

Of course, you can't really start planning that until you do all the incremental steps, the sharing of these missions by the end of this decade, and then the planning for an unmanned mission, where you could have two separate missions that taken together would be the combined mission, but no transfer of technology. For example, one nation could land on Mars, scoop up the samples, and bring them back to a predetermined position, where the other nation could land its spacecraft, receive the samples, and return to Earth.

WHITE: We seem to draw a lesson out of space missions, saying, "If we can send a man to the moon, why can't we build better cities or feed the hungry?" If we do have a joint mission with the Soviets, the message might be, "If we can go to Mars together, why can't we . . ." You fill in the blanks.

NELSON: You're getting into a different realm of political thought that I, having been in space and looked back at the Earth, think could be very real. It's a unique environment in which, if you put aside the politics of the moment, and you don't look for excuses not to cooperate in space, then you have a unique environment in which adversaries can cooperate. It's an area of exploration that lends itself to joint participation for highly advanced societies. It's not in anybody's territory — not in the West, not in the Eastern bloc, not in the nonaligned nations. It's in a common ground of space.

WHITE: The East, the West, the blocs, all those terms don't make any sense when you're in space, so it's hard to maintain them when you're not on the planet.

NELSON: You're not going to get leaders of nations going into space while it is so risky to fly. But once that risk comes down, it's very likely to happen. I think the world would be better off for it, because the perspective of the leaders would change.

WHITE: You have no question that if any of the leaders go into space, they will definitely experience the unity of the planet?

NELSON: That's right.

WHITE: When you're talking to your colleagues in Congress, do some of them say, "That's all very nice, but we know that the Soviet Union's goal is to dominate not only this planet, but space, and we have to be careful about them."

NELSON: Sure, and that commentary will continue. The Soviets have done a lot of things that lead people to be suspicious. On the other hand, they're suspicious about us. We happen to think that truth and justice are usually on our side, so we have a few more suspicions of them. Of course, there are always going to be those considerations. When you have an adversary, that's the nature of warfare/competition.

WHITE: How do you respond? Do you say, "I know that that's so, but for common survival purposes, we have to find ways to work together"? What is your basic reaction to that argument?

NELSON: My response is that whether we like our adversary or not, the realities are that we have to try to seek accommodation and keep from blowing up the planet.

WHITE: What do you think of the scenario the National Commission on Space laid out? That is a fairly comprehensive vision of an American future in space that focuses on cooperation and a broadly based view of the future. Where do you see it in terms of its becoming an integral part of American space development? Or do you think it will become such?

NELSON: I think it will because it traces the future of the next fifty years. That committee's report could have been written in Moscow as well as in Washington; it could have been written ten years ago or it could be written ten years from now, and it would be essentially the same thing.

WHITE: Finally, if there were one key message you'd like to get across to people, what would it be?

NELSON: That it's very important for us to have a robust space program to complement the character of the American people as adventurers and explorers. If we are to fulfill our potential, we have to act on that characteristic.

Appendix A

Rationale for Exploring and Settling the Solar System

Our Vision: The Solar System as the Home of Humanity. The Solar System is our extended home. Five centuries after Columbus opened access to "The New World" we can initiate the settlement of worlds beyond our planet of birth. The promise of virgin lands and the opportunity to live in freedom brought our ancestors to the shores of North America. Now space technology has freed humankind to move outward from Earth as a species destined to expand to other worlds.

Our Purpose: Free Societies on New Worlds. The settlement of North America and other continents was a prelude to humanity's greater challenge: the space frontier. As we develop new lands of opportunity for ourselves and our descendants, we must carry with us the guarantees expressed in our Bill of Rights: to think, communicate, and live in freedom. We must stimulate individual initiative and free enterprise in space.

Our Ambition: Opening New Resources to Benefit Humanity. Historically, wealth has been created when the power of the human intellect combined abundant energy with rich material resources. Now America can create new wealth on the space frontier to benefit the entire human community by combining the energy of the Sun with materials left in space during the formation of the Solar System.

Our Method: Efficiency and Systematic Progression. In undertaking this great venture we must plan logically and build wisely. Each new step

National Commission on Space, *Pioneering the Space Frontier* (New York: Bantam Books, 1986), 3–4.

must be justified on its own merits and make possible additional steps. American investments on the space frontier should be sustained at a small but steady fraction of our national budget.

Our Hope: Increased World Cooperation. In his essay *Common Sense,* published in January of 1776, Tom Paine said of American independence, " 'Tis not the affair of a City, County, a Province, or a Kingdom; but of a Continent . . . 'Tis not the concern of a day, a year, or an age; posterity are virtually involved in the contest, and will be more or less affected even to the end of time, by the proceedings now." Exploring the Universe is neither one nation's issue, nor relevant only to our time. Accordingly, America must work with other nations in a manner consistent with our Constitution, national security, and international agreements.

Our Aspiration: American Leadership on the Space Frontier. With America's pioneer heritage, technological preeminence, and economic strength, it is fitting that we should lead the people of this planet into space. Our leadership role should challenge the visions, talents, and energies of young and old alike, and inspire other nations to contribute their best talents to expand humanity's future.

Our Need: Balance and Common Sense. Settling North America required the sustained efforts of laborers and farmers, merchants and ministers, artisans and adventurers, scientists and seafarers. In the same way, our space program must combine with vigor and continuity the elements of scientific research, technological advance, the discovery and development of new resources in space, and the provision of essential institutions and systems to extend America's reach in science, industry, and the settlement of space.

Our Approach: The Critical Lead Role of Government. As formerly on the western frontier, now similarly on the space frontier, Government should support exploration and science, advance critical technologies, and provide the transportation systems and administration required to open broad access to new lands. The investment will again generate in value many times its cost to the benefit of all.

Our Resolve: To Go Forth "In Peace for All Mankind." When the first Apollo astronauts stepped onto the Moon, they emplaced a plaque upon which were inscribed the words, "We came in peace for all mankind." As we move outward into the Solar System, we must remain true to our values as Americans: To go forward peacefully and to respect the integrity of planetary bodies and alien life forms, with equality of opportunity for all.

Appendix B

Organizations and Institutions Supporting the Exploration and Development of Space

National Space Society: Formed as a result of the merger of the L-5 Society and the National Space Institute, NSS is an active organization with local chapters all over the country. The society holds an annual space development conference, publishes a magazine, and alerts its members to important developments on the space exploration front.

For information: 922 Pennsylvania Avenue, S.E., Washington, DC 20023.

Planetary Society: Founded by astronomer Carl Sagan, this society supports unmanned and manned exploration of space, including a joint US-Soviet mission to Mars. The society also publishes a magazine and holds conferences of interest to its members.

For information: 65 North Catalina Avenue, Pasadena, CA 91106.

Space Studies Institute: SSI focuses on research aimed at supporting large-scale human settlement of space, utilizing extraterrestrial materials. Founded by Dr. Gerard K. O'Neill, SSI holds a biennial conference and publishes a monthly newsletter.

For informaton: P.O. Box 82, Princeton, N.J. 08540.

Students for the Exploration and Development of Space: SEDS is a student-oriented organization, the purpose of which is to support and constructively channel student interest in space exploration and development.

For information: Massachusetts Institute of Technology, W20-445, Cambridge, MA 02139.

Space Generation Foundation/International Space University Project: With a name reflecting the aspirations of those born since the launching of

Sputnik in 1957, the foundation supports a number of innovative space-related activities, including the International Space University.

For information: 636 Beacon Street, Suite 201, Boston, MA 02215.

Institute for Security and Cooperation in Outer Space: ISCOS promotes international cooperative space activities as an alternative to deployment of space weapons. ISCOS activities include research, activism, and outreach.

For information: 8 Logan Circle, Washington, DC 20004-3727.

Association of Space Explorers: The Association of Space Explorers is a global organization of cosmonauts and astronauts that encourages the cooperative exploration and development of space for the benefit of all humanity. Membership is open to people who have flown in space, and the Association holds annual meetings of its members.

For information: 3278 Sacramento Street, San Francisco, CA 94115.

Notes

Chapter 1

1. Willis Harman and Howard Rheingold, *Higher Creativity: Liberating the Unconscious for Breakthrough Insights* (Los Angeles: J. P. Tarcher, 1984), 174.
2. Ibid., 175.

Chapter 2

1. Telephone interview with Edward G. Gibson, August 15, 1985.

Chapter 3

1. Russell L. Schweickart, *No Frames, No Boundaries,* film commentary (Palo Alto, Calif.: Creative Initiative/Beyond War). From *Earth's Answer: Explorations of Planetary Culture at the Lindesfarne Conferences* (West Stockbridge, Mass.: Lindesfarne/Harper & Row, 1977).
2. The best source for this type of information is Tim Furniss, *Space Flight: The Records* (Enfield, England: Guinness Books, 1985). This edition listed 165 people as having been in space. In addition, Charles Walker supplied me with a "Spacefarers Roster" compiled by author and space expert James E. Oberg, which lists 111 missions and 199 people in space as of January 22, 1986. Oberg does not count the two Mercury suborbital hops; with them, the totals are 113 and 201.
3. Julian Jaynes, *The Origin of Consciousness in the Breakdown of the Bicameral Mind* (Boston: Houghton Mifflin, 1976), 48–49.
4. Interview with Marc Garneau, Ottawa, Canada, July 11, 1986.
5. Interview with Jake Garn, Washington, D.C., July 23, 1986.

6. Interview with Garneau.
7. Interview with Byron K. Lichtenberg, Wellesley, Massachusetts, August 19, 1986.
8. Telephone interview with Edward G. Gibson, August 15, 1985.
9. Interview with Don L. Lind, Johnson Space Center, Houston, November 12, 1985.
10. Telephone interview with Alan L. Bean, July 28, 1986.
11. A number of excellent firsthand accounts of Soviet cosmonauts have been published in Soviet journals and newspapers. Excerpts used in this book were kindly provided to me by Marcia S. Smith, former executive director of the National Commission on Space and an expert on the Soviet program.
12. *Life,* March 9, 1962, 4.
13. Interview with Bean.
14. Because of the force of gravity, it is as if this gravity well were actually four thousand miles deep. An excellent explanation of this concept appears in National Commission on Space, *Pioneering the Space Frontier* (New York: Bantam Books, 1986), 61.
15. Interview with Lind.
16. Excerpts from an audiotape of a radio interview, "Conversations with the *Christian Science Monitor*," conducted by Bob MacDonald, September 10, 1985.
17. Interview with Garn.
18. Interview with Jeffrey A. Hoffman, Johnson Space Center, Houston, November 12, 1985.
19. Telephone interview with Eugene A. Cernan, December 3, 1985.
20. M. Scott Carpenter et al., *We Seven* (New York: Simon and Schuster, 1962), 449.
21. Excerpt from cosmonaut Valentin Lebedev's flight diary, *Pravda,* August 15, 1983, 7.
22. Carpenter, *We Seven,* 393.
23. Interview with Lichtenberg.
24. Interview with Cernan.
25. "An Astronaut's Diary," audiotape (Washington, D.C.: National Public Radio, 1985). From René Daumal, *Mount Analogue,* trans. Roger Shattuck. Translation copyright © 1959 by Vincent Stuart Ltd.
26. L-5 Society, Fourth Annual Conference on Space Development, Washington, D.C., April 27–28, 1985.
27. Interview with Lind.
28. Interview with Edgar D. Mitchell, Palm Beach, Florida, November 18, 1986.

Chapter 4

1. Yuri Gagarin and Valentin Lebedev, *Survival in Space* (New York: Frederick Praeger, 1969), 3.
2. *We Seven* (New York: Simon and Schuster, 1962), 254.
3. Ibid., 388.
4. Ibid., 395–396.
5. Ibid., 450.
6. Ibid.
7. Richard S. Lewis, *Appointment on the Moon* (New York: Ballantine Books, 1969), 227.
8. Ibid.
9. *We Seven*, 465.
10. *Life*, March 9, 1962, 4.
11. Press release, "Remarks of Senator John Glenn, Declaration of Candidacy for Re-election, February 19–20, 1986."

Chapter 5

1. Telephone interview with Eugene A. Cernan, December 3, 1985.
2. Telephone interview with Russell L. Schweickart, October 29, 1985.
3. Tim Furniss, *Space Flight: The Records* (Enfield, England: Guinness Books, 1985), 122.
4. Russell L. Schweickart, *No Frames, No Boundaries*, film commentary (Palo Alto, Calif.: Creative Initiative/Beyond War). From *Earth's Answer: Explorations of Planetary Culture at the Lindesfarne Conferences* (West Stockbridge, Mass.: Lindesfarne/Harper & Row, 1977).
5. Ibid.
6. Interview with Cernan.
7. Michael Collins, *Carrying the Fire* (New York: Farrar, Straus and Giroux, 1974), 471.
8. Ibid., 470.
9. Telephone interview with Michael Collins, January 17, 1986.
10. Eugene A. Cernan, "The Price of Being a Space Hero," *TV Guide*, April 13–19, 1985, 4.
11. James Gorman, "The Righteous Stuff," *Omni*, May 1984, 48.
12. Interview with Edgar D. Mitchell, Palm Beach, November 18, 1986.
13. Interview with Cernan.
14. Henry S. F. Cooper, *A House in Space* (New York: Holt, Rinehart and Winston, 1976), 166–167.

15. Ibid.
16. Ibid.
17. Ibid., 136–137.
18. Telephone interview with Edward G. Gibson.
19. Telephone interview with Gerald P. Carr, February 6, 1986.
20. Interview with Gibson.

Chapter 6

1. Presidential support, which appears to be a necessary element in a strong space program, has continued at various levels through seven presidencies.
2. Joseph P. Allen, "Diary of a Shuttle Launch," *Science Digest*, September 1984.
3. "Good Morning America," December 12, 1984.
4. L-5 Society, Fourth Annual Conference on Space Development, Washington, D.C., April 27–28, 1985.
5. "Discovery Due to Land in Calif. This Morning," *Boston Globe*, June 24, 1985.
6. Telephone interview with Charles D. Walker, July 2, 1985.
7. Telephone interview with Loren W. Acton, July 15, 1986.
8. Ibid.
9. Interview with Jake Garn, Washington, D.C., July 23, 1986.
10. Ibid.
11. Telephone interview with Bill Nelson, August 7, 1986.
12. Ibid.

Chapter 7

1. Interview with Edgar D. Mitchell, November 18, 1986.
2. Ibid.
3. Interview with Charles D. Walker, Seattle, Washington, May 1986.
4. "First Chinese Manned Space Shot Is 'Not Far Off,' Party Paper Says," *Boston Globe*, September 1, 1986, 6.
5. Ibid.
6. Details of all of these flights are included in Tim Furniss, *Space Flight: The Records* (Enfield, England: Guinness Books, 1985). It is an excellent source for American readers who wish to keep current on the Soviet program.
7. The Soviet experience on long-duration missions is consistent with

the American Skylab experience; these appear to be cross-cultural issues.

8. Press release issued by the Association of Space Explorers, First Planetary Congress, Cernay, France, October 2–6, 1985.

Chapter 8

1. Geoffrey K. C. Pardoe, *The Future for Space Technology* (London and Dover, N.H.: Frances Pinter, 1984), 64.
2. Ibid., 67.
3. "Communications, the Information Society and Space," talk delivered at Space Policy Seminar, Kennedy School for Government, Harvard University, Cambridge, Massachusetts, 1986.
4. Interview with Don L. Lind, Johnson Space Center, Houston, November 12, 1985.
5. The Geostar Corporation, founded by Gerard K. O'Neill, also founder of the Space Studies Institute, is one of the early leaders in this area.
6. Edgar Mitchell has written a book about SDI. It should be valuable reading for those who want to understand SDI against the backdrop of space exploration and human evolution. A book about his overall philosophy is forthcoming.
7. Patrick O'Driscoll, Julia Lawlor, and William Dunn, "Space Future: Trips to Mars, Moon Colony," *USA Today,* June 10, 1986, 2A.
8. Telephone interview with Michael Collins, January 17, 1986.
9. "Earth System Science: A Preview," Earth System Sciences Committee, University Corporation for Atmospheric Research, Boulder, Colorado, 1986.
10. Ibid.
11. James E. Lovelock, *Gaia: A New Look at Life on Earth* (Oxford: Oxford University Press, 1979), 1–2.
12. National Commission on Space, *Pioneering the Space Frontier* (New York: Bantam Books, 1986), 52–53.
13. Ibid., 56–57.
14. Interview with Paul Blanchard, Washington, D.C., July 22, 1986.

Chapter 9

1. L-5 Society, Space Development Conference, Seattle, Washington, May 1986.

2. Michael Collins, *Carrying the Fire* (New York: Farrar, Straus and Giroux, 1974).
3. A good summary of diffusion of innovation theory is available from Creative Initiative/Beyond War, 222 High Street, Palo Alto, CA 94301.
4. Michael Rozek, "Bioflight," *Air & Space* (June/July 1986): 84.
5. Ibid.
6. Telephone interview with Martin Rutte, July 16, 1986.
7. Ibid.
8. Ibid.
9. Peter Russell, *The Global Brain* (Los Angeles: J. P. Tarcher, 1983), 18.
10. "Leadership and Mastery," brochure of Innovation Associates, P.O. Box 2008, Framingham, MA 01701, 1985.

Chapter 10

1. Arthur Koestler, *The Ghost in the Machine* (London: Hutchinson, 1967), 46–47.
2. Interview with Edgar D. Mitchell, November 18, 1986.
3. As with other components of my conceptual framework, I am adapting elements of general systems theory and human systems theory to the requirements of this analysis. Readers interested in more detail should explore the references provided, particularly Jeffrey S. Stamps, *Holonomy: A Human Systems Theory* (Seaside, Calif.: Intersystems Publications, 1980), an excellent synthesis of systems thinking.

   The holonomic model expands on many ideas presented here. For example, the cycle of emergence broadens the notion of system states into four levels. These are slow change, accelerated change, a period of uncertainty and confusion in which the system may step back in order to make a leap forward, and a new level of stability at which new qualities emerge and become a part of the system. See *Holonomy*, page 97.
4. For a system to have a purpose or to behave purposively does not imply a teleological force at work. For example, systems theorists see a kind of purposive behavior in all systems, including human ones. See *Holonomy*, page 75.

Chapter 11

1. Peter Russell, *The Global Brain* (Los Angeles: J. P. Tarcher, 1983), 32.
2. There are, of course, theories about how human beings came into existence that do not use evolution as an explanation, the best known of which is the Genesis story. There is also a modern update on this "Creationist" approach, which suggests that humans are the descendants of extraterrestrial space travelers who colonized the planet long ago. However, regardless of which explanation or combination of explanations is chosen, the question of the human purpose or function in the universe would remain.
3. Jeffrey S. Stamps, in *Holonomy: A Human Systems Theory* (Seaside, Calif.: Intersystems Publications, 1980), suggests that mind is a complementarity to systems. Wherever a system exists, an appropriate level of mind and awareness exist. Using that perspective, we could say that the purpose of building overview systems is to create planetary, solar, galactic, and universal minds.
4. Norman Myers, ed., *Gaia: An Atlas of Planet Management* (Garden City, N.Y.: Anchor Books, 1984), 100.
5. Ibid., 12.
6. Ibid., 100.
7. Russell, *The Global Brain*, 95–97.
8. Ibid., 100.
9. Ibid., 232–233.
10. R. Buckminster Fuller, *Critical Path* (New York: St. Martin's Press, 1981), 27.
11. Michael Holmquist, "The Philosophical Bases of Soviet Space Exploration," *Key Reporter* (Winter 1985–86): 3.
12. Yuri Gagarin and Valentin Lebedev, *Survival in Space* (New York: Frederick Praeger, 1969), 3.

Chapter 12

1. Patrick O'Driscoll, Julia Lawlor, and William Dunn, "Space Future: Trips to Mars, Moon Colony," *USA Today*, June 10, 1986, 2A.
2. Trudy E. Bell, "The Evolution of American Space Interest Groups: 1980–1985," *Space Manufacturing* 5, Proceedings of the Seventh Princeton/AIAA/SSI Conference, May 8–11, 1985, ed. Barbara Faughnan and Gregg Maryniak (New York: American Institute of Aeronautics and Astronautics, 1985), 187.

3. Michael Rozek, "Bioflight," *Air & Space* (June/July 1986): 84. It is worth noting that the ideas discussed here are gaining general currency. For example, the terms "old space" and "new space" were used frequently in a talk given by Ken Sweezey at the L-5 Society's 1986 Space Development Conference. In addition, "the new space movement" is a prime focus in Michael A. G. Michaud, *Reaching for the High Frontier: The American Pro-Space Movement 1972–1984* (New York: Praeger, 1986).

Chapter 13

1. Frank White, "Understanding Space Settlements as Human Systems," in *Space Manufacturing 1983*, vol. 53, *Advances in the Astronautical Sciences*, Proceedings of the Sixth Princeton/SSI Conference on Space Manufacturing, ed. James D. Burke and April S. Whitt (San Diego: Univelt, 1983), 59.
2. Michael Collins, *Carrying the Fire* (New York: Farrar, Straus and Giroux, 1974), 462.

Chapter 14

1. James E. Lovelock, *Gaia: A New Look at Life on Earth* (Oxford: Oxford University Press, 1979), 148.
2. Ibid.

Chapter 15

1. Telephone interview with Edward G. Gibson, August 15, 1985.
2. Telephone interview with Russell L. Schweickart, October 29, 1985.
3. Telephone interview with Michael Collins, January 17, 1986.

Chapter 16

1. Letter from commission chairman Thomas O. Paine to those who had participated in or supported the work of the commission.
2. National Commission on Space, *Pioneering the Space Frontier* (New York: Bantam Books, 1986), 60.
3. Using extraterrestrial materials to build space structures and habitats

creates a wholly different mind-set about every aspect of space exploration, from propulsion systems to population levels. It is for this reason that the commission's endorsement of the concept is so important.

4. It is reasonable to ask whether the American value system, with its emphasis on individual freedoms, could have existed without an open frontier available for expansion. It is also reasonable to ask whether it can survive on a finite and increasingly restricted planetary surface.

5. See testimony on the commission report before the relevant Senate and House subcommittees in *America's Future in Space: Final Report of the National Commission on Space*, July 22, 1986. Statements by Thomas O. Paine, chairman, Laurel L. Wilkenning, vice chairman, and commissioners George Field, Jack L. Kerrebrock, and Kathryn D. Sullivan.

6. Professor George Field, a member of the commission, and I wrote the first drafts of several sections of the Declaration for Space, in particular the Rationale for Exploring and Settling the Solar System. These drafts were modified and rewritten by other members of the commission before being included in the final report.

7. For additional thoughts on this subject, see George Field and Frank White, "Principles for Pioneers" in *Space Policy Journal* (Guildford, England: Butterworth Scientific, February 1987). The article contains a detailed analysis of the principles enunciated in the commission's report.

8. The process of developing such a document has already begun under the joint auspices of the National Air and Space Museum, Washington, D.C., and the Center for Democracy, Boston, Massachusetts.

9. *Pioneering the Space Frontier*, 2.

10. Ibid., 15.

11. This statement has drawn a good deal of comment from members of the new space movement and from the media, because it is the fundamental principle from which the others follow.

12. *Pioneering the Space Frontier*, 107–142.

13. Ibid., 16.

14. Telephone interview with Bill Nelson.

Chapter 17

1. Senator Spark Matsunaga, "Marsquest," *Omni*, June 1986, 22.

2. Ibid., 125.

3. This process has already begun and can be seen in the growing pressure from many quarters for a joint U.S.-Soviet Mars mission. If that takes place, it would be more than a one-shot project, because it might become the model for future exploration of the solar system.
4. Hearings were held in both the House and Senate in the spring of 1986, and the report was presented to the president at that time.
5. Article 2 of the 1967 United Nations treaty on space forbids any sovereign claims in outer space.
6. Telephone interview with Eugene A. Cernan, December 3, 1985.
7. National Commission on Space, *Pioneering the Space Frontier* (New York: Bantam Books, 1986), 70–71.
8. Press release, "Remarks of Senator John Glenn, Declaration of Candidacy for Re-election," February 19–20, 1986.
9. Press release, First Planetary Congress, Association of Space Explorers, Cernay, France, October 2–6, 1985.
10. Seminar on exploration of space, Boston, May 6, 1986.
11. Both Jeffrey S. Stamps, *Holonomy: A Human Systems Theory* (Seaside, Calif.: Intersystems Publications, 1980), 57, and I. S. Shklovskii and Carl Sagan, *Intelligent Life in the Universe* (New York: Dell, 1966), 412–413, offer valuable discussions of this issue.

Chapter 18

1. James E. Lovelock, *Gaia: A New Look at Life on Earth* (Oxford: Oxford University Press, 1979), 148.
2. David Lacey, "Some Social Implications of a Generation Starship," *Journal of the British Interplanetary Society* 37 (1984): 499–501, is well worth reading.
3. Charles D. Walker, addendum to interview, August 7, 1986.

Chapter 19

1. National Commission on Space, *Pioneering the Space Frontier* (New York: Bantam Books, 1986), 25.
2. Ibid., 30.
3. Ibid., 27.
4. Willis Harman and Howard Rheingold, *Higher Creativity: Liberating the Unconscious for Breakthrough Insights* (Los Angeles: J. P. Tarcher, 1984), 177–182.
5. Joanne Irene Gabrynowicz, a New York City lawyer and writer, is

doing innovative work on how the Founding Fathers applied the principles of systems thinking to the Constitution and the implications for planetary and space-based civilizations. Her views are summarized in a paper, "Space Development and the American Experiment: A Context and Model for International Progress." For information, write to The Human Side of Law, 67 Murray Street, New York, NY 10007.
6. Telephone interview with Eugene A. Cernan, December 3, 1985.
7. William Y. Elliott and Neil A. McDonald, *Western Political Heritage* (Englewood Cliffs, N.J.: Prentice-Hall, 1955), 492, 500.

Chapter 20

1. In very large populations on Earth, mutations may occur but not be noticed because they simply cannot get a foothold and are weeded out over time. This is why it is so important not only to have an environment that encourages mutation, but also one where small, isolated groups can come together.
2. Ben R. Finney and Eric M. Jones, "From Africa to the Stars: The Evolution of the Exploring Animal," *Space Manufacturing 1983*, vol. 53, *Advances in the Astronautical Sciences*, Proceedings of the Sixth Princeton/SSI Conference on Space Manufacturing, ed. James D. Burke and April S. Whitt (San Diego: Univelt, 1983), 85–100.
3. Ibid., 96–97.
4. Ibid., 100.

Chapter 21

1. Ben R. Finney, "SETI and Interstellar Migration," *Journal of the British Interplanetary Society* 38 (1985): 274–275.
2. Telephone interview with Michael Collins, January 17, 1986.
3. The Greek gods apparently were believed to intervene in human society in much the same way that extraterrestrials are reputed to involve themselves today. The difference seems to be that the intervention fit into that society's basic paradigm of reality, but does not fit into ours.
4. I. S. Shklovskii and Carl Sagan, *Intelligent Life in the Universe* (New York: Dell, 1966), 409–418.
5. National Commission on Space, *Pioneering the Space Frontier* (New York: Bantam Books, 1986), 4.

Chapter 22

1. William Y. Elliott and Neil A. McDonald, *Western Political Heritage* (Englewood Cliffs, N.J.: Prentice-Hall, 1955), 145.
2. Ibid., 145–146.
3. Brian O'Leary, "Duality, Oneness, and Outer Space," *The Movement* (March 1985): 11.

Bibliography

Allen, Joseph P. *Entering Space: An Astronaut's Odyssey*. New York: Stewart, Tabori & Chang, 1984.
———. "Diary of a Shuttle Launch." *Science Digest*, September 1984.
Bertalanffy, Ludwig von. *General Systems Theory: Foundations, Development, Applications*. New York: George Braziller. 1968.
Carpenter, M. Scott, et al. *We Seven: By the Astronauts Themselves*. New York: Simon and Schuster, 1962.
Cernan, Eugene. "The Price of Being a Space Hero." *TV Guide*, April 13–19, 1985.
Collins, Michael. *Carrying the Fire*. New York: Farrar, Straus and Giroux, 1974.
Cooper, Henry S. F. *A House in Space*. New York: Holt, Rinehart and Winston, 1976.
Finney, Ben R. "SETI and Interstellar Migration." *Journal of the British Interplanetary Society*, vol. 38, 1985.
Finney, Ben R., and Jones, Eric M. "From Africa to the Stars: The Evolution of the Exploring Animal." *Space Manufacturing 1983*, vol. 53, *Advances in the Astronautical Sciences*, Proceedings of the Sixth Princeton/SSI Conference on Space Manufacturing, ed. James D. Burke and April S. Whitt. San Diego: Univelt, 1983.
Fuller, R. Buckminster. *Critical Path*. New York: St. Martin's Press, 1981.
Furniss, Tim. *Space Flight: The Records*. Enfield, England: Guinness Books, 1985.
Gagarin, Yuri, and Lebedev, Valentin. *Survival in Space*. New York: Frederick Praeger, 1969.
Georgescu-Roegen, Nicholas. *The Entropy Law and the Economic Process*. Cambridge: Harvard University Press, 1971.
Gor'kov, V., and Kon'kov, N. "211 Days in Orbit," Moscow *Aviatsiya I*

Kosmonavtika, no. 7, July 1983, no. 8, August 1983, no. 9, September 1983.

Gorman, James. "The Righteous Stuff." *Omni,* May 1984.

Harman, Willis, and Rheingold, Howard. *Higher Creativity: Liberating the Unconscious for Breakthrough Insights.* Los Angeles: J. P. Tarcher, 1984.

Hoffman, Jeffrey A. "An Astronaut's Diary." Audiotape. Washington, D.C.: National Public Radio, 1985.

Holmquist, Michael. "The Philosophical Bases of Soviet Space Exploration." *Key Reporter* (Winter 1985–86).

Huxley, Aldous. *The Perennial Philosophy.* New York and London: Harper & Brothers, 1944.

Jaynes, Julian. *The Origin of Consciousness in the Breakdown of the Bicameral Mind.* Boston: Houghton Mifflin, 1976.

Koestler, Arthur. *The Ghost in the Machine.* London: Hutchinson, 1967.

Lebedev, Valentin. Flight diary excerpts in Moscow *Pravda,* August 15, 1983.

Lewis, Richard S. *Appointment on the Moon.* New York: Ballantine Books, 1969.

Lovelock, James E. *Gaia: A New Look at Life on Earth.* Oxford: Oxford University Press, 1979.

MacDonald, Bob. "Conversations with the Christian Science Monitor," Boston: Christian Science Monitor Publishing Society, 1985.

Mitchell, Edgar D. "Perspective Is an Interesting Word." *Exploring New Perspectives of Humankind.* Sausalito, Calif.: Institute of Noetic Sciences, n.d.

Myers, Norman, ed. *Gaia: An Atlas of Planet Management.* Garden City, New York: Anchor Books, Anchor Press/Doubleday, 1984.

National Commission on Space. *Pioneering the Space Frontier.* New York: Bantam Books, 1986.

O'Leary, Brian. "Duality, Oneness and Outer Space." *The Movement,* March 1985.

Pardoe, Geoffrey K.C. *The Future for Space Technology.* London and Dover, N.H.: Frances Pinter, 1984.

Rozek, Michael. "Bioflight." *Air & Space,* June/July 1986.

Russell, Peter. *The Global Brain: Speculations on the Evolutionary Leap to Planetary Consciousness.* Los Angeles: J. P. Tarcher, 1983.

Schweickart, Russell L. *No Frames, No Boundaries.* Palo Alto, Calif.: Creative Initiative/Beyond War. From *Earth's Answer: Explorations of Planetary Culture at the Lindesfarne Conferences.* West Stockbridge, Mass.: Lindesfarne/Harper & Row, 1977.

Shklovskii, I. S., and Sagan, Carl. *Intelligent Life in the Universe.* New York: Dell, 1966.

Smith, Anthony P. "Mutiny on the Beagle." *ReVision* 7, no. 1 (Spring 1984).

Smothermon, Ron. *Mastery of Context Creation.* Audiotape. San Francisco: Context Publications, n.d.

Stamps, Jeffrey S. *Holonomy: A Human Systems Theory.* Seaside, Calif.: Intersystems Publications, 1980.

Titov, Gherman. "A Test in Orbit." *Moscow Krasnaya Zvezda,* 1983.

White, Frank. "Humanity's Next Step." Unpublished manuscript. Newton, Mass.: Human Systems Incorporated, 1983.

———. "Space Exploration and Human Evolution." Testimony at Boston Public Forum, National Commission on Space, October 28, 1985.

———. "Understanding Space Settlements as Human Systems." *Space Manufacturing 1983,* vol. 53, *Advances in the Astronautical Sciences,* Proceedings of the Sixth Princeton/SSI Conference on Space Manufacturing, ed. James D. Burke and April S. Whitt. San Diego: Univelt, 1983.

Wilber, Ken. *Eye to Eye: The Quest for the New Paradigm.* Garden City, N.Y.: Anchor Books, Anchor Press/Doubleday, 1983.

Wolfe, Tom. *The Right Stuff.* New York: Farrar, Straus and Giroux, 1979.

Index